D1278731

The Geological Society of America, Inc.
Memoir 96

FAUNAS AND STRATIGRAPHY OF THE SNOWY RANGE FORMATION (UPPER CAMBRIAN) IN SOUTHWESTERN MONTANA AND NORTHWESTERN WYOMING

By
RICHARD E. GRANT
E-316 Natural History Building, Washington, D.C.

1965

Library of Congress Catalog Card Number 65–26558

PUBLISHED BY
THE GEOLOGICAL SOCIETY OF AMERICA, INC.
231 East 46th Street
New York, New York 10017

Made in the United States of America

The printing of this Memoir
has been made possible
by the bequest of
Richard Alexander Fullerton Penrose, Jr.

ACKNOWLEDGMENTS

I am grateful to the many people who have aided in the progress of this project and who have made suggestions concerning the final form of the manuscript. Principal acknowledgment is due Prof. W. C. Bell, Geology Department, University of Texas, who suggested the problem, supervised the field and laboratory work and criticized the manuscript; and my parents, the Rev. and Mrs. Charles L. Grant, St. Paul, Minnesota, for support and encouragement. Thanks are extended to Dr. Christina Lochman, New Mexico Bureau of Mines, for suggestions concerning collecting localities, trilobite taxonomy, and stratigraphic nomenclature, for contributing her collections of Franconian fossils from southwestern Montana, and for critical reading of the original manuscript; to Mr. O. M. Hackett, U.S. Geological Survey, and Dr. W. J. McMannis, Montana State College, for help with the geography and geology of the Horseshoe Hills and Bridger Mountains; to Dr. J. L. Wilson, Shell Development Company, for suggestions involving trilobite taxonomy and distribution; to Prof. E. A. Frederickson, University of Oklahoma, for the loan of type specimens and for conversations on trilobite taxonomy; to Prof. W. T. Thom, Jr., Yellowstone-Bighorn Research Association, for providing field assistants; to Dr. A. R. Palmer, U.S. Geological Survey, for critical reading of the manuscript; to Messrs. Paul Benedum, Richard Buckley, Lawrence Corbett, Ivan Gibbs, Neal McLean, and S. Dennison Whitford, Jr., for assistance in the field during parts of the summers of 1952 and 1954; and to Profs. R. K. DeFord, R. L. Folk, and J. A. Wilson, University of Texas, for critical reading of the manuscript.

Thanks also are due the following institutions: the Geology Department of the University of Texas for office and laboratory space and financial assistance; the National Science Foundation and the Shell Oil Company Fellowship Committee for scholarships at the University of Texas; the Yellowstone-Bighorn Research Association, Red Lodge, Montana, for hospitality during field seasons; and the U.S. National Park Service for permission to collect fossils in Yellowstone National Park.

CONTENTS

	Page
ABSTRACT	1
INTRODUCTION	3
LOCATION AND DESCRIPTION OF AREA	5
LITHOSTRATIGRAPHY	9
General statement	9
Cambrian System	9
Pilgrim Formation	9
Snowy Range Formation	9
Ordovician System	17
Bighorn Formation	17
Devonian System	18
Maywood unit	18
Jefferson Formation	21
PETROGRAPHY	23
General statement	23
Thin-section descriptions	23
Summary	27
Snowy Range Formation, Dry Creek Member	27
Snowy Range Formation, Saga Member	28
Snowy Range Formation, Grove Creek Member	29
Maywood unit	30
Measured sections and faunal lists	30
BIOSTRATIGRAPHY	79
General statement	79
Trilobite zonation	79
General statement	79
Dresbachian Stage	80
Franconian Stage	81
Trempealeauan Stage	88
Brachiopod zonation	88
General statement	88
Brachiopod Stage 1 (equivalent to Dresbachian Stage)	89
Brachiopod Stage 2 (equivalent to part of Franconian Stage)	89
Brachiopod Stage 3 (equivalent to upper part of Franconian Stage and lower part of Trempealeauan Stage)	91
SYSTEMATIC PALEONTOLOGY: CROIXAN FAUNAS	93
Phylum PORIFERA	94
Family MULTIVASCULATIDAE	94
Phylum BRACHIOPODA	95
Superfamily OBOLACEA	95
Superfamily PATERINACEA	96
Superfamily ACROTRETACEA	97
Superfamily ORTHACEA	101
Superfamily SYNTROPHIACEA	104
Phylum MOLLUSCA	105
Class GASTROPODA	105
Class INCERTAE SEDIS	106
Phylum ARTHROPODA	107

Page
Class TRILOBITA 107
Family AGNOSTIDAE 107
Family PSEUDAGNOSTIDAE 108
Family ANOMOCARIDAE 109
Family CHEILOCEPHALIDAE 109
Family DIKELOCEPHALIDAE 110
Family DOKIMOCEPHALIDAE 110
Family ELVINIIDAE 114
Family EUREKIIDAE 116
Family HOUSIIDAE 117
Family IDAHOIIDAE 117
Family ILLAENURIDAE 124
Family KINGSTONIIDAE 125
Family KOMASPIDIDAE 126
Family LECANOPYGIDAE 127
Family MARJUMIIDAE 128
Family PAGODIIDAE 130
Family PARABOLINOIDIDAE 131
Family PLETHOPELTIDAE 138
Family PTEROCEPHALIIDAE 138
Family PTYCHASPIDIDAE 141
Family SAUKIIDAE 142
Family SHUMARDIIDAE 142
Family INCERTAE SEDIS 143
Class ARACHNIDA 143
Phylum ECHINODERMATA 143
Subphylum PELMATOZOA 143
Phylum CHORDATA (?) 144
Class GRAPTOLITHINA 144
Conodonts 144
Problematicum 145
Calcareous algae 145
REFERENCES 147
EXPLANATION OF PLATES 155
INDEX 167

ILLUSTRATIONS

PLATES

Plate
1. Columnar sections, Horseshoe Hills, Montana .... In pocket, back cover
2. Columnar sections, Bridger Mountains to Squaw Creek, Montana .... In pocket, back cover
3. Columnar sections, Crowfoot Ridge to Grove Creek, Wyoming .... In pocket, back cover
4. Ranges of genera and species in Snowy Range Formation, Montana and Wyoming .... In pocket, back cover

Facing page
5. Photographs of outcrops and calcareous algae 156
6. Limestone-pebble conglomerate 157
7. Photomicrographs of rocks, Snowy Range Formation 158
8. Dresbachian and *Elvinia* Zone fossils 159
9. *Elvinia* Zone fossils 160
10. *Elvinia* Zone and *Taenicephalus* Zone fossils 161
11. *Taenicephalus* Zone fossils 162

Facing page

12. *Taenicephalus* Zone fossils 163
13. *Taenicephalus* Zone and *Idahoia* Zone fossils 164
14. *Idahoia* Zone and *Prosaukia* Zone fossils 165
15. *Illaenurus* Zone fossils 166

FIGURE

Figure Page

1. Locations of sections measured in the Snowy Range Formation, southwestern Montana and northwestern Wyoming 6

ABSTRACT

Fossils and rock samples were collected from the Snowy Range Formation at 24 sections measured in the Horseshoe Hills and Bridger Mountains of Montana and eight sections in the vicinity of Yellowstone National Park in Montana and Wyoming. Where the Snowy Range Formation is overlain by the Maywood unit (Devonian), both were measured and sampled, although the Maywood proved to be unfossiliferous.

Lowermost of the three members of the Snowy Range is the Dry Creek Shale which lies conformably on the Pilgrim Limestone. It consists of about 50 feet of purplish, thin-bedded, fissile to slightly plastic shale with a few irregular beds of brownish-gray, platy, dolomitic siltstone in the lower three fourths, and some thin beds of silty limestone or limestone-pebble conglomerate in the upper quarter. No evidence is present in this area for subaerial erosion between the Pilgrim and Snowy Range Formations, although beds of siltstone in the Dry Creek may reflect uplift and erosion at the source of terrigenous sediments.

The middle member is the Sage, which averages about 200 feet thick where complete. Its base is marked at most localities by a 1–20-foot bioherm of columnar algal limestone; the remainder is a fairly regular alternation of 1–2-foot beds of limestone or limestone-pebble conglomerate with 2–4-foot beds of green shale or very argillaceous greenish-gray limestone. The upper part contains beds of noncolumnar algal limestone. This member was deposited far from shore in shallow turbid water that contained abundant calcium in solution. Microcrystalline calcite ooze, along with fine fragments of fossils and pellets, collected in ripple troughs and other depressions in the mud of the sea floor. These small accumulations became sufficiently consolidated to maintain coherence when excavated by currents that swept away clay particles and concentrated the limestone "pods" into beds that later were cemented to form limestone-pebble conglomerate.

The uppermost member, the Grove Creek, is nowhere complete in this area; the upper part was removed by erosion at some localities and by faulting at others. The member consists of about 25 feet of dolomitized limestone-pebble or cobble conglomerate with intercalated beds of dolomitized, gray, splintery shale. This member owes much of its distinctive character to weathering that took place before deposition of the Upper Ordovician Bighorn Formation.

The Maywood unit is a Devonian soil or weathered zone that overlies some part of the Snowy Range Formation in the northwestern part of the area of study but overlies formations as low as those in the Precambrian Belt Series or as high as the Upper Ordovician Bighorn Formation in other parts of Montana. It consists of a greatly varying thickness (averaging about 55 feet) of reddish-orange or brown, thin-bedded, silty dolomite or dolomitic limestone. At a few localities it is coarse-grained, thick-bedded, light-brown dolomite. No fossils were found in the Maywood of the area studied, but Devonian fossils have been collected from it in other parts of Montana.

Fossils described are 80 species assigned to 48 genera of trilobites, 20 species assigned to 14 genera of brachiopods, four species in four genera of gastropods, two species in one genus of conodonts, one species of sponge, one of graptolite, two form species of algal limestone, and *problematica.* New taxa are the trilobites *Comanchia lippa* n.sp., *Geragnostus ? insolitus* n.sp., *Monocheilus demissus* n.sp., *Pinctus ? artus* n.sp., *P. ? pullus* n.sp., *Pseudagnostus sentosus* n.sp., *Rasettia snowyensis* n.sp., *Saratogia carita* n.sp., *S. fracida* n.sp., and *Taenicephalus gallupensis* n.sp.; the brachiopods *Angulotreta catheta* n.sp., *A. glabra* n.sp., *A. vescula* n.sp., *Eoorthis remnicha* var. *A.* n. var. and *Huenella texana* var. *fortis* n.var.

Fossil species in the Snowy Range Formation are assigned to local zones that are based on ranges of genera and species of trilobites and which can be correlated with standard zones of the Cambrian Correlation Chart or with local zones of other areas. A few species from scattered localities near the base of the formation belong to the *Aphelaspis* or *Dunderbergia* zones of the Dresbachian Stage. Most species belong to zones in the Franconian. Lowermost of these is the *Elvinia* Zone (with *Camaraspis* Subzone and *Irvingella major* Zonule in the upper part) which corresponds to the *Elvinia* Zone of the Cambrian Correlation Chart. Next higher is the *Taenicephalus* Zone (with *Parabolinoides* Subzone at base) which correlates with the *Conaspis* Zone of the Chart. Above this is the *Idahoia* Zone (with basal *I. wyomingensis* Subzone, middle *I. wisconsensis* Subzone, and upper *I. serapio* Subzone) which correlates with the *Ptychaspis* Subzone of the *Ptychaspis-Prosaukia* Zone of the Chart. The uppermost zone of the Franconian is the *Prosaukia* Zone, which is equivalent to the *Prosaukia* Subzone of the Chart. Species of the Trempealeauan Stage are assigned to the *Illaenurus* Zone which corresponds to the Lower Trempealeauan of Texas or the lower part of the *Saukia* Zone of the upper Mississippi Valley.

An alternative zonation is offered, based on the ranges of genera and species of brachiopods. Boundaries of most brachiopod zones fall near the levels of the boundaries of trilobite zones, but some do not. The *Apsotreta expansa* Zone belongs to the Dresbachian Stage. The *Linnarssonella* Zone and the *Angulotreta tetonensis* Zone (with *Ceratreta-Eoorthis* Subzone at base) correspond respectively to the *Elvinia* and *Taenicephalus* Zones of the lower part of the Franconian Stage. The *Angulotreta vescula* Zone corresponds to all but the uppermost part of the *Idahoia* Zone, and the *A. catheta* Zone (with *Finkelnburgia osceola* Subzone at top) is equivalent to this uppermost part of the *Idahoia* Zone and the entire *Prosaukia* Zone of the Franconian Stage as well as the entire *Illaenurus* Zone of the Trempealeauan Stage. No Franconian-Trempealeauan boundary is apparent in the brachiopod zonation.

INTRODUCTION

Detailed modern investigations of Upper Cambrian lithostratigraphy, paleontology, and biostratigraphy in several widely separated regions of the United States have made the Croixan Series one of the best understood parts of the North American stratigraphic sequence. Some of these studies were undertaken in preparation of the Cambrian Correlation Chart (Howell and others, 1944), and others were begun after the chart showed gaps in knowledge of Croixan biostratigraphy, even in the Croixan type area.

The present study is one of a series of investigations of Upper Cambrian lithostratigraphy and biostratigraphy in several parts of the United States. Franconian paleontology and biostratigraphy of the central Appalachians are described by Wilson (1951), and the stratigraphy by Wilson (1952) and Rodgers (1956). Stratigraphy of the Franconia Formation in the Croixan type area in the upper Mississippi Valley is presented in papers by Berg (1954); Bell, Berg, and Nelson (1956); and Berg, Nelson, and Bell (1956). That of the Upper Croixan St. Lawrence and Jordan formations is summarized by Nelson (1956); Bell, Berg, and Nelson (1956); and Berg, Nelson, and Bell (1956). Paleontology and biostratigraphy of the Franconian and Trempealeauan Stages of the same area are described by Nelson (1951; 1956); Bell, Feniak, and Kurtz (1952); Bell, Berg, and Nelson (1956); Berg, Nelson, and Bell (1956); and Grant (1962).

Similar investigations have been made in Central Texas. Cambrian stratigraphy is described by Bridge, Barnes, and Cloud (1947), and a brief summary is given by Barnes and Bell (1954). The paleontology and biostratigraphy are described by Lochman (1938), Wilson (1949), and Palmer (1955a). Frederickson presented the biostratigraphy of the Upper Cambrian of Oklahoma in 1949 and a summary of the stratigraphy in 1956.

Cambrian stratigraphy of southwestern Montana and northwestern Wyoming is well known from papers by Dorf and Lochman (1940), Hanson (1952), and McMannis (1955). Available knowledge is summarized in papers by Lochman (1949) and Lochman-Balk (1956b). Paleontology and biostratigraphy of the Dresbachian part of the Croixan Series are described in detail by Lochman and Duncan (1944). DeLand and Shaw (1956) studied trilobites from the Dresbachian and lower Franconian of western Wyoming and presented brief summaries of the biostratigraphy in 1955 (Shaw and DeLand) and 1956 (Shaw). They are the only previous workers who have studied the Franconian part of the Croixan of western Wyoming in detail, and their basic framework of nomenclature for the local Franconian zonation (Shaw, 1954; Shaw and DeLand, 1955) is used here. Lochman-Balk and Wilson (1958) summarized much of this work.

This paper attempts to fill some of the remaining gaps in knowledge of the

Croixan of southwestern Montana and northwestern Wyoming. It describes the faunas and rocks in terms of the biostratigraphic and lithostratigraphic successions, comparing them with documented successions in other areas. It is hoped that the data here presented will aid in the formulation of a comprehensive picture of North America during the Late Cambrian.

In terms of lithostratigraphy the present study concerns the Snowy Range Formation and the overlying Devonian Maywood unit. No fossils were found in the Maywood; the faunas are entirely those of the Snowy Range Formation. Collections were made on the basis of lithic succession rather than faunal succession; therefore although most species are Franconian and Trempealeauan, a few from near the base of the Snowy Range are Dresbachian.

LOCATION AND DESCRIPTION OF AREA

Fossils and rock samples were collected from measured sections in the Horseshoe Hills and Bridger Mountains of Montana and in parts of Montana and Wyoming near Yellowstone National Park between the Missouri River and the Clark Fork of the Yellowstone River, all in Gallatin, Park, and Carbon counties, Montana, and Park County, Wyoming (Fig. 1).

The Horseshoe Hills are east-northeast trending hogbacks between Logan and Dry Creek, Montana. Strata are moderately folded and simply faulted, with many small normal faults and a few thrusts. The Snowy Range Formation underlies part of the antidip slope of one of the southernmost hogbacks. It is exposed well enough to be measured and sampled in several stream valleys and at scattered localities along the face of the hogback where the slope is steep. Access to exposures in the Horseshoe Hills is simple. Several roads enter the hills from the south: one from Logan, one from Manhattan, one from Belgrade, and another skirts their eastern end along Dry Creek. Sections between the roads are easily reached on foot. Geology of the Horseshoe Hills has been mapped in detail by Verall (1954, Ph.D. thesis, Princeton Univ.).

The Bridger Mountains extend for 23 miles from slightly northeast of Bozeman, Montana, in a direction slightly west of north. Their highest summit is Sacajawea Peak which reaches an elevation of 9,669 feet. Rocks in the Bridger Mountains dip steeply to the east, except at the extremities of the range where they are overturned. The Snowy Range Formation commonly underlies a grass-covered slope between the resistant limestones of the Pilgrim and Jefferson Formations. It is best exposed in valleys and on sharp ridges. The only easily accessible exposures are those immediately north of Flathead Pass (Sections FP, FC) and at Sacajawea Peak. Sections at Bighorn Lake, Bill Smith Creek, Sacajawea Peak, and Ross Peak can be reached most conveniently from the campground at Fairy Lake on the east side of the range; others are best reached by way of the valleys of streams that flow down the west side of the range. Geology of the Bridger Range has been mapped in detail by McMannis (1955).

Sections along Soda Butte Creek and the Clark Fork are exposed by erosion where dips are gentle and structural complications few. The Snowy Range Formation is exposed in the north-facing wall of the edge of the blanket of Paleozoic and younger rocks that borders the granitic and gneissic terrane of the Beartooth Mountains. According to Pierce (1957) the base of the Heart Mountain thrust sheet is formed by part of the Grove Creek Member of the Snowy Range Formation. He believes that the contact between the Snowy Range Formation and the overlying strata is a fault contact. Therefore, some of the upper part of the Grove Creek may be missing. Most of the Snowy

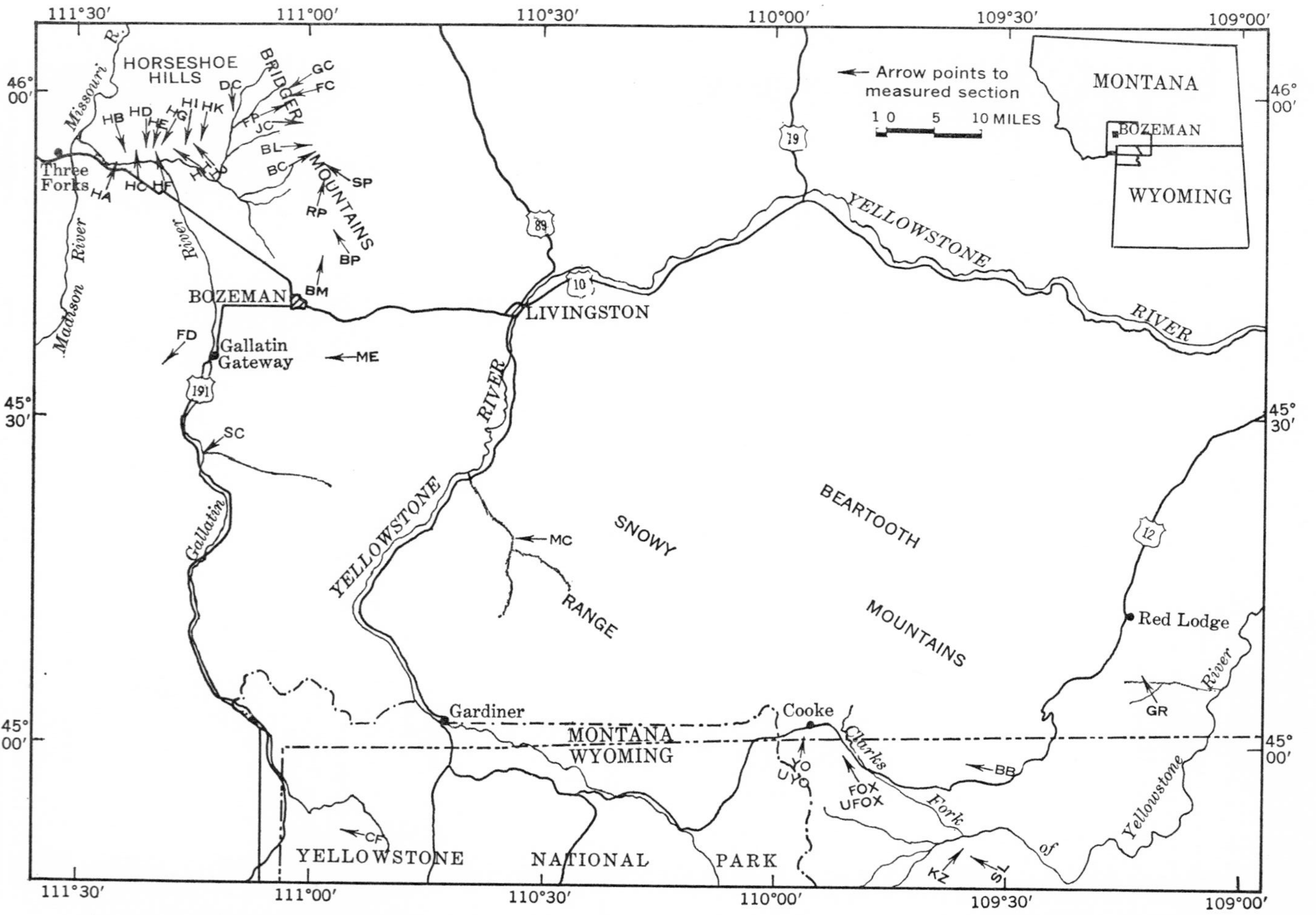

Figure 1. Locations of sections measured in the Snowy Range Formation, southwestern Montana and northwestern Wyoming

Range Formation is better exposed in this area than in other parts of the study area. Beartooth Butte is an outlier of the same sheet of Paleozoic rock, but exposures of the Snowy Range Formation there are poor.

Exposures between the Bridgers and the Clark Fork are widely scattered. Those at Flying "D," Squaw Creek, Mill Creek, Crowfoot Ridge, and North Grove Creek were measured on steep slopes at the peripheries of the Snowy and Beartooth ranges.

LITHOSTRATIGRAPHY

GENERAL STATEMENT

The following discussion of the Snowy Range Formation and of the rocks immediately above and below it provides a framework upon which to base paleontologic and biostratigraphic considerations. Rock units are discussed from oldest to youngest, with brief statements concerning those above and below the Snowy Range and Maywood units; hypotheses concerning their origins are offered.

CAMBRIAN SYSTEM

Pilgrim Formation (Weed, 1899a). Weed first used the name "Pilgrim Limestone" in his Fort Benton folio (1899a) and Little Belt Mountains folio (1899b), but his first adequate description appeared in 1900 (p. 286). Deiss (1936, p. 1283) designated a type locality for the Pilgrim Formation at Dry Wolf Creek in the Little Belt Mountains, Montana.

Dorf and Lochman (1940, p. 547–550) proposed the name "Maurice" for the same unit in southern Montana. Lochman (Lochman-Balk, 1956b, p. 603) now considers the Maurice to be the lithic equivalent of the Pilgrim and suggests that the name "Maurice" be dropped in favor of the prior name Pilgrim.

DISTRIBUTION AND THICKNESS: The uppermost of the three members of the Pilgrim Formation in this area of study is a massive limestone that forms a cliff below the normally covered slope of the Snowy Range Formation. In the Horseshoe Hills this upper member is about 200 feet thick (Hanson, 1952, p. 36); in the Bridger Mountains it is about 235 feet thick (McMannis, 1955, p. 1394); between the Bridgers and Yellowstone National Park it averages about 100 feet thick (Hanson, 1952, p. 37), thinning to about 60 feet at Crowfoot Ridge (Deiss, 1936, p. 1319). Along Soda Butte Creek and Clark Fork Canyon it averages about 130 feet thick (Hanson, 1952, p. 40) but is only about 100 feet thick at Beartooth Butte (Hanson, 1952, p. 41) and at North Grove Creek (Dorf and Lochman, 1940, p. 548).

LITHOLOGY: The upper member of the Pilgrim Formation is massive, dark-gray, mottled, dolomitic limestone that is arenaceous at the top in southwestern Montana (Lochman-Balk, 1956b, p. 602–603). The top of the Pilgrim cliff was used as a base for most measurements of the Snowy Range Formation.

Snowy Range Formation (Dorf and Lochman, 1940, p. 545–547). At its type locality near Mill Creek the Snowy Range Formation consists of three members: the Dry Creek Shale at the base, the Sage Limestone-Pebble Conglomerate in the middle, and the Grove Creek Dolomitic Limestone at the top. The Grove Creek Member and the upper part of the Sage Member are absent at many localities. Parts of all three members are present only at Section HJ in the Horseshoe Hills (Pl. 1) and at Sections RP, BP, and BM in the Bridger Mountains (Pl. 2). Most of the formation is present where it is overlain by the Bighorn Formation and has not been affected by post-Ordovician to pre-Late Devonian weathering and erosion. It is protected in this manner at Mill Creek and eastward to North Grove Creek, including the area immediately to the east of Yellowstone National Park (Pl. 3). Total thicknesses show no trend toward thinning or thickening in any one direction; Hanson's (1952, p. 8) isopach of the formation indicates depth of removal of the upper part of the formation but not original thickness.

The Snowy Range Formation occurs in southwestern Montana and northern Wyoming. Its western edge is in the vicinity of Three Forks, Montana, north and west of which it changes to dark shale and reddish-purple limestone of the Red Lion Formation (Hanson, 1952, p. 17–19; Lochman-Balk, 1956b, p. 608). In the Big Snowy Mountains rocks of the same age belong to the Zortman Member of the Emerson Formation (Lochman-Balk, 1956b, p. 605), as in the Little Rocky Mountains farther to the north and east.

In northern Wyoming the Snowy Range Formation extends eastward to the Powder River Basin, beyond which it changes to the Deadwood Formation which also contains beds of micaceous shale and sandstone (Lochman-Balk, 1956b, p. 600–601, Fig. 12, p. 613–618). Shaw and DeLand (1955, p. 38) propose the name "Open Door" for the equivalent of the Snowy Range Formation in northwestern Wyoming, but Lochman-Balk (1956b, p. 615) considers the name superfluous; not a lithic but a paleontologic unit.

West of Yellowstone National Park, in Montana and Idaho, the Snowy Range Formation is absent (Hanson, 1952, p. 21, 38–39, Pl. 8, fig. B). According to Lochman-Balk (1956b, p. 608), it has been removed by pre-Late Devonian erosion.

Thickness of the Snowy Range Formation depends in part on the depth of pre-Late Devonian erosion. In the Horseshoe Hills the minimum thickness is about 50 feet at Section HA, and the maximum is about 265 feet at Section HJ where most of the Grove Creek Member is present. In most other sections in the Horseshoe Hills its thickness is nearer the minimum than the maximum. In the Bridger Mountains it ranges from 140 feet at Gallup Creek to 325 feet at Baldy Mountain. Between the Bridgers and Yellowstone National Park the thickness is between 60 and 80 feet. From Mill Creek eastward to Swamp Lake and North Grove Creek the Snowy Range Formation is overlain by the Bighorn Formation; here the thickness was not reduced by post-Cambrian erosion. It averages about 300 feet, although thicknesses of the individual members vary.

DRY CREEK MEMBER (PEALE, 1893, p. 24): Since Peale's proposal of the name "Dry Creek Shale," much confusion has attended its use. Many authors followed Weed's (1900, p. 286) incorrect use of the name for the entire interval that now includes both the Snowy Range Formation and the Maywood unit (*e.g.*, Deiss, 1936; Lochman and Duncan, 1944; Sloss and Laird, 1947).

This confusion in nomenclature has been cleared up by Lochman (1950b), and present use of the name "Dry Creek" follows the original definition by Peale.

Peale did not designate a type locality for the Dry Creek Shale, but the name implies that he studied exposures along Dry Creek at the eastern end of the Horseshoe Hills, Montana. Deiss (1936, p. 1285–1286) attempted to establish a type locality in the Little Belt Mountains, but his concept of the Dry Creek Shale was based on Weed's use of the name and involved rock that differs in position and lithology from Peale's Dry Creek Shale. Lochman (1950b, p. 2218–2221) has investigated the rocks along Dry Creek and believes that Peale saw the section on the west side of the creek just south of Accola, where faulting is least severe. She (p. 2219) has designated this as the type locality of the Dry Creek Member. The character of the member at this locality is about the same as it is in the Horseshoe Hills (Pl. 1) and Bridger Mountains (Pl. 2).

The Dry Creek Member is commonly grayish-green, soft, fissile to crumbly shale that forms gentle, partly covered slopes. At several localities some of the shale beds are dusky purple, probably the result of recent weathering. The shale is somewhat silty at some localities and may be slightly micaceous. Interbedded with the shale are several thin beds of brownish-gray, platy, irregularly bedded, calcareous or dolomitic siltstone. These thin beds are more common in the lower part of the member but occur in the upper part as well. Just east of Yellowstone National Park a few of these beds are silty limestone rather than calcareous siltstone and contain abundant phosphatic inarticulate brachiopods. The member contains few beds of limestone or limestone-pebble conglomerate, although a bed of limestone-pebble conglomerate containing trilobites and brachiopods occurs near its base at sections BL and BC in the Bridger Range.

The Dry Creek Member is present in every section measured except that at Mount Ellis, where it is faulted out. It is a persistent lower member of the Snowy Range Formation, although most of its outcrops are at least partly covered and its thickness varies considerably. In the Horseshoe Hills (Pl. 1) its thickness ranges from 30 feet at Section HA to 95 feet at Section HJ, averaging about 55 feet. In the Bridger Mountains (Pl. 2) it ranges from 45 feet at Section BC to 105 feet at Section FP, averaging about 65 feet. Between the Bridgers and Yellowstone National Park it is rather thin — only about 15 feet thick at Sections FD and CF and 30 feet thick at Squaw Creek. At Mill Creek the member is about 105 feet thick, but east of Yellowstone National Park (Pl. 3) it has a relatively constant thickness of about 50 feet.

The base of the Dry Creek Member overlies the uppermost bed of massive limestone in the Pilgrim Formation with a sharp contact. Thin lenses of limestone-pebble conglomerate that occur near the base of the Dry Creek may have derived their pebbles from the Pilgrim, but some shale occurs below them and they differ sufficiently from Pilgrim Limestone to be considered parts of the Dry Creek Member.

The top of the Dry Creek Member is the base of the lowest bed of columnar limestone of the Sage Member. Where the columnar limestone is absent, the top of the Dry Creek is the base of the lowest bed of limestone-pebble conglomerate or limestone. Where the columnar limestone is present, beds of limestone or limestone-pebble conglomerate may occur below it; they are placed in the Dry Creek Member (Hanson, 1952, p. 18; Lochman-Balk, 1956b, p. 608; Shaw and DeLand, 1955, p. 39, Fig. 1; Shaw, 1956, p. 49). The columnar limestone present at most localities studied is a reliable marker for the top of the Dry Creek Member and the base of the Sage Member. For a map of the areal extent of the columnar limestone see Lochman (1949, Pl. 6).

SAGE MEMBER (LOCHMAN, 1950b, p. 2212): The Sage Limestone-Pebble Conglomerate is the middle member of the Snowy Range Formation. Its type locality was established by Lochman (1950b) at the type locality of the Snowy Range Formation on the south slope of Castle Rock above Mill Creek (Section MC). The name is derived from Sage Creek, a nearby tributary of Mill Creek (Fig. 1).

The Sage Member is characterized by several types of limestone with intercalated beds of grayish-green shale. The most striking type of limestone is that of the bioherm of calcareous algae (*Collenia magna*) that occurs at the base of the member at most localities. It is composed of vertical columns 8–18 inches in diameter, commonly 1–6 feet high; pebbly limestone fills the space between closely adjacent columns. At some localities the entire bioherm consists of one thin bed of columns, whereas at others three or four beds of high columns with thin beds of shale and conglomerate between them may total as much as 25 feet. The limestone is very pure, fine-grained, greenish gray, and commonly unfossiliferous, with irregular stylolite-like flutings randomly distributed. The matrix is greenish gray, pebbly, and locally moderately fossiliferous (*see* description of *Collenia magna,* p. 145).

At Fox Creek, Wyoming Creek, and Swamp Lake the edge of the bioherm is exposed in stream cuts where adjacent beds can be measured and sampled. These beds consist of green shale, coarse-grained limestone or pebble conglomerate, and fragmental algal debris that was eroded from the bioherm. They are not very fossiliferous, but some contain abundant crinoid columnals and phosphatic brachiopods. Limestone beds adjacent to the bioherm thicken toward it and butt directly against it. Shale beds do not thicken toward the bioherm; most bend upward near it to accommodate the thickening of the limestone beds, and the uppermost shale beds arch over the top of the bioherm. The bioherm terminates abruptly; it is thickest in the three sections where its edge is exposed and other beds butt against it.

Above the columnar bioherm are thin beds of fine- to medium-grained limestone and limestone-pebble conglomerate interbedded with beds of shale or very shaly, fine-grained, crinkly bedded limestone. At most localities several beds of brachiopod coquinite (*Eoorthis-Ceratreta* Subzone) occur 10–20 feet above the top of the bioherm.

The upper three fourths of the Sage Member exhibits a subtle change in aspect from west to east. In the Horseshoe Hills, most of the Bridger Mountains, and in Yellowstone National Park the member is composed chiefly of limestone. Beds of limestone-pebble conglomerate or fine- to medium-grained hard limestone are interbedded with beds of fine-grained, light-gray, crinkly bedded, very shaly limestone, or occasionally of hard calcareous shale. In the southeasternmost part of the Bridger Mountains and from Mill Creek eastward, the limestone and conglomerate beds alternate with beds of soft, grayish-green, fissile to crumbly shale. Many beds of this shale simulate those to the west by containing thin stringers of limestone or abundant limestone pods, but the shale itself is soft and green and cannot be considered shaly limestone.

Many of the limestone beds are fossiliferous and slightly dolomitic, and most are somewhat argillaceous. The presence of clay is not obvious at the outcrop but becomes apparent in insoluble residues. The shale beds are rarely fossiliferous, although lenses and stringers of limestone within shale beds may contain abundant fossils. Wherever the Sage Member is exposed, it is characterized by prominent limestone beds between recesses of shale or crinkly, shaly limestone.

At most sections a 10–20-foot ledge of limestone and limestone-pebble conglomerate occurs 30–60 feet above the top of the columnar bioherm. Limestone of this ledge is brownish gray and dolomitic, with very few interbeds of shale, and normally contains fossils of the *Idahoia wyomingensis* Subzone.

Immediately above this ledge is a fairly uniform sequence of alternating beds of limestone and shale in the east and limestone and crinkly argillaceous limestone in the west. The thickness of the average bed of grayish-green shale or greenish-gray argillaceous limestone is about 2 feet. Intercalated beds of limestone or limestone-pebble conglomerate are commonly slightly thinner than the beds of shale or argillaceous limestone and may be quite fossiliferous.

Except at localities just east of Yellowstone National Park, alternating beds of shale and limestone or limestone-pebble conglomerate continue to the base of the overlying Grove Creek Member or the Maywood unit. In sections along Soda Butte Creek and Clark Fork Canyon the upper quarter of the Sage Member contains many biostromes of *Tetonophycus blackwelderi,* a bedded algal limestone that differs in gross form from the columnar *Collenia magna* of the lower part of the member but is similar in thin section. Beds of this algal limestone consist of two parts: the base is very pebbly; the pebbles probably provided a substrate upon which the algae grew. The upper part of the bed is algal limestone; it is fine-grained and dolomitic, with visible growth lines and an upper surface of low, rounded, convex mounds. A sharp contact separates the upper algal part from the basal pebbly part of each bed. Beds of *T. blackwelderi* alternate with beds of green shale, as do beds of nonalgal limestone in the middle half of the Sage Member.

The Sage Member is the thickest and most fossiliferous of the three members of the Snowy Range Formation. As originally deposited it probably ranged in thickness from about 120 to 220 feet, averaging close to 200 feet, but at many localities the upper part has been removed or altered by pre-Late Devonian weathering and erosion. Its thickness in the Horseshoe Hills (Pl. 1) ranges from slightly less than 15 feet at Section HB to 120 feet at Section HJ where none has been removed. The average thickness in the Horseshoe Hills is about 55 feet. Pre-Late Devonian erosion has cut deeper toward the west, so the member thickens gradually but erratically toward the east. In the Bridger Mountains (Pl. 2) the thickness ranges from 70 feet at Flathead Pass to 215 feet at Baldy Mountain, averaging about 120 feet. From the Bridger Mountains to Yellowstone National Park (excluding Mill Creek) the average thickness is slightly over 50 feet. From Mill Creek to Swamp Lake (Pl. 3) none of the member was removed by pre-Late Devonian erosion; its thickness is relatively constant near 200 feet.

Throughout the Sage Member most beds of limestone and limestone-pebble conglomerate are somewhat glauconitic and dolomitic, and the pebbles of the conglomerate are small, flat, rounded, and actually of pebble or granule size; many with oxidized outer rims are stained by limonite (*see* Pl. 6, fig. 1). Shale beds of the Sage Member are grayish green, soft, and commonly contain stringers or pods of limestone. These characteristics distinguish it from the overlying Grove Creek Member. The top is above the highest bed of soft green shale, or the highest bed of glauconitic limestone that occurs near a change in slope in the upper part of the Snowy Range Formation. The Grove Creek Member contains beds of cobble or boulder conglomerate, and if one of these occurs near the break in slope, it is chosen as the base of the Grove Creek Member.

The base of the Sage Member is the base of the lowest bed of columnar limestone. Where columnar limestone is absent the base of the member is the base of the lowest bed of relatively pure, (containing little silt) gray limestone or limestone-pebble conglomerate.

Study of very well-exposed sections along Soda Butte Creek and Clark Fork Canyon has provided clues to the origin of the most common type of limestone-pebble conglomerate of the Sage Member (Type 2 of Lochman, 1949, p. 52; Lochman-Balk, 1957, p. 143). Evidence suggests that beds of limestone-pebble conglomerate are concentrates of limestone "pods" that had formed in slight depressions such as ripple marks (*see* Pl. 6, figs. 3, 4).

Pods from beds of shale have been examined in thin section and on acid-etched surfaces. They are composed of microcrystalline calcite or dolomite with high percentages of clay. Apparently they formed from an original small concentration of microcrystalline ooze or pellets, along with clay and a few tiny fragments of fossils. These pods are remarkably similar to the pebbles that occur in limestone-pebble conglomerate.

Bed GR 235.6 at North Grove Creek illustrates clearly the mode of occurrence of pods (*see* Pl. 6, fig. 3). This thin bed of calcareous shale or argillaceous limestone has ripples on its upper surface. In the troughs are elongate, flat, subrounded pods of limestone. At Fox Creek and other localities where shale beds of the Sage Member are exposed such pods can be seen lying parallel to bedding surfaces (*see* Pl. 6, fig. 4). Thin sections show that pods in shale are accumulations of lime ooze or fecal pellets and lime in depressions on the Cambrian sea floor.

Thin sections of limestone-pebble conglomerate (Pl. 7, fig. 3) show that the pebbles are not composed of the same kind of limestone as that of the matrix that surrounds them (*e.g.*, FOX 92.4) but of microcrystalline limestone or dolomite, or pellet limestone or dolomite, resembling the composition of pods from shale. Pellet-bearing and nonpellet-bearing pebbles both contain much clay, bespeaking deposition in turbid water (Lochman, 1957, p. 144). Matrix that surrounds the pebbles is mainly composed of fossil fragments and sparry calcite, with local admixtures of glauconite, quartz silt, pyrite, and other minor constituents. The fabric of beds of limestone-pebble conglomerate indicates deposition by currents that were strong enough to transport pebbles and fossil fragments and to sweep away clay-size particles. The rounded pebbles do not necessarily mean that currents were strong enough, or transportation far enough to round them; the pebbles were already flat and round as they existed in the shale prior to their concentration into beds of limestone-pebble conglomerate.

The history of formation of a bed of limestone-pebble conglomerate may be reconstructed as follows. Currents that were carrying particles of clay and depositing them as shale had sufficient velocity to ripple the muddy surface of the sea floor and to carry particles of microcrystalline calcite or minute fecal pellets and concentrate them in troughs of ripples. These small accumulations of calcareous material became semiconsolidated. Perhaps the water was lime-saturated or lime was concentrated and secreted by algae that preferred the incipient "pods" over the soft shale as a substrate upon which to grow (*see* description of *Tetonophycus blackwelderi*). After several feet of shale and pods had accumulated, some disturbance such as a storm created stronger currents that swept away the upper surface of shale and concentrated the pods and large fragments of fossils into loosely packed beds. This accumulation of pods and fossils provided a porous framework that later was cemented by sparry calcite. Deposition of conglomerate by currents produced by local disturbances such as storms may account for the lenticular shape of most beds (Pl. 5, fig. 1; Pl. 6, figs. 4, 5). Except for a thick ledge in the *Idahoia wyomingensis* Subzone that is pebbly at most localities, individual beds of limestone-pebble conglomerate are not traceable for more than short distances.

Lochman (1949, p. 54) believes that this type of limestone-pebble conglomerate was deposited at depths of less than 75 feet. Its presence in association with algal limestone bears out this conjecture (Cloud, 1942, p. 370–372; Cloud and Barnes, 1957, p. 194–197). The uniformly fine grain size of the terrigenous sediments implies deposition at considerable distance from shore, estimated by Lochman (1957, p. 144) to be anywhere from 100 to 1500 miles.

GROVE CREEK MEMBER (DORF AND LOCHMAN, 1940, p. 543–545): The Grove Creek Limestone-Pebble Conglomerate was described as a formation, but

Lochman-Balk (1956b, p. 609–613) proposed that it be considered a member of the Snowy Range Formation; this usage is accepted here.

The type locality of the Grove Creek Member is on the south bank of North Grove Creek, a few miles east of Red Lodge, Montana (*see* Grove Creek section, easternmost of the measured sections, p. 76).

The Grove Creek Member is Trempealeauan in the area studied. However, it is no longer considered the "Trempealeau equivalent" (Dorf and Lochman, 1940, p. 543), because the Franconian-Trempealeauan boundary now is drawn at the top of the *Ptychaspis-Prosaukia* Zone (Bell, Berg, and Nelson, 1956, p. 435) instead of at the higher "*Dikelocephalus postrectus* Zone" (Howell and others, 1944).

The top of the Grove Creek Member has been removed by faulting or erosion throughout the area of study; no Ordovician fossils have been found.

The Grove Creek Member commonly stands as a vertical cliff of dolomitic yellowish-orange limestone or limestone-pebble conglomerate and hard, dolomitic or calcareous, dusky-gray shale. At the type locality and at Mill Creek, however, it is less resistant and makes a more gentle slope than is typical. Even at these localities it is more resistant to weathering than is the shaly Sage Member and makes a steeper slope. In the Horseshoe Hills and Bridger Mountains, dips are so high that the break in slope between the Sage and Grove Creek members is less apparent.

In typical exposures the base of the member occurs very near the base of a vertical cliff. Where it is pebbly many of the "pebbles" are larger than those of the Sage Member. Some cobbles are composed of rounded fragments of limestone-pebble conglomerate. Many cobbles and pebbles of the Grove Creek Member are partly or completely penetrated by peculiar holes (Dorf and Lochman, 1940, p. 543) which have about the same diameter as the abundant crinoid columnals in the adjacent matrix. Possibly the holes in the pebbles mark places of attachment of crinoids or similar pelmatozoans (Pl. 6, fig. 2).

The Grove Creek Member contains more dolomite and less glauconite than the Sage Member. The shale of the Grove Creek Member is not soft and green like that of the Sage, but hard, splintery, and dusky gray. The base is the bed nearest the level at which most of these lithologic changes occur. At some localities it is the lowest cobble conglomerate; at others it is the bed above the highest glauconite bed. A reliable marker for the base of the member is a change in the shale from soft and green to hard and dusky gray. These lithologic changes commonly occur within a few feet of the break in slope near the top of the formation; any combination of them defines the lower boundary.

The top of the Grove Creek Member and of the Snowy Range Formation is the boundary between it and the Maywood unit or the Bighorn Formation. Where Maywood beds overlie the Grove Creek Member the latter either is altered or truncated at the top. The average thickness of beds is greater in the Grove Creek Member than in the Maywood; the Grove Creek is yellowish orange rather than dusky brown or purple, and it is not petroliferous like the Maywood where it overlies the Grove Creek.

Where the Grove Creek is overlain by the Bighorn Formation the boundary is sharp, but except at Mill Creek and North Grove Creek this boundary is produced by a fault (Pierce, 1957). At these two localities the Bighorn Dolomite is more resistant than the Grove Creek and stands out as a cliff above the steplike ledges of the Grove Creek. Along Soda Butte Creek and Clark Fork Canyon the Grove Creek and Bighorn are in fault contact, and the Bighorn forms a slope above the vertical dolomitic cliff of the Grove Creek (Pl. 5, fig. 2). Here the base of the Bighorn Formation contains blocks of limestone-pebble conglomerate as much as 1 foot in length that obviously are derived from some part of the Snowy Range Formation. Pierce has demonstrated the existence of a great thrust sheet in this area (the Heart Mountain thrust), so the blocks of conglomerate probably are constituents of a dolomitized breccia associated with the lower part of the thrust sheet.

The Grove Creek is the thinnest member of the Snowy Range Formation. Its position at the top of the formation made it the member most affected by Ordovician and/or Devonian weathering and erosion, so its distribution is more irregular than is that of the lower two members. It is present only at one locality in the Horseshoe Hills; it is 48 feet thick at Section HJ (Pl. 1). The member is present at four localities in the Bridger Mountains (Pl. 2), but there it is overlain by the Maywood unit, indicating possible removal or alteration of an indeterminate footage of rock at its top. Its thickness ranges from 6 feet at Sacajawea Peak to 44 feet at Bridger Peak. This maximum is not much less than the thickness of the member at its type locality; therefore, little may have been eroded at Bridger Peak. The Grove Creek is absent between the Bridgers and Mill Creek and at Crowfoot Ridge. Where it is present, and the Maywood unit is absent, its thickness ranges from about 15 feet at Mill Creek and Upper Fox Creek (Pl. 3) to 48 feet at North Grove Creek.

ORDOVICIAN SYSTEM

Bighorn Formation (Darton, 1904, p. 395–396). The Bighorn Dolomite overlies the Grove Creek Member of the Snowy Range Formation at all measured sections from Mill Creek eastward. At Mill Creek and North Grove Creek it stands as a cliff above the more gently sloping Grove Creek Member. At the localities along Soda Butte Creek and Clark Fork Canyon the Bighorn makes a gentle slope immediately above the Grove Creek Member, but where it is not covered by Tertiary pyroclastic breccia the main part of the formation stands in a high vertical cliff.

The lower part of the Bighorn Formation is pale yellow to brownish-yellow, medium- to coarse-grained dolomite. The darker parts are petroliferous but not as much so as the Jefferson Formation.

Where the Bighorn Formation overlies the Snowy Range Formation, the latter has not been affected by the pre-Late Devonian weathering and erosion that produced the Maywood unit. Instead, it was subject only to pre-Upper Ordovician erosion that gave the Grove Creek Member some of its distinctive characteristics.

BOUNDARIES: Only at Mill Creek and North Grove Creek was the lower part of the Bighorn Formation observed in normal stratigraphic contact with the Snowy Range Formation. There the beds of the two formations appear to be concordant, but Hanson (1952, p. 22) presents convincing evidence for pre-Upper Ordovician erosion which removed an undetermined number of feet of rock from the top of the Snowy Range Formation. This concordant disconformity merely shows that there was no strong local deformation of the Snowy Range Formation during the pre-Upper Ordovician interval of erosion.

According to Sloss and Laird (1947, p. 1408, Fig. 2) the Bighorn is overlain by the Maywood unit in the Little Rocky Mountains.

DEVONIAN SYSTEM

Maywood unit (Emmons and Calkins, 1913, p. 64–65). Strata that lie between limestone-pebble conglomerate of the Snowy Range Formation and dusky-brown thick-bedded limestone or dolomite of the Jefferson Formation in southwestern Montana and northwestern Wyoming comprise the Maywood unit. Emmons and Calkins (1913) described it as a formation in the Philipsburg quadrangle; its type locality is at Maywood Ridge, west of Princeton, Montana.

ORIGIN: Lochman (1950b, p. 2221) and Hanson (1952, p. 20–22) present convincing evidence that the Maywood unit is the preserved remnant of a soil or zone of chemical weathering that developed before advance of the sea in which the Jefferson Formation was deposited. The thickness of the Maywood unit and the depth to which weathering and erosion cut into underlying formations depended upon regional structure and local topography. Considering its somewhat erratic thickness, the different depths to which it has penetrated underlying rocks, and the variety of formations that it overlies (Hanson, 1952, p. 21), no other hypothesis seems to explain all the facts.

NOMENCLATURE: Lochman (1950b, p. 2213) treated the Maywood as a formation, and Hanson (1952), Verall (1954, Ph.D. thesis, Princeton Univ.), and McMannis (1955) follow this usage. Her hypothesis as to the origin of this unit is accepted here, but the recommendation of the Stratigraphic Commission (Cohee and others, 1956, p. 2009) concerning the naming of soil-stratigraphic units ("paleosols") is followed. The suggestion is made that such a unit be given a geographic name, but that it not be given formal status as a formation or member.

Many authors (*e.g.*, Deiss, 1936; Lochman and Duncan, 1944; Sloss and Laird, 1947) referred the rock of the Maywood unit to the "Dry Creek Shale" ever since Weed (1900, p. 286) introduced this error into the literature. According to Lochman (1950b, p. 2213) the "beds of undetermined age" and the "basal Devonian unit" of Sloss and Laird (1947) are parts of the Maywood unit.

AGE: Commonly the entire Maywood unit is unfossiliferous (Emmons and Calkins, 1913, p. 65; Deiss, 1936, p. 1310; Lochman and Duncan, 1944, p. 3, 8–9; Sloss and Laird, 1947, p. 1407; Lochman, 1950b, p. 2209; Hanson, 1952, p. 17; McMannis, 1955, p. 1396; and personal observation). McMannis (1955, p. 1396) cites evidence for a possible Middle Devonian age based on identification of fossils from the upper part of the unit. This corroborates Sloss and Laird's (1947, p. 1407) stratigraphic evidence that the Maywood beds are part of the Devonian cycle of sedimentation. They record (Sloss and Laird, 1947, p. 1407–1409; Fig. 2) Maywood-type rock above Cambrian rocks in the Horseshoe Hills and above Upper Ordovician rocks in the Little Rocky Mountains. Hanson (1952, p. 11, 20–22) has seen the Maywood unit in contact with the Middle Cambrian Park Shale Formation in the Madison Range and cites evidence that it lies on rock of the Precambrian Belt Series in the southwestern corner of Montana. Regardless of what underlies it, the Maywood always occurs directly below the Upper Devonian Jefferson Formation, with a gradational boundary (Emmons and Calkins, 1913, p. 64; Sloss and Laird, 1947, p. 1407). Available faunal and stratigraphic evidence supports the contention of Sloss and Laird that the Maywood unit (*i.e.,* their units between the "Dry Creek Shale" and the Jefferson Formation) belongs to the Devonian cycle of sedimentation. They hypothesize (Sloss and Laird, 1947, p. 1409) that their unfossiliferous "beds of undetermined age" may be weathered or otherwise altered Cambrian rock that was reworked by an advancing Devonian sea.

LITHOLOGY AND BOUNDARIES: The base of the Maywood unit appears to be concordant with beds of the Snowy Range Formation below it. Where Maywood is present, the portion of the Snowy Range Formation that is just below the boundary is more dolomitic and limonitic than is normal for Snowy Range. The dolomite content gradually increases upward in the Snowy Range Formation, and glauconite and fossils decrease until both are absent. The base of the Maywood is placed at the lowest bed above which no fossils and little glauconite occur, the consequence of dolomitization that has obliterated most of the original features of the rock, including limestone-pebble conglomerate. Beds of the Maywood unit are much thinner and redder than those of the Snowy Range.

At Squaw Creek and Flying "D" Ranch the Maywood differs somewhat from its normal manifestation in the Horseshoe Hills and Bridger Mountains. At these two localities it is more completely dolomitic, with thick beds of coarse-grained dolomite and no intervening thin beds of limestone or reddish-purple silty dolomite. The color is light tan or gray, and from a distance it looks much like the limestone ledge locally present near the middle of the Sage Member of the Snowy Range. When broken, it is seen to be unfossiliferous and uniform in texture. Instead of forming a slope like the normal, purple, thin-bedded Maywood, it stands up as a resistant ledge above the slope of the Sage Member. This appears to represent a more complete alteration of some of the Sage beds during the pre-Late Devonian interval of erosion that produced the Maywood.

At Crowfoot Ridge alteration of the Sage beds is so complete that recognition of the Maywood unit is difficult. The only difference between the 23 feet of rock that may be considered Maywood and the overlying Jefferson Formation is a subtle difference in bedding. For purposes of mapping, the dolomite cliff above the Snowy Range Formation must be included with the Jefferson Formation. However, the lowermost 23 feet has bedding characteristics similar to the underlying Sage Member and similar to the Maywood unit at Sections FD and SC. The Jefferson Formation is much more dolomitic here than is normal. Perhaps it has been secondarily dolomitized along with the underlying "Maywood" part; this might account for their close resemblance.

Above the thin zone of transition between normal Maywood and the Snowy Range Formation, the Maywood consists of thin beds of yellow, reddish-orange or brown dolomite or very dolomitic limestone and a few beds of gray dolomitic shale. The upper part of the unit becomes increasingly petroliferous subjacent to the very petroliferous lower beds of the Jefferson Formation. The uppermost beds of the Maywood are less red and more brown in color; they resemble the lower Jefferson in color and odor but resemble the rest of the Maywood in bedding and weathering characteristics.

The top of the Maywood unit in the Horseshoe Hills and Bridger Mountains is the base of a prominent and persistent 3-foot ledge of dusky-brown, medium-bedded, petroliferous limestone or dolomite at the base of the Jefferson Formation. South of the Bridger Mountains the boundary is drawn where the light-gray to yellow, thin-bedded dolomite of the Maywood gives way to the thicker-bedded, dusky-brown, petroliferous limestone or dolomite of the Jefferson Formation.

DISTRIBUTION: Where studied, the basal part of the Maywood unit is transitional with some portion of the Snowy Range Formation. In the Horseshoe Hills (Pl. 1) it lies on the Sage Member everywhere except at Section HJ where it lies on altered Grove Creek rock. In the northern half of the Bridger Range (Pl. 2) the Maywood overlies the Sage Member. It lies on some portion of the Grove Creek Member at Ross Peak, Bridger Peak, and Baldy Mountain in the Bridgers, and at Mount Ellis. In the sections at Flying "D" and Squaw Creek the Maywood unit again overlies the Sage Member. At Crowfoot Ridge (Pl. 3) the rock above the Snowy Range Formation is assigned to the Jefferson Formation (Deiss, 1936, p. 1324, Fig. 10) because the entire cliff of Devonian rock is a homogenous white dolomite. The lowermost 23 feet of this formation is bedded somewhat differently from the remainder and may have been Maywood-type rock before its final dolomitization. The Maywood unit is not present in measured sections from Mill Creek eastward (Pl. 3).

THICKNESS: The thickness of the Maywood unit depends upon depth of weathering and erosion of the formations that contributed its material, upon the amount of this material deposited, and upon the topography of the land surface that it covered. Pre-Late Devonian weathering and erosion cut deepest in the southwestern part of Montana (*illustrated by* Hanson, 1952, Pl. 8, fig. B). In the Horseshoe Hills and Bridger Mountains the thickness ranges between 15 and 110 feet, averaging about 55 feet. The peculiar Maywood lithology at Flying "D," Squaw Creek, and perhaps at Crowfoot Ridge is fairly uniform in thickness: 42 feet at Flying "D"; 32 feet at Squaw Creek; and a possible 23 feet at Crowfoot Ridge.

Jefferson Formation (Peale, 1893, p. 27). Limestone or dolomite of the Jefferson Formation overlies the Maywood unit in southwestern Montana (Sloss and Laird, 1947, p. 1408; Sloss and Moritz, 1951, p. 2151). The usual practice in this area is to map the Maywood along with the Snowy Range Formation and to draw a boundary between the top of the Maywood and the base of the Jefferson (P. Verall, 1954, Ph.D. thesis, Princeton Univ., Pl. 1; McMannis, 1955, Pl. 1). In the Horseshoe Hills and the Bridger Mountains the base of the Jefferson Formation is mapped on a prominent 3-foot ledge of dusky-brown petroliferous limestone or dolomite. Above this basal bed is a short interval of thin-bedded, less resistant limestone that weathers to a gentle recess, above which is a high cliff of dusky-brown limestone and dolomite. Where the Bighorn Formation is absent, the high cliff of the Jefferson Formation makes it easy to find the Snowy Range-Maywood interval that forms a slope below it.

PETROGRAPHY

GENERAL STATEMENT

Representative samples of rock from the Snowy Range Formation and Maywood unit were studied in thin section and by means of sawed and acid-etched surfaces in order to compare rock types and to interpret sources of sediment and environments of deposition. The results are summarized below, and a few representative thin sections are described and illustrated. Terminology and classification of sedimentary rocks originate with Folk (1954; 1957; 1959; *in* Barnes and others, 1959) to whose work the reader is referred for definitions. Photomicrographs are by J. S. Pittman, Jr.

THIN-SECTION DESCRIPTIONS

Snowy Range Formation, Dry Creek Member

Sample number. FOX 7.8

Rock name. Slightly clayey siltstone; calcitic submature glauconitic arkose

Composition. Terrigenous: 40 per cent angular quartz silt, average size about .015 mm (15 per cent with straight extinction, 25 per cent with undulose extinction), some with authigenic overgrowths; 20 per cent angular to subangular, fresh orthoclase silt, average size about .015 mm, some with authigenic overgrowths; 8 per cent flakey, slightly parallel-oriented illite clay. Allochemical: 3 per cent glauconite pellets. Orthochemical: 22 per cent sparry calcite cement; 5 per cent medium-crystalline euhedral dolomite; 2 per cent pyrite cubes; stains of limonite and hematite.

Fabric. Terrigenous grains are well sorted; illite flakes are slightly oriented, giving weak bedding; calcite cement is evenly distributed.

Interpretation. Silt-size quartz and orthoclase were derived from a distant granitic and gneissic terrane, possibly outcroppings of the Belt Series and rocks of the Canadian Shield. Freshness of feldspar indicates a moderate to cold or arid climate in the source area and low humidity. Angularity of quartz and feldspar is the result of the small size of the grains. Illite may be derived from the same source area or may have formed on the sea floor in a potassium-rich environment. Deposition probably was in shallow water, far from shore, in an area of gentle currents that were competent to transport silt and to orient illite flakes. Dolomite probably formed during diagenesis, and limonite formed around the rhombs, probably deposited by solutions during and after diagenesis. These solutions may be responsible for authigenic overgrowths on some grains of quartz and feldspar.

Sample number. FOX 31.2

Rock name. Sandy glauconitic biosparite

Composition. Terrigenous: 20 per cent angular very fine quartz sand, average size about .08 mm (10 per cent with straight extinction, 10 per cent with undulose extinction); 5 per cent angular very fine orthoclase sand, average size about .08 mm, some with authigenic overgrowths, some with incipient glauconitization around edges; 2 per cent illite clay flakes. Allochemical: 15 per cent glauconite pellets. Biogenic: 45 per cent pelmatozoan, trilobite and brachiopod fragments. Orthochemical: 10 per cent sparry calcite cement; 3 per cent limonite stain.

Fabric. Terrigenous grains are well sorted; packing and cementation are very loose (rock very friable in hand specimen); there is little evidence of bedding.

Interpretation. Very fine sand-size quartz and orthoclase were derived from erosion of a distant granitic and gneissic terrane under nonhumid conditions. Small size of terrigenous grains throughout the member indicates the distant source; freshness of feldspar postulates a nonhumid or cool climate; quartz with undulose extinction is evidence for gneissic rocks in the source area. Terrigenous grains were deposited with fossil fragments and glauconite pellets, then partly cemented by sparry calcite. Later, solutions produced the limonite stain by oxidizing iron present in glauconite or pyrite or by introducing the stain from elsewhere.

Snowy Range Formation, Sage Member

Sample number. HA 45.8 (Pl. 7, fig. 1)

Rock name. Dolomitized glauconitic intraclastic biosparite

Composition. Terrigenous: 1 per cent rounded fine quartz sand (0.4 mm). Allochemical: 44 per cent intraclasts of medium-crystalline dolomite; 5 per cent glauconite pellets. Biogenic: 20 per cent fossils (replaced by dolomite, hence not identifiable). Orthochemical: 30 per cent matrix of rock, replaced by medium-crystalline dolomite; trace of limonite stain.

Fabric. Intraclasts of biomicrite, sparry calcite cement, and fossil fragments are replaced by medium-crystalline dolomite making outlines of fossils and intraclasts irregular and vague. Dolomite rhombs pit a few quartz grains.

Interpretation. Original intraclastic biosparite was secondarily dolomitized, probably by weathering. Stratigraphic evidence indicates that this took place in the Devonian.

Sample number. HG 45.8 (Pl. 5, figs. 5, 7–8)

Rock name. Algal limestone (*Collenia magna*)

Composition. Terrigenous: trace of quartz and illite. Orthochemical: 99 per cent algal microcrystalline calcite; 1 per cent medium crystalline sparry calcite as pore filling.

Fabric. Homogenous micrite with stylolite-like markings that may contain illite; areas of recrystallization; a few pellets.

Interpretation. Microcrystalline calcite was precipitated by algae, growing into high columns known as *Collenia magna.* Some quartz grains and fossil fragments (seen in other samples) may have been washed in while the algae grew; it probably projected a few inches above the sea floor, or it would contain more detrital material.

Sample number. YO 196.9 (Pl. 6, fig. 1; Pl. 7, fig. 3)

Rock name. Fossiliferous intrasparite

Composition. Allochemical: 64 per cent intraclasts composed of microcrystalline calcite; 1 per cent glauconite pellets. Biogenic: 10 per cent elongate curved trilobite and brachiopod fragments. Orthochemical: 20 per cent coarsely crystalline sparry calcite cement; 5 per cent finely crystalline dolomite in intraclasts; trace of pyrite cubes; limonite stain.

Fabric. Dolomitic pelmicrite intraclasts oriented at random in a hash of fossil fragments and allochemical calcite, cemented by sparry calcite. Some intraclasts with limonite rims; some truncated at upper bedding plane where microcrystalline algal calcite adjoins.

Interpretation. Intraclasts and fossil fragments were deposited on the sea bottom. Intraclasts contained some pyrite or iron-bearing dolomite that was oxidized around the edges, giving each intraclast a limonite rim. This hash was all buried and partly or completely cemented by sparry calcite. Then solutions or currents excavated some and dissolved off the tops of the limestone pebbles that projected above the cement. Algae or gentle currents then deposited microcrystalline ooze on the surface that had been exposed, and the whole rock became cemented together. The little corrosion surface is typical of many diastems that occur in the Sage Member. The algal limestone above the corrosion surface may be a bed of *Tetonophycus blackwelderi.*

Sample number. YO 238.2 (Pl. 7, fig. 6)

Rock name. Dolomitic illitic shale with limonite stain

Composition. Terrigenous: 90 per cent illite clay flakes. Allochemical: trace of glauconite pellets. Biogenic: trace of fossil fragments. Orthochemical: 8 per cent medium-crystalline euhedral dolomite; 2 per cent finely crystalline sparry calcite cement; 1 per cent pyrite cubes.

Fabric. Illite flakes all oriented parallel to bedding and fissility; other minerals distributed randomly.

Interpretation. Illite mud was deposited on the sea floor along with a few fossil fragments and glauconite pellets. The mud probably contained some organic matter which decayed and aided formation of tiny crystals of pyrite. Later solutions introduced dolomite, and recent weathering produced the limonite stain by oxidation of some of the iron in the pyrite.

Sample number. FOX 94.2

Rock name. Fossiliferous intrasparrudite with intraclasts of biopelsparite, biopelmicrite, and micrite

Composition. Allochemical: 55 per cent intraclasts composed of microcrystalline calcite; 1 per cent glauconite pellets. Biogenic: 6 per cent trilobite and brachiopod fragments. Orthochemical: 35 per cent sparry calcite cement; 3 per cent medium-crystalline euhedral dolomite; trace of pyrite; limonite stain.

Fabric. Intraclasts of biopelsparite, biopelmicrite, and micrite in matrix of fossil fragments and microcrystalline calcite, all cemented by sparry calcite. Dolomite rhombs, rimmed with limonite, cut into edges of fossils. Coarse sparry calcite below each intraclast and fossil. One intraclast is broken, and the fracture filled with brachiopod fragments and sparry calcite.

Interpretation. Intraclasts and fossil fragments were deposited; then a microcrystalline ooze settled down over them falling into interstices but not filling in under the large fragments. Compaction or shrinkage during diagenesis broke some intraclasts and packed the mass somewhat. Sparry calcite cemented the rock together; then dolomite replaced some of the calcite, cutting into the edges of some fossil fragments. Limonite rims of the dolomite rhombs indicate oxidation, at least during diagenesis. Intraclasts have pyrite, indicating that they formed under more reducing conditions, probably along with mud and organic matter from which they later were excavated by currents and concentrated into the bed where they now lie.

Sample number. FOX 202.4

Rock name. Very finely crystalline microsparite. (This is a limestone pod from a shale bed.)

Composition. Terrigenous: 5 per cent illite flakes. Orthochemical: 95 per cent homogeneous very finely crystalline (.015 mm) clear calcite; trace of euhedral dolomite.

Fabric. Calcite distributed homogeneously, illite in two wavy bands about .02 mm wide, along with a few dolomite rhombs. Calcite shows possible relict pellet structure near edges of pod.

Interpretation. Microcrystalline calcite ooze and possibly some fecal pellets were deposited with a few clay flakes in a ripple or other depression in greenish gray shale. This later recrystallized to a microsparite (very finely crystalline [.015 mm], clear sparry calcite). Pods like this one, when excavated by currents, were slightly rounded and accumulated in beds; they form the limestone-pebble conglomerates that characterize the Snowy Range Formation.

Sample number. UFOX 39.5

Rock name. Slightly recrystallized intraclastic biomicrite

Composition. Allochemical: 85 per cent microcrystalline calcite. Biogenic: 5 per cent fossil fragments, chiefly trilobites. Orthochemical: 10 per cent sparry calcite cement; trace of dolomite.

Fabric. Coarse sand- to granule-size intraclasts of biopelmicrite with worn ends of fossils at their edges showing abrasion of intraclasts, in matrix of biomicrite, all cemented by sparry calcite. Rock is cut by many little fractures that are filled with sparry calcite. Incipient recrystallization has altered some intraclasts to dismicrites.

Interpretation. Intraclasts and fossils were picked up by currents and carried into an area where microcrystalline ooze (perhaps precipitated by algae) covered them. Fractures in the rock were caused by compaction and burrowing organisms. (Some areas of sparry calcite look like worm burrows.) Incipient recrystallization is indicated by fuzzy outlines of some intraclasts. This may be a bed of *Tetonophycus blackwelderi,* although it was not recognized as such in the field.

Sample number. FOX 146.2

Rock name. Partly recrystallized biopelsparite

Composition. Biogenic: 15 per cent trilobite fragments, commonly unbroken. Orthochemical: 45 per cent sparry calcite cement; 35 per cent pellets, many of which have formed by recrystallization; 5 per cent medium-crystalline euhedral dolomite; trace of pyrite; limonite stain.

Fabric. Fossils oriented subparallel, with pellets on top of them, and coarsely crystalline sparry calcite under the arcs of curved fossils. A few dolomite rhombs cut edges of fossils. Many pellets and much coarsely crystalline sparry calcite has formed by recrystallization.

Interpretation. Gentle currents deposited fossils and allochemical constituents as a loose ooze. Orthochemical calcite cemented them together, large crystals growing in the pore spaces beneath fossil fragments. Later dolomite rhombs replaced some calcite, cutting edges of fossils. Loose packing of fossils and pellets may indicate replacement of original pelmicrite by coarse sparry calcite, the detrital constituents of the rock being spread apart by growth of large calcite crystals.

Snowy Range Formation, Grove Creek Member

Sample number. BP 245.5 (Pl. 7, fig. 5)

Rock name. Fossiliferous finely and coarsely crystalline dolomite

Composition. Terrigenous: trace of fine quartz silt. Allochemical: 2 per cent glauconite pellets. Biogenic: 8 per cent fossil fragments in various stages of replacement by dolomite. Orthochemical: 85 per cent finely and coarsely crystalline euhedral dolomite (two distinct sizes); 5 per cent sparry calcite cement in patches; trace of hematite.

Fabric. Not obviously bedded, but fossils oriented subparallel. Few coarse sand-size intraclasts present. Fossils in several stages of replacement by dolomite: (1) unaltered; (2) rhombs of finely crystalline dolomite within boundaries of original shell material; (3) slightly larger rhombs of dolomite, some cutting edges of fossil; (4) patches of coarse crystalline dolomite arranged in the shape of fossil (fossil completely replaced). Finely crystalline dolomite rhombs have no obvious nuclei; coarsely crystalline rhombs have nuclei of hematite or pyrite and limonite bands outlining zoned crystals. Some pellets of glauconite partly replaced by dolomite. Quartz grains have overgrowths.

Interpretation. Intraclastic biomicrite or biosparite was deposited, then cemented by sparry calcite. Some dolomite formed during diagenesis, especially under the curves of fossils and intraclasts. The rock was then subjected to weathering or to the action of magnesium-bearing solutions that produced large crystals of dolomite that replaced some of all previous constituents, including some of the diagenetic dolomite. This late dolomite is recognizable by its high content of iron, probably derived from the weathering of grains of pyrite, hematite, or glauconite. Stratigraphic evidence indicates that this weathering took place in the Ordovician.

Sample number. FOX 257.3

Rock name. Recrystallized dolomitized intrasparrudite

Composition. Terrigenous: 5 per cent illite clay flakes; 2 per cent angular quartz and microcline silt. Allochemical: 40 per cent intraclasts composed of microcrystalline calcite with pellets, partly replaced by dolomite; 10 per cent medium-crystalline, slightly rounded calcite grains; 5 per cent microcrystalline calcite. Biogenic: 5 per cent elongate fossil fragments, trilobites, and brachiopods. Orthochemical: 43 per cent medium-crystalline (.03–.15 mm) euhedral dolomite rhombs, many with pyrite nuclei and iron-stain banding; 30 per cent sparry calcite cement; trace of pyrite and limonite in dolomite rhombs.

Fabric. Granule-size intraclasts of pelsparite and micrite bedded with limonite-stained clay and euhedral dolomite, cemented by sparry calcite. Original fabric obscured by dolomite replacement. Terrigenous grains, some with overgrowths, scattered throughout.

Interpretation. Intraclasts and fossil fragments were deposited and buried by microcrystalline ooze. Compaction broke some intraclasts and diagenesis produced a few crystals of dolomite around the fossils. Later dolomitization and recrystallization produced coarse crystalline sparry calcite and coarse crystalline dolomite. The late dolomite occurs without preference in both intraclasts and matrix. Iron bands in dolomite rhombs show that late dolomitization took place under oxidizing conditions, probably weathering during part of the Ordovician.

Sample number. UFOX 57.6 (Pl. 5, figs. 3–4, 6)

Rock name. Algal limestone (*Tetonophycus blackwelderi*)

Composition. Terrigenous: trace of illite in stylolites. Allochemical: 80 per cent microcrystalline calcite, precipitated or trapped by algae. Biogenic: 10 per cent elongate trilobite and brachiopod fragments. Orthochemical: 10 per cent finely crystalline sparry calcite cement.

Fabric. Irregular patches of microcrystalline calcite in matrix of biomicrite and sparry calcite cement, some irregular stylolite-like lines, and patches of incipient recrystallization to coarser sparry calcite.

Interpretation. Algal colonies either precipitated or trapped particles of microcrystalline calcite ooze; shells fell in and were buried. Compaction produced small fractures that were filled by sparry calcite. There are some peculiar chainlike structures in this slide that resemble tiny cells.

Maywood unit

Sample number. HA 65.7 (Pl. 7, fig. 2)

Rock name. Finely crystalline dolomite

Composition. Terrigenous: 5 per cent angular quartz (and feldspar ?) silt. Allochemical: 10 per cent granular microcrystalline calcite; traces of glauconite pellets and collophane. Orthochemical: 70 per cent finely crystalline (.03 mm) euhedral dolomite, replacing other minerals; 15 per cent sparry calcite cement; traces of pyrite, hematite, and limonite.

Fabric. Bedding irregular, with beds of fine-grained and coarser-grained material. Dolomite replaces most other minerals. Some quartz grains have overgrowths. A few fine-grained areas may be intraclasts that have been almost obliterated by dolomitization.

Interpretation. Calcite, quartz, and other minerals were deposited in irregular beds by gentle currents. Some finely crystalline dolomite formed during diagenesis. Later, weathering (stratigraphic evidence indicating Devonian weathering) caused further growth of dolomite crystals which replaced other minerals, and oxidized pyrite to limonite and hematite.

Sample number. FD 98 (Pl. 7, fig. 4)

Rock name. Homogeneous medium-crystalline dolomite

Composition. Orthochemical: 95 per cent medium crystalline (.08 mm) subhedral dolomite; 5 per cent sparry calcite cement; trace of limonite.

Fabric. Irregularly bedded, with stylolite-like bands, a few healed fractures containing sparry calcite.

Interpretation. The entire sample is dolomitized; it probably was algal limestone of the Snowy Range Formation that was dolomitized during Devonian weathering. It strongly resembles unaltered algal limestone from other localities.

SUMMARY

Snowy Range Formation, Dry Creek Member. Only siltstone and limestone beds of the Dry Creek Member were studied in thin section. An X-rayed sample of the shale was shown to be composed of illite, with slight admixtures of quartz.

Beds of terrigenous material in the Dry Creek Member contain grains of angular quartz and feldspar that range in size from very fine silt to very fine sand (about .015–.08 mm). Terrigenous grains along with some transported and some authigenic glauconite were deposited with loose packing and later cemented by sparry calcite. Angularity and freshness of silt-size feldspar grains show that the climate in the source area was not excessively humid or hot. A high percentage of quartz with undulose extinction (50 per cent or more of total quartz) is evidence for derivation from terrane containing some metamorphic rocks. Terrigenous grains may have come from erosion of the Belt rocks and igneous rocks of the shield areas (*see* paleogeographic map by Lochman, 1949, Pl. 6).

Presence of a predominantly terrigenous unit above the chemical rock of the Pilgrim Formation probably reflects a tectonic event in the source area of the terrigenous material. The source area may have been uplifted slightly, initiating renewed erosion, or the sea may have withdrawn enough to bring the area of deposition of the Dry Creek Member closer to the supply of terrigenous material. Perhaps both events transpired at once, with uplift causing withdrawal. The lithic change between the Pilgrim Formation and the Dry Creek Member is considered to be the most significant and widespread in the entire Cambrian sequence of this area (Lochman-Balk, 1956b, p. 620). The change occurs near the Dresbachian-Franconian boundary as does the disconformity at the top of the Dresbach Formation in the Croixan type area (Berg and others, 1956, p. 7).

Limestone beds near the top of the Dry Creek Member appear to be similar to those in the Sage Member. They are concentrations of fossil fragments (predominantly trilobites and brachiopods) and glauconite, with a few grains of silt, cemented by sparry calcite; some beds are limestone-pebble conglomerate. These are included with the Dry Creek Member because they occur below the base of the columnar limestone that marks the bottom of the Sage Member.

Snowy Range Formation, Sage Member. This unit contains five major rock types; in all, dolomite content increases with proximity to the Maywood unit. Most limestone beds contain dolomite, especially around the fossil fragments, but where they are near the Maywood unit, there is evidence for two stages of dolomitization: one during diagenesis, the other later. Stratigraphic and petrographic evidence point to post-Cambrian, pre-Late Devonian erosion and weathering for the later stage of dolomitization.

(1) LIMESTONE-PEBBLE CONGLOMERATE (INTRACLASTIC LIMESTONE): Limestone-pebble conglomerate (intrasparrudite) is composed of intraclasts of micrite, biomicrite, pelmicrite, or biopelmicrite loosely packed with a matrix of abundant fossil fragments, some glauconite and silt grains, all cemented by sparry calcite with varying amounts of replacement dolomite. The fabric indicates deposition by moderately strong currents that were able to move limestone pebbles and fossil fragments and to wash away microcrystalline ooze. Several beds show evidence of solution on their upper surfaces; pebbles at the tops of the beds are truncated and overlain by fine-grained nonpebbly limestone. Pebbles in many beds have limonitic rims around their peripheries, indicating oxidation during the Cambrian.

(2) ALGAL LIMESTONE: Limestone masses in the form of two "species" of algae are present in the Sage Member. The masses differ in gross form and stratigraphic position and grew on different kinds of substrate but are similar petrographically. *Collenia magna* forms tall, thin columns at the base of the member. It grew directly on clay bottom with no hard substrate. *Tetonophycus blackwelderi* forms beds rather than columns, and it normally overlies a bed of limestone-pebble conglomerate in which the tops of some pebbles have been truncated by action of solutions or currents (Pl. 5, fig. 3; Pl. 6, fig. 1; Pl. 7, fig. 3).

Both forms of algal limestone are composed largely of microcrystalline calcite with stylolite-like bands of clay or dolomite and a few randomly scattered fossil fragments, pellet clusters, or silt grains. Algal limestone is distinguished by its fine grain size and by the presence of irregular streaks that may represent growth lines.

(3) BEDDED LIMESTONE; NONPEBBLY, NONALGAL: Ordinary limestone beds of the Sage Member are trilobite and brachiopod biomicrite, biopelmicrite, biosparite or biopelsparite, with glauconite, dolomite, and pyrite. In many the rhombs of dolomite are concentrated below the concave sides of fossil fragments, with pellets lying on the convex sides. Many have patches where finely crystalline calcite is recrystallized to coarse sparry calcite.

(4) LIMESTONE PODS IN SHALE: Shale beds in the Sage Member contain many rounded, flat, sometimes elongate pods of limestone that occupy ripple troughs and other depressions in the bedding of the shale. The pods are composed of micrite, pelmicrite, or microsparite (micrite that has recrystallized to slightly larger grain size). The fabric is homogeneous, but there may be streaks of clay with tiny crystals of pyrite or dolomite and a few streaks of limonite. Such limestone pods, when excavated from the shale by strong currents, concentrated into beds with fossil fragments, and cemented by sparry calcite, formed beds of limestone-pebble conglomerate. Most pebbles in limestone-pebble conglomerate bear close petrographic resemblance to pods from shale and little resemblance to the limestone matrix in which they occur. This problem is discussed above, with the stratigraphy of the Sage Member.

(5) SHALE: X-ray patterns from shale of the Sage Member bear out petrographic evidence from index of refraction that the clay is illite. Thin sections contain dolomite rhombs, pyrite cubes, glauconite pellets, or limonite stain in small quantities. The shale commonly is fissile, but where weathered it is crumbly or slightly plastic. Some shale beds contain flakes of muscovite that are larger than illite flakes.

Snowy Range Formation, Grove Creek Member. This member differs from the Sage primarily in its higher content of dolomite. Evidence from thin sections suggests that the Grove Creek dolomite is postdiagenetic. The Grove Creek underlies the Bighorn Formation at most localities, so was not affected by post-Upper Ordovician to pre-Late Devonian weathering that produced dolomite in the Maywood unit. Limestone-cobble conglomerate and very little glauconite in the Grove Creek indicate that it may have been deposited under conditions more turbulent than those under which the Sage Member was deposited.

Probable postdiagenetic dolomite of the Grove Creek Member differs from diagenetic (early replacement) dolomite in its larger grain size and high iron content. Large rhombs of late dolomite are zoned, with bands of iron oxide marking the zones. These large rhombs cut the edges of fossil fragments, intraclasts, and glauconite pellets. Diagenetic dolomite is present only in sparry calcite cement, but large rhombs of later dolomite occur in microcrystalline intraclasts as well as sparry calcite cement, with no preference.

Maywood Unit. Like the Grove Creek Member, the Maywood unit is chiefly dolomite. Evidence from thin sections suggests that much of it is the result of weathering and that there were two stages of dolomitization. The first stage probably was during diagenesis of the original rock; the second is shown by stratigraphic evidence to have been the result of a period of weathering during the Devonian. Dolomitization of the Maywood unit was much more complete than that of the Grove Creek Member. Most intraclasts and glauconite pellets have been obscured by dolomitization, quartz and feldspar grains are pitted by dolomite rhombs, and fossils that may have been present were obliterated. Some chert formed during Devonian weathering, possibly through action of ground water.

These findings corroborate those of O. Tweto (1937, M.A. thesis, Montana State Univ., p. 141) who recognized two phases of dolomitization in the basal Maywood, which he called basal "Dry Creek," at Nixon Gulch. He identified the high-iron form of dolomite as ankerite.

MEASURED SECTIONS AND FAUNAL LISTS

Data upon which the major portion of this paper is based are presented in the form of 36 measured sections — 34 original and two from published literature (Sections NG, YG). They are arranged in the order that they appear in the lists of occurrences following the description of each fossil species. First are the sections in the Horseshoe Hills, in alphabetical order from west to east, then those in the Bridger Mountains, listed from north to south along the strike of the range. These are followed by sections between the Bridger Mountains and the eastern boundary of Yellowstone National Park, and finally by sections along Soda Butte Creek and Clark Fork Canyon, and the single section east of Red Lodge, Montana. Section YG is in the Little Belt Mountains of Montana and appears at the end of the list.

Each section is described from top to bottom. Formation and member names are indicated, and standard biostratigraphic subdivisions based on trilobites are inserted. Where biostratigraphic boundaries occur within covered intervals or unfossiliferous rock, they are drawn at the most likely horizon indicated by evidence from sections where boundaries are exposed.

Rock descriptions are given in field terms and contain information largely derived from examination in the field. Some information from insoluble residues has been included, namely, indications of presence and amounts of dolomite, glauconite, sand, and silt. Dolomite and glauconite are observable in the field and in hand specimen, but sand or silt are not. Bedding is described as "thin," laminae up to half an inch thick; "medium," beds from one-half to 6 inches thick; or "thick," beds from 6 inches to 2 feet thick. The term "massive" is used in reference to the Pilgrim Limestone in which beds commonly are 2–3 feet thick. Grain size of limestone is described as "fine," meaning that transported grains or constituent crystals are just at or below the threshold of visibility ("lithographic" of other workers), "medium," meaning that they are visible, but less than 0.5 mm. in diameter; or "coarse," meaning that they are larger than 0.5 mm. "Sugary" refers to dolomite or limestone that is weathered in such a way that medium to coarse grains stand out in slight relief and look like sugar. The term "hash" or "hashy" is contracted from "fossil hash" and refers to weathered coquinite of fossil fragments.

Lists of fossil species accompany lithologic descriptions of the beds from which they were obtained. Species are arranged by phylum according to the biological classification of Shrock and Twenhofel (1953): (1) Porifera, (2) Brachiopoda, (3) Mollusca, (4) Arthropoda, (5) Echinoderma, (6) Hemichordata. Within each phylum the species are listed alphabetically.

Immediately to the right of the description of each bed are two columns of numbers. The first gives the thickness of the beds; the second shows the footage from the base of the section to the base of the bed. Footages in the second column correspond to those in the list of occurrences that follows the description of each fossil species.

Locations of measured sections are given in terms of section, township, and range. These differ in accuracy according to the accuracy and scale of the map used to establish the location. Where recent and detailed geologic maps are available, accuracy is considered to be high; these are the maps by McMannis (1955, Pl. 1), Verall (1954, Ph.D. thesis, Princeton Univ., Pl. 1), and Wilson (1936, M.A. thesis, Montana State Univ.). Maps by the U.S. Department of Agriculture Forest Service for the Gallatin and Shoshone National forests are of unknown accuracy. The source for the location data is given at the beginning of each measured section.

Horseshoe Hills Section A (HA)

Section measured on side of gully, reached by crossing Gallatin River just west of Logan, Montana, keeping to east fork of road and leaving main gravel road for jeep road that leads past outcrops of Jefferson and Pilgrim limestones, with thin Snowy Range–Maywood interval between them, SW.¼sec. 30, T. 2 N., R. 3. E., Gallatin County, Montana, near western end of Horseshoe Hills. (Map by Verall, 1954, Ph.D. thesis, Princeton Univ.)

At this locality, rock between the Pilgrim and Jefferson formations is red, silty, and dolomitic. The Maywood unit occupies most of the interval, its base lying just above the base of the Sage Member of the Snowy Range Formation. The Grove Creek Member of the Snowy Range Formation has been removed, and most of the Sage either removed or altered to Maywood lithology by post-Cambrian, pre-Late Devonian weathering and erosion.

This locality is near the section measured and described by Sloss and Laird (1947, p. 1411–1413) and discussed and diagrammed by Lochman (1950b, p. 2213–2217, Fig. 2, sec. B).

Horseshoe Hills Section A (HA) *Continued*

DEVONIAN SYSTEM

	Bed thickness in feet	Feet above base
Jefferson Formation—3 feet measured		
Limestone: brownish gray, weathers gray, very dolomitic, stands out as traceable gray ledge	3.0	123.5
Maywood unit—77 feet thick		
Limestone: medium-grained, thin- to medium-bedded, dolomitic, petroliferous	17.0	106.5
Limestone: yellowish to brownish gray, thin-bedded, weathers platy, dolomitic, shaly	22.3	84.2
Limestone: moderate yellow to pale purple and dark red, thin-bedded, vuggy, dolomitic, shaly, outlines of pebbles in base	11.2	73.0
Dolomite and limestone: thin-bedded, medium-grained, beds of dark red, purple, and moderate yellow to nearly white, silty	18.8	54.2
Limestone: very dark red, mottled with grayish yellow, thin-bedded, very dolomitic, shaly, lower 1.5 feet covered	3.3	50.9
Limestone: greenish gray, thin-bedded, very dolomitic, arenaceous, lower 3.5 feet covered	4.4	46.5
CAMBRIAN SYSTEM		
Snowy Range Formation—46.5 feet thick		
Sage Member—15.9 feet thick (altered by post-Cambrian weathering; resembles Maywood unit but contains pebble conglomerate, glauconite, and Franconian fossils)		
FRANCONIAN STAGE		
Idahoia Zone		
I. wyomingensis Subzone		
Limestone: moderate yellow, medium-grained, dolomitic, arenaceous, outlines of limestone pebbles, *Sinuella vaticina*	0.7	45.8
(probably top of *Taenicephalus* Zone)		
Limestone: moderate yellow with purple stains, thin- to thick-bedded, slightly glauconitic, very dolomitic, looks like strongly altered (dolomitized) limestone-pebble conglomerate, interbedded with thin beds of crinkly, purplish-gray limestone; Linguloid fragments	15.2	30.6
Dry Creek Member—30.6 feet thick		
Elvinia Zone		
Shale: greenish gray, fissile to hard, calcareous and nonfissile, alternating with thin beds of siltstone: gray, weathering to brownish gray, thin-bedded; flaggy, wavy-bedded; *Lingulella perattenuata, Linnarssonella girtyi*	27.0	3.6
Shale: greenish gray, fissile, with lenses of limestone-pebble conglomerate: rusty brown, silty, thin-bedded, hard	3.6	0
Pilgrim Formation		
Limestone: top of Pilgrim Limestone datum for measurements		

Horseshoe Hills Section B (HB)

Section measured in SE.¼sec. 19, T. 2 N., R. 3 E., Gallatin County, Montana, reached from road that crosses Gallatin River just west of Logan, taking east fork of road where it branches north of river. Strike and dip: N. 25° E., 40° N. (Map by Verall, 1954, Ph.D. thesis, Princeton Univ.)

DEVONIAN SYSTEM

	Bed thickness in feet	Feet above base
Jefferson Formation—4 feet measured		
Limestone: dusky brown, weathers gray, medium-grained, thick-bedded, petroliferous, dolomitic, forms ledge	4.0	142.1
Maywood unit—62 feet thick		
Limestone: brownish gray, thin- to medium-bedded, petroliferous	10.0	132.1
Covered: rubble is platy limestone and dolomite, 1.5-foot bed near middle is limestone, moderate yellow, medium-grained, thin-bedded	52.0	80.1

CAMBRIAN SYSTEM

Snowy Range Formation—80.1 feet thick
Sage Member—about 21 feet present

FRANCONIAN STAGE

Taenicephalus Zone
Parabolinoides Subzone

Limestone: three 2-foot beds with covered between, gray, dusky red at top, coarse-grained with chert on bedding planes, dolomitic, slightly glauconitic, very fossiliferous; *Angulotreta tetonensis, Billingsella perfecta, B. plicatella, Ceratreta hebes, Pseudodicellomus mosaicus, Eoorthis remnicha, E. remnicha* var. *A., Huenella abnormis, H. texana, Lingulella desiderata, Orygmaspis firma, Parabolinoides cordillerensis, P. hebe, Taenicephalus gallupensis, T. gouldi, T. shumardi,* crinoid columnals, and calyx	12.8	67.3

Elvinia Zone

Covered: base of Sage Member and entire Dry Creek Member lie within covered interval	67.3	0

Pilgrim Formation
Limestone: top of Pilgrim Limestone datum for measurements

Horseshoe Hills Section C (HC)

Section in SW.¼sec. 21, T. 2 N., R. 3 E., Gallatin County, Montana, reached from road that crosses Gallatin River just west of Logan, keeping to east fork where road branches just north of river. Strike and dip: N. 40° E., 47° NW. (Map by Verall, 1954, Ph.D. thesis, Princeton Univ.)

DEVONIAN SYSTEM

	Bed thickness in feet	Feet above base
Jefferson Formation—4 feet measured		
Limestone: dusky brown, weathers gray, massive dolomitic, forms traceable gray ledge	4.0	94.9
Maywood unit—58.8 feet thick		
Limestone: dusky brown, pale yellowish orange and dusky red, smooth, petroliferous odor near top, dolomitic, dense to porous, lower 26 feet covered	58.8	36.1

CAMBRIAN SYSTEM

Snowy Range Formation—36.1 feet measured
Sage Member—36.1 feet thick

Horseshoe Hills Section C (HC) *Continued*
Cambrian System *Continued*

FRANCONIAN STAGE

	Bed thickness in feet	Feet above base
Taenicephalus Zone		
Limestone: gray, fine- and medium-grained, thin-bedded, irregularly bedded, with pebbly layers, slightly dolomitic, glauconitic, chert on bedding planes; *Angulotreta tetonensis, A. vescula, Billingsella plicatella,* alternating with thicker intervals of covered: probably shale or shaly limestone	18.5	17.6
Parabolinoides Subzone		
Limestone: gray, medium-grained, thick-bedded, very fossiliferous, glauconitic, chert on bedding planes, thin shale breaks between limestone beds; *Angulotreta tetonensis, Billingsella perfecta, B. plicatella, Ceratreta hebes, Eoorthis remnicha, E. remnicha* var. *A. Lingulella* sp., *Orygmaspis llanoensis, Parabolinoides expansus, P. hebe, Taenicephalus shumardi, Wilbernia halli,* Crinoid columnals	6.2	11.4
Elvinia Zone		
Camaraspis Subzone		
Limestone and limestone-pebble conglomerate: gray and grayish green, silty, medium-grained, pebbles small, flat, some imbricated, in two beds separated by 1-foot covered shale interval; *Linnarssonella girtyi, Camaraspis convexa*	3.6	7.8
Base of *Camaraspis* Subzone		
Limestone: light gray, coarse-grained, dolomitic, silty; *Linnarssonella girtyi, Dellea saratogensis, Dellea,* sp., *Pseudagnostus sentosus*	1.3	6.5
Limestone: greenish gray, fine-grained columns of *Collenia magna.* Base of bioherm datum for measurements	6.5	0

Horseshoe Hills Section D (HD)

Section measured in sharp V-shaped gulley in NE.¼sec. 21, T. 2 N., R. 3 E., Gallatin County, Montana, reached by walking west from branch of road that crosses Gallatin River at Manhattan. Strike and dip: N. 30° E., 62° N. (Map by Verall, 1954, Ph.D. thesis, Princeton Univ.)

DEVONIAN SYSTEM

	Bed thickness in feet	Feet above base
Jefferson Formation—3 feet measured		
Limestone: dusky brown, weathers medium gray, surface hackly, odor petroliferous, dolomitic, stands out as prominent ledge	3.0	185.1
Maywood unit—34 feet thick		
Limestone: dusky brown, medium-grained, thin-bedded, petroliferous odor, weathers into thin plates	10.3	174.8
Covered: probably dusky brown and yellow limestone and dolomite, thin-bedded, platy, with 1-foot bed of limestone: light gray and moderate yellow, medium-grained, thin-bedded, dolomitic, weathers into thin plates, base at 160.9 feet	23.7	151.1

CAMBRIAN SYSTEM

Snowy Range Formation—151.1 feet thick
Sage Member—89 feet thick

FRANCONIAN STAGE

	Bed thickness in feet	Feet above base
Idahoia Zone		
Idahoia serapio Subzone		
Limestone: light gray, medium-grained, weathers into 4-inch beds with smooth surfaces, slightly pebbly; *Angulotreta vescula, Billingsella perfecta, Pseudodicellomus mosaicus, Lingulella* sp., *Lytospira* sp., *Sinuella vaticina, Drumaspis idahoensis, Idahoia serapio, I. wisconsensis, Maladia americana, Pinctus ? pullus, Pseudagnostus josephus, P. sentosus, Ptychaspis granulosa, Wilbernia expansa,* Crinoid columnals	6.9	144.2
Idahoia wisconsensis Subzone		
Limestone: gray, intermixed fine- and medium-grained, evenly to crinkly bedded (1.5 feet at base covered); *Billingsella perfecta, Pseudodicellomus mosaicus, Sinuella vaticina, Drumaspis briscoensis, D. idahoensis, Idahoia wisconsensis, I. wyomingensis, Maladia americana, Pinctus ? pullus, Pseudagnostus sentosus, Ptychaspis granulosa*	5.3	138.9
Idahoia wyomingensis Subzone		
Limestone and dolomite: gray and dusky red, very lumpy, with irregular cherty bedding surfaces: thin beds of shale; *Billingsella perfecta, Pseudodicellomus mosaicus, Lingulella* sp., *Sinuella vaticina, Drumaspis briscoensis, Idahoia wyomingensis, Monocheilus demissus, Pseudagnostus josephus, P. sentosus, Saratogia fria, Wilbernia pero,* Crinoid columnals	10.5	128.4
Limestone: brownish gray to gray, weathers dark gray, smooth to hackly surface, forms ledge, fine-grained intermixed with coarse-grained, latter with pebbles. Some bedding planes look like corrosion surfaces: small pebbles of underlying bed worked into overlying bed. Slightly glauconitic, dolomitic, cherty, in 1–3-foot beds with a few 2–3-foot intervals of green shale, crinkly bedded shaly limestone, or covered; *Multivasculatus ovatus, Billingsella perfecta, Pseudodicellomus mosaicus, Lingulella* sp., *Lytospira* ? sp., *Sinuella vaticina, Idahoia wyomingensis, Pseudagnostus sentosus, Ptychaspis granulosa, Saratogia carita, S. fracida, Wilbernia expansa,* Crinoid columnals	16.0	112.4
Taenicephalus Zone		
Limestone and limestone-pebble conglomerate: gray, weathers dark gray or dusky yellow, hackly surface, silty, glauconitic, dolomitic, limonite on bedding surfaces, in 1–2-foot beds alternating with greenish-gray lumpy-bedded shale, fossils at 90.1 feet; *Angulotreta tetonensis, A. vescula, Billingsella perfecta, Pseudodicellomus mosaicus, Eoorthis remnicha, Huenella texana, Lingulella desiderata, Pelagiella primordialis, Croixana bipunctata, Kendallina eryon, Maustonia nasuta* Crinoid columnals	24.3	88.1
Parabolinoides Subzone		
Limestone and limestone-pebble conglomerate: brownish gray, fine-grained, arenaceous to silty, limonitic; *Angulotreta tetonensis, Billingsella perfecta, B. plicatella, Ceratreta hebes, Eoorthis remnicha, Huenella texana, Lingulella desiderata, Pelagiella primordialis, Kendallina eryon, Orygmaspis firma, Parabolinoides contractus, P. cordillerensis, P. expansus, P. hebe, Taenicephalus shumardi,* Crinoid columnals	3.5	84.6

Horseshoe Hills Section D (HD) *Continued*
Cambrian System *Continued*
Franconian Stage *Continued*

Elvinia Zone
Camaraspis Subzone

	Bed thickness in feet	Feet above base
Limestone: gray, medium-grained, very pebbly, (lower 1.2 feet covered); *Pseudodicellomus mosaicus, Linnarssonella girtyi, Camaraspis convexa*	1.7	82.9
Base of *Camaraspis* Subzone		
Limestone: light gray, weathers darker gray mottled with brownish gray, fine- to medium-grained, slightly glauconitic, silty, pebbly in middle, irregularly bedded, alternating with covered shale or shaly limestone; *Linnarssonella girtyi, Burnetiella ectypa, Dellea saratogensis, D. suada, Dokimocephalus intermedius, Irvingella major* (pygidium), Crinoid columnals	2.8	80.1
Limestone: greenish gray, columns of *Collenia magna,* pebbly matrix between columns has Crinoid columnals	18.0	62.1
Dry Creek Member—62.1 feet thick		
Shale: commonly covered, green fissile, in 2–4-foot beds, alternating with siltstone: brownish gray, platy, calcareous, limonitic in 1–2-foot beds: top 18 feet covered, basal 27 feet covered	62.1	0
Pilgrim Formation		
Limestone: top of massive Pilgrim Limestone datum for measurements		

Horseshoe Hills Section E (HE)

Section measured on south-facing slope of hogback in NW.1/4sec. 22, T. 2 N., R. 3 E., Gallatin County, Montana, reached by walking east from west branch of road that crosses Gallatin River at Manhattan. Strike and dip: N. 80° E., 35° N. (Map by Verall, 1954, Ph.D. thesis, Princeton Univ.)

DEVONIAN SYSTEM

	Bed thickness in feet	Feet above base
Jefferson Formation—2.7 feet measured		
Limestone: dusky brown, weathers medium gray, dolomitic, forms traceable ledge	2.7	196.6
Maywood unit—74.7 feet thick		
Covered: slope covered by rubble consisting of moderate-yellow and dusky-red fragments of limestone and dolomite	74.7	121.9

CAMBRIAN SYSTEM

Snowy Range Formation—121.9 feet thick
Sage Member—45.9 feet thick

FRANCONIAN STAGE

Idahoia Zone
Idahoia wyomingensis Subzone

Limestone: mottled light gray to dusky yellow, thin-bedded, dolomitic, weathers smooth, glauconitic, limonitic; *Angulotreta vescula, Sinuella vaticina,* Crinoid columnals (12 feet in middle covered)	19.8	102.1

Taenicephalus Zone

	Bed thickness in feet	Feet above base
Limestone: gray, mottled with brownish gray, dolomitic, weathers smooth to hackly, limonitic, in two 1-foot beds with middle and top covered; *Angulotreta vescula, Lingulella perattenuata*	9.8	92.3
Parabolinoides Subzone		
Limestone: gray, crinkly bedded, pebbly, dolomitic, glauconitic, upper 3 feet fossiliferous; *Angulotreta tetonensis, A. vescula, Billingsella perfecta, B. plicatella, Ceratreta hebes, Eoorthis remnicha, E. remnicha* var. *A., Huenella texana, Lingulella* sp., *Pelagiella primordialis, Maustonia nasuta, Orygmaspis llanoensis, Parabolinoides contractus, P. expansus, Taenicephalus gallupensis, T. gouldi, T. shumardi,* Crinoid columnals	4.0	88.3
Elvinia Zone (Top of zone probably near 85 feet)		
Limestone and limestone-pebble conglomerate: light gray, pebbles weather out in relief, top exposed bed has fossil-fragment coquina too fine to identify, Linguloid fragments, Crinoid columnals, top 6.5 feet of interval covered, basal 3.5 feet columns of *Collenia magna* ...	12.3	76.0
Dry Creek Member—70.7 feet thick		
Shale: grayish green to dusky green, thin-bedded, fissile, bands of dusky red purple, one thin bed of siltstone in middle: dark reddish brown, platy, calcareous	70.7	0
Pilgrim Formation		
Limestone: top of Pilgrim Limestone datum for measurements		

Horseshoe Hills Section F (HF)

Section measured on south-facing slope of hogback in NE.¼sec. 22, T. 2 N., R. 3 E., Gallatin County, Montana, reached by walking west from Nixon Gulch. Strike and dip: N. 55° E., 37° N. (Map by Verall, 1954, Ph.D. thesis, Princeton Univ.)

DEVONIAN SYSTEM

	Bed thickness in feet	Feet above base
Maywood unit—14 feet measured		
Covered: slope with rubble of yellow and dusky-red dolomite fragments (not measured)		50.5
Limestone: moderate yellow with streaks of dusky red, medium-grained, thin-bedded, moderately hard, arenaceous, lower 8.8 feet covered ..	14.0	36.5

CAMBRIAN SYSTEM

Snowy Range Formation—36.5 feet measured
Sage Member—36.5 feet thick

FRANCONIAN STAGE

Taenicephalus Zone ?

Limestone: gray, fine-grained, thin-bedded, thin stringers of chert on bedding surfaces, weathers pitted, alternating with shale and crinkly limestone, partly covered, lumpy, grayish green	5.2	31.3

Horseshoe Hills Section F (HF) *Continued*
Cambrian System *Continued*
Franconian Stage *Continued*
Taenicephalus Zone *Continued*

	Bed thickness in feet	Feet above base
Limestone: brownish gray, evenly bedded, fine-grained, argillaceous, and limestone-pebble conglomerate; weathers gray, pebbles brownish gray, small, flat, randomly oriented, matrix gray, fine-grained, slightly dolomitic, in half-foot beds, alternating with shale and crinkly limestone; *Angulotreta tetonensis, A. vescula, Lingulella perattenuata, Taenicephalus shumardi*	15.5	15.8
Parabolinoides Subzone		
Limestone: gray and dark yellowish orange, weathered, slightly glauconitic, silty, fossiliferous, thin-bedded; *Angulotreta tetonensis, A. vescula, Billingsella perfecta, B. plicatella, Ceratreta hebes, Pseudodicellomus mosaicus, Eoorthis remnicha, E. remincha* var. *A., Huenella texana, Lingulella desiderata, Micromitra modesta, Orygmaspis firma, O. llanoesis, Parabolinoides cordillerensis, P. hebe, Taenicephalus gallupensis, T. gouldi, T. shumardi*	1.2	14.6
Elvinia Zone (Top within covered interval)		
Limestone: gray, arenaceous, thin-bedded with shale streaks, with beds of small limestone pebbles, chert on bedding surfaces, *Burnetiella ectypa, Kyphocephalus* ? sp., top 5 feet covered, lower 5 feet columnar limestone; *Collenia magna*	14.6	0
Dry Creek Member—not measured		
Covered: shale with dolomitic siltstone layers		

Horseshoe Hills Section G (HG)
(Same locality as Lochman's NIXON GULCH section)

Section measured on west side of Mr. Sinton's road from Manhattan, where it bends to go through deep Nixon Gulch in hogback formed by Pilgrim and Jefferson formations, on boundary between SW.¼ and SE.¼ sec. 14, T. 2 N., R. 3 E., Gallatin County, Montana. This is the section measured by Deiss (1936, p. 1311–1317), Lochman and Duncan (1944, p. 7), and Lochman (1950b, p. 2217–2218). Strike and dip: N. 65° E., 41° N. (Map by Verall, 1954, Ph.D. thesis, Princeton Univ.)

Devonian System

	Bed thickness in feet	Feet above base
Jefferson Formation—2 feet measured		
Limestone: dusky brown, weathers medium gray, fine-grained, hard, forms ledge, weathers hackly, unfossiliferous	2.0	108.4
Maywood unit—25.1 feet thick		
Limestone and dolomite: commonly covered, moderate yellow and dusky red, thin-bedded, platy	25.1	83.3

Cambrian System

Snowy Range Formation—83.3 feet thick
Sage Member—47.3 feet thick

FRANCONIAN STAGE

Idahoia Zone

	Bed thickness in feet	Feet above base
Idahoia wyomingensis Subzone		
Limestone: gray and dusky red, thin-bedded, with beds of limestone-pebble conglomerate and fossil hash; *Billingsella perfecta, Pseudodicellomus mosaicus, Hyolithes primordialis, Sinuella vaticina, Croixana bipunctata, Idahoia wyomingensis, Pseudagnostus josephus, P. sentosus, Saratogia carita, S. fracida, S. fria, Wilbernia diademata,* Crinoid columnals	6.8	76.5
Taenicephalus Zone		
(Top of zone probably in 10-foot covered interval at top)		
Limestone: gray, coarsely crystalline, dolomitic, slightly pebbly, in 1–2-foot beds, alternating with 2–4-foot covered intervals, probably shale or shaly limestone, top 10 feet of interval covered; *Angulotreta tetonensis, Billingsella perfecta, Pseudodicellomus mosaicus, Lingulella desiderata, L. perattenuata, Kendallina eryon, Maustonia nasuta, Pseudagnostus josephus, P. sentosus, Taenicephalus shumardi*	20.5	56.0
Parabolinoides Subzone		
Limestone and limestone-pebble conglomerate: gray, coarse-grained, dolomitic, pebbles small and flat, beds 6–10 inches thick; *Angulotreta tetonensis, Billingsella perfecta, B. plicatella, Ceratreta hebes, Pseudodicellomus mosaicus, Eoorthis remnicha, E. remnicha* var. *A., Huenella texana, Lingulella perattenuata, Micromitra modesta, Otusia sandbergi, Irvingella major, Orygmaspis firma, O. llanoensis, Parabolinoides contractus, P. cordillerensis, P. expansus, P. hebe, Taenicephalus gallupensis, T. gouldi, T. shumardi, Wilbernia halli,* Crinoid columnals	8.3	47.7
Elvinia Zone		
Camaraspis Subzone		
Limestone: coarse-grained, silty, and shale: greenish gray, fissile; *Linnarssonella girtyi, Sulcocephalus* sp., *Burnetiella ectypa, Camaraspis berkeyi, Dellea butlerensis, D. saratogensis, Homagnostus* cf. *H. tumidosus, Irvingella major, Pinctus ? artus, Pseudagnostus sentosus, Pterocephalia sanctisabae*	0.4	47.3
Limestone: light greenish gray, fine-grained, stylolitic, columns of *Collenia magna,* with fossiliferous dolomitic matrix between columns; *Linnarssonella girtyi, Burnetiella ectypa, Camaraspis convexa, Dellea suada, Pinctus ? artus, Pseudagnostus sentosus, Pterocephalia sanctisabae*	1.5	45.8
Base of *Camaraspis* Subzone		
Limestone: greenish gray, fine-grained, columns of *Collenia magna.* Pebbly matrix between columns has *Lingulella desiderata, Linnarssonella girtyi, Hyolithes primordialis, Sulcocephalus granulosus, Burnetiella ectypa, Deadwoodia duris, Dellea butlerensis, D. saratogensis, D. snoburgensis, D. suada, Irvingella (Parairvingella) eurekensis, Pinctus ? artus,* Crinoid columnals	9.8	36.0

Horseshoe Hills Section G (HG) *Continued*
Cambrian System *Continued*
Franconian Stage *Continued*
Base of *Camaraspis* Subzone *Continued*

	Bed thickness in feet	Feet above base
Dry Creek Member—36 feet thick		
Covered: shale and thin beds of dolomitic siltstone. Thickness given by Lochman (1950b, p. 2214; Fig. 2)	36.0	0
Pilgrim Formation		
Limestone: top of Pilgrim Limestone datum for measurements		

Nixon Gulch Section (NG)

In 1936, 1940, and 1949 Dr. C. Lochman-Balk collected Franconian fossils from the Nixon Gulch section in the Horseshoe Hills, Gallatin County, Montana. This section corresponds to Section HG of this study. Collections from the Snowy Range Formation at this locality containing species from the *Elvinia* Zone, *Taenicephalus* Zone, and *Idahoia wyomingensis* Subzone were supplied by Dr. Lochman-Balk.

These collections are listed according to zone, and each is designated by an original collection number (written communication, 1955). Each is accompanied by a brief lithologic description, but no attempt to give footages is made here. Height above the top of the Pilgrim Limestone can be approximated by reference to Section HG.

CAMBRIAN SYSTEM

Snowy Range Formation
Sage Member

FRANCONIAN STAGE

Idahoia Zone
Idahoia wyomingensis Subzone

Coll. 2.8: Yellow and red dolomite with thin, discontinuous beds of fine-grained, gray limestone; *Hyolithes primordialis, Sinuella vaticina, Idahoia wyomingensis. Pseudagnostus sentosus, Saratogia fracida,* Crinoid columnals

Coll. 4 (Lochman and Duncan, 1944, p. 7): "Massive pebble conglomerate with many red and a few gray-green pebbles, interbedded with 3–4 inch irregular beds of red sandy argillaceous limestone. . . . 4.7 feet"; *Billingsella perfecta, Pseudodicellomus mosaicus, Sinuella vaticina, Idahoia wyomingensis, Pseudagnostus sentosus, Ptychaspis granulosa* (pygidium), *Saratogia fracida, Wilbernia diademata,* Crinoid columnals

Coll. "Highest bed of pebble conglomerate in Snowy Range Formation": *Billingsella perfecta, Pseudodicellomus mosaicus, Sinuella vaticina, Idahoia wyomingensis, Pseudagnostus sentosus, Wilbernia expansa*

Colls. 4e, 4x, 4y, "*Ptychaspis* Zone ledge" (all same bed): Yellow platy limestone, medium-grained; *Billingsella perfecta, Pseudodicellomus mosaicus, Hyolithes primordialis, Sinuella vaticina, Idahoia wyomingensis, Pseudagnostus sentosus, Saratogia fracida,* Crinoid columnals

Colls. 4d, $4d_1$: Yellow crystalline limestone above a red-yellow shale break; *Pseudodicellomus mosaicus, Sinuella vaticina, Idahoia wyomingensis, Saratogia fracida, Wilbernia diademata*

Colls. 4a, 4b, 4c, $4c_1$, and "float from level of 4c": Thin bed of light-purple limestone and pebble or granule conglomerate; *Billingsella perfecta, Pesudodicellomus mosaicus, Hyolithes primordialis, Sinuella vaticina, Idahoia wyomingensis, Pseudagnostus sentosus, Saratogia carita, S. fracida, S. fria,* Crinoid columnals

Coll. 3g: 2½ feet above 3f, gray, medium-grained limestone with greenish-gray pebbles; *Pseudodicellomus mosaicus,* Linguloid fragments, *Wilbernia expansa*

Taenicephalus Zone

Colls. 3e, 3f, "*Conaspis* Zone," and "Upper *Conaspis* Zone": light-gray, medium-grained, glauconitic, dolomitic, slightly pebbly limestone; *Angulotreta tetonensis, Billingsella perfecta, B. plicatella, Ceratreta hebes, Pseudodicellomus mosaicus, Eoorthis remnicha, E. remnicha* var. *A., Huenella abnormis, H. texana, Lingulella desiderata, Maustonia nasuta, Orygmaspis llanoensis, Taenicephalus gallupensis, T. shumardi, Wilbernia halli,* Crinoid columnals

Parabolinoides Subzone

Colls. C (float), 3c, 3d: gray, fine-grained very shaly limestone; *Angulotreta tetonensis, Billingsella perfecta, B. plicatella, Pseudodicellomus mosaicus, Huenella abnormis, H. texana, Lingulella perattenuata, Kendallina eryon, Orygmaspis firma, Parabolinoides expansus, Taenicephalus gallupensis, T. gouldi, T. shumardi, Wilbernia halli*

Colls. 2.6 and "Lower *Conaspis* Zone": gray, fine-grained, dolomitic limestone; *Billingsella perfecta, B. plicatella, Pseudodicellomus mosaicus, Eoorthis remnicha, E. remnicha* var. *A., Otusia sandbergi, Kendallina eryon, Parabolinoides hebe*

Colls. 3, 3a and "*Conaspis* Zone float": light-gray, medium-grained, slightly dolomitic limestone; *Angulotreta tetonensis, Billingsella perfecta, B. plicatella, Pseudodicellomus mosaicus, Eoorthis remnicha, E. remnicha* var. *A., Huenella texana, Otusia sandbergi, Kendallina eryon, Maustonia nasuta, Parabolinoides cordillerensis, P. hebe, Taenicephalus gallupensis, T. shumardi, Wilbernia halli.*

Elvinia Zone

Coll. 2: thin bed of fine-grained limestone interbedded between two beds of coarse limestone-pebble conglomerate; *Linnarssonella girtyi, Burnetiella ectypa, Camaraspis convexa*

Colls. 1 and "Top of columnar reef" (*Collenia magna*): greenish-gray pebbly limestone, not actually part of bioherm but of matrix around columns; *Linnarssonella girtyi, Hyolithes primordialis, Deadwoodia duris, Dellea butlerensis, D. juvenalis, D. saratogensis, D. suada, Kyphocephalus bridgerensis, Pterocephalia sanctisabae,* Crinoid columnals

Horseshoe Hills Section H (HH)

Section measured in first major gulley east of a broad, flat wheat field in Horseshoe Hills, NE.¼sec. 24, T. 2 N., R. 3 E., Gallatin County, Montana. Strike and dip: N. 65° E., 44° NW. (Map by Verall, 1954, Ph.D. thesis, Princeton Univ.)

Horseshoe Hills Section (HH) *Continued*

DEVONIAN SYSTEM

	Bed thickness in feet	Feet above base
Maywood unit—52.4 feet thick		
Limestone: dusky yellow, thin-bedded, dolomitic, petroliferous at top, weathers into curved plates, forms slope	12.4	171.7
Limestone: dusky yellow to dusky red, dolomitic, thin-bedded, alternating with limestone-granule conglomerate; weathered, soft, lower 16 feet covered	40.0	131.7

CAMBRIAN SYSTEM

Snowy Range Formation—131.7 feet thick

Sage Member—81.1 feet thick

FRANCONIAN STAGE

Idahoia Zone

Idahoia serapio Subzone

	Bed thickness in feet	Feet above base
Limestone: gray, medium-bedded, hard, slightly glauconitic and dolomitic, in 0.5–1-foot beds with somewhat thicker, covered intervals between; *Billingsella perfecta, Pseudodicellomus mosaicus, Lingulella desiderata, Drumaspis idahoensis, Idahoia serapio, I. wisconsensis, Pinctus ? pullus, Pseudagnostus josephus, P. sentosus, Ptychaspis granulosa, P.* cf. *P. miniscaensis*	7.1	124.6
Idahoia wisconsensis Subzone		
Limestone: dark gray, fine- and medium-grained, dolomitic, hard, glauconitic, lower 6 feet covered; *Lingulella* sp., *Sinuella vaticina, Drumaspis briscoensis, D. idahoensis, Idahoia wisconsensis, Pseudagnostus josephus, P. sentosus, Ptychaspis granulosa, Wilbernia expansa*	7.2	117.4
Idahoia wyomingensis Subzone		
Covered: probably shaly limestone. Top 1.5 feet is limestone: gray, fine- and medium-grained, dolomitic, slightly pebbly; *Billingsella perfecta, Pseudodicellomus mosaicus, Sinuella vaticina, Idahoia wyomingensis, Pseudagnostus sentosus, Saratogia carita, Wilbernia expansa*	10.0	107.4
Limestone: gray or brownish gray, medium-bedded, medium-grained or pebbly, slightly glauconitic, dolomitic, forms ledge; *Billingsella perfecta, Pseudodicellomus mosaicus, Sinuella vaticina, Idahoia wyomingensis, Pseudagnostus sentosus, Saratogia carita, Wilbernia expansa*	7.9	99.5
Taenicephalus Zone		
Covered: probably shale or shaly limestone, with four 1-foot beds of limestone-pebble conglomerate; dark gray with flat, light-gray pebbles lying flat or imbricated; *Angulotreta tetonensis, A. vescula, Billingsella perfecta*	23.7	75.8
Parabolinoides Subzone		
Limestone-pebble conglomerate and fossil-fragment coquina: gray, in 2-foot beds, dolomitic, glauconitic, silty; *Angulotreta tetonensis, Billingsella perfecta, B. plicatella, Ceratreta hebes, Pseudodicellomus mosaicus, Eoorthis remnicha, E. remnicha* var. *A., Huenella abnormis, Otusia sandbergi, Orygmaspis firma, Parabolinoides hebe, Taenicephalus gallupensis, T. gouldi, T. shumardi,* Crinoid columnals	5.5	70.3
Limestone-pebble conglomerate: light gray, silty, medium- to coarse-grained, in two thin beds separated by covered interval; *Linnarsso-*		

Elvinia Zone
Camaraspis Subzone

	Bed thickness in feet	Feet above base
nella girtyi, Ocnerorthis monticola, Camaraspis convexa, Pinctus ? artus, Pseudagnostus sentosus	4.4	65.9
Base of *Camaraspis* Subzone		
Limestone: greenish gray, fine-grained, columns of *Collenia magna,* with 1-foot beds of limestone-pebble conglomerate at top and bottom, pebbly matrix between columns; *Linnarssonella girtyi, Deadwoodia duris, Dellea butlerensis, D. snoburgensis, D. suada*	15.3	50.6
Dry Creek Member—50.6 feet thick		
Shale: mostly covered, greenish gray and purple, fissile, slightly calcareous, unfossiliferous	16.3	34.3
Shale: greenish gray (as above) with 6–8-inch beds of siltstone; grayish brown, limonitic, very calcareous, irregularly bedded, platy	34.3	0
Pilgrim Formation		
Limestone: top of Pilgrim Limestone datum for measurements		

Horseshoe Hills Section I (HI)

Section measured on slope west of big gulley between section HH and road from Belgrade, SE.1/4sec. 18, T. 2N., R. 4 E., Gallatin County, Montana. Strike and dip: N. 70° E., 30° NW. (Map by Verall, 1954, Ph.D. thesis, Princeton Univ.)

DEVONIAN SYSTEM

	Bed thickness in feet	Feet above base
Jefferson Formation—2.4 feet measured		
Limestone: dusky brown, weathers gray, dolomitic, forms traceable ledge	2.4	188.4
Maywood unit—63.5 feet thick		
Limestone: dusky brown to dusky red, hard, petroliferous odor at top, alternating with thin beds of similarly colored, shaly and lumpy limestone	63.5	124.9
(Maywood unit measured about 300 yards east of remainder of section)		

CAMBRIAN SYSTEM

Snowy Range Formation—124.9 feet thick
Sage Member—67.9 feet thick

FRANCONIAN STAGE

Idahoia Zone
Idahoia serapio Subzone

	Bed thickness in feet	Feet above base
Limestone: light gray, coarse- to medium-grained, glauconitic, slightly pebbly, in two half-foot beds with 2.5 feet covered between; *Pseudodicellomus mosaicus,* Phosphatic balls, *Sinuella vaticina, Drumaspis idahoensis, Idahoia serapio, I. wisconsensis, Maladia americana, Pseudagnostus sentosus, Ptychaspis granulosa, P.* cf. *P. miniscaensis, Westergaardodina bicuspidata*	3.7	121.2
Idahoia wisconsensis Subzone?		
Covered: probably shale or shaly limestone. *Idahoia wisconsensis* not found at this locality	4.7	116.5

Horseshoe Hills Section I (HI) *Continued*
Cambrian System *Continued*
Franconian Stage *Continued*

	Bed thickness in feet	Feet above base
Idahoia wyomingensis Subzone		
Limestone: gray to light gray, medium-grained, glauconitic, dolomitic, basal 8 feet forms ledge, beds separated by thin, shaly, or covered intervals; *Multivasculatus ovatus, Angulotreta vescula, Billingsella perfecta, B. plicatella, Pseudodicellomus mosaicus, Lingulella* sp., Phosphatic balls, *Sinuella vaticina, Idahoia wyomingensis, Monocheilus demissus, Pseudagnostus josephus, P. sentosus, Ptychaspis granulosa, Saratogia fria, Wilbernia diademata, W. expansa*	18.4	98.1
Taenicephalus Zone (Top of zone probably within covered interval)		
Covered: probably shale and shaly limestone. Basal 1.5 feet is limestone, gray, medium- to coarse-grained, slightly glauconitic, dolomitic, with *Angulotreta vescula*	13.8	84.3
Covered: probably shale and shaly limestone. Basal 1.5 feet is limestone, gray, coquina of fossil fragments, dolomitic; *Angulotreta tetonensis, Billingsella perfecta, B. plicatella, Pseudodicellomus mosaicus, Eoorthis remnicha, Huenella abnormis, Lingulella* sp., *Pelagiella primordialis, Taenicephalus gallupensis, T. gouldi, T. shumardi,* Crinoid columnals	14.8	69.5
Parabolinoides Subzone		
Limestone and limestone-pebble conglomerate: upper 1.3 feet fossil coquinite, basal 5.7 feet covered; *Angulotreta tetonensis, A. vescula, Billingsella perfecta, B. plicatella, Ceratreta hebes, Pseudodicellomus mosaicus, Eoorthis remnicha, E. remnicha* var. *A.*, *Kendallina eryon, Orygmaspis firma, O. llanoensis, Parabolinoides contractus, P. cordillerensis,* Crinoid columnals	7.5	62.0
Elvinia Zone		
Limestone: gray, fine-grained, some limestone pebbles, middle 3.5 feet covered, basal foot columns of *Collenia magna,* top has *Linnarssonella girtyi*	5.0	57.0
Dry Creek Member—57 feet thick		
Mostly covered: greenish-gray, fissile, calcareous shale with thin stringers of brownish-gray calcareous siltstone	57.0	0
Pilgrim Formation		
Limestone: top of Pilgrim Limestone datum for measurements		

Horseshoe Hills Section J (HJ)

Section measured on east side of Benson's road from Belgrade, SE.¼sec. 17, T. 2 N., R. 4 E., Gallatin County, Montana. Strike and dip: N. 80° E., 30° N. (Map by Verall, 1954, Ph.D. thesis, Princeton Univ.)

Devonian System

	Bed thickness in feet	Feet above base
Jefferson Formation—3.5 feet measured		
Limestone: dusky brown, weathers gray, dolomitic, top half massive, bottom half thin-bedded, forms traceable gray ledge	3.5	291.8

	Bed thickness in feet	Feet above base
Maywood unit—23.8 feet thick		
Limestone: partly covered, brownish gray, thin-bedded, petroliferous. Basal 11 feet partly covered dolomite, coarse-grained, yellow, thin-bedded, forms rubbly slope	23.8	268.0

CAMBRIAN SYSTEM

Snowy Range Formation—268.0 feet thick		
Grove Creek Member—52.6 feet thick		
TREMPEALEAUAN STAGE		
Illaenurus Zone		
Limestone and limestone-pebble conglomerate: light brown, weathers to light orange, fine-grained with patches medium-grained, thinly laminated but weathers into 0.5–1.5-foot beds alternating with 1–2-foot covered intervals, probably shaly limestone; *Rasettia snowyensis* at 246.2 feet, Saukid fragments at 255.2 feet, *Finkelnburgia osceola* at 266.6 feet	52.6	215.4
Sage Member—120.2 feet thick		
(Probably FRANCONIAN STAGE, no collections)		
Limestone: brownish gray to gray, fine- to medium-grained, very hard, slightly glauconitic, pebbly, some beds fossiliferous, alternating with thin, covered intervals. Top 42 feet covered	63.5	151.9
Limestone: brownish gray, alternating fine- and medium-grained, pebbly, slightly glauconitic, finely laminated but weathers into 1-foot beds, forms ledge	7.2	144.7
Limestone and limestone-pebble conglomerate: light gray, fine- to medium-grained, pebbles large, slightly glauconitic, fossiliferous, alternating with thicker intervals covered: probably shaly limestone	49.5	95.2
Dry Creek Member—95.2 feet thick		
Covered: probably green fissile shale and thin beds of brown calcareous siltstone	95.2	0
Pilgrim Formation		
Limestone: top of Pilgrim Limestone datum for measurements		

Horseshoe Hills Section K (HK)

Section measured on south slope of hogback half way between Benson's road from Belgrade and west fork of road along Dry Creek, NW.¼sec. 16, T. 2 N., R. 4 E., Gallatin County, Montana. Strike and dip: N. 20° E., 23° NW. (Map by Verall, 1954, Ph.D. thesis, Princeton Univ.)

DEVONIAN SYSTEM

	Bed thickness in feet	Feet above base
Jefferson Formation—2.1 feet measured		
Limestone: dusky brown, weathers gray, lower part thin-bedded, upper part massive, petroliferous odor, dolomitic, forms ledge	2.1	213.0
Maywood unit—96.8 feet thick		
Covered: by float of thin-bedded, platy, dusky-red, yellowish-brown or silty, dolomitic limestone, upper part petroliferous	75.8	137.2

Horseshoe Hills Section K (HK) *Continued*
Devonian System *Continued*

	Bed thickness in feet	Feet above base
Limestone: moderate yellow with greenish tinge, thin-bedded but weathers into 4–8-inch beds, dolomitic, glauconitic, unfossiliferous, lower 11 feet covered by red and yellow limestone float	21.0	116.2
CAMBRIAN SYSTEM		
Snowy Range Formation—116.2 feet thick		
Sage Member—48.4 feet thick		
FRANCONIAN STAGE		
Idahoia Zone		
Idahoia wyomingensis Subzone		
Limestone: dusky red to yellow, fine- to coarse-grained, glauconitic, dolomitic, some pebbles, unit split by 1-foot covered interval; *Pseudodicellomus mosaicus, Sinuella vaticina, Idahoia wyomingensis, Pseudagnostus josephus, Wilbernia* sp.	7.1	109.1
Taenicephalus Zone		
Mostly covered: probably shale or shaly limestone with four projecting 0.5–1.5-foot beds of limestone and limestone-pebble conglomerate: gray, weathers light brownish gray, small limonitic pebbles; *Angulotreta tetonensis, A. vescula, Pseudodicellomus mosaicus, Lingulella* sp. in basal bed. *Kendallina eryon* at 92.4	22.6	86.5
Covered: probably shale and shaly limestone. Basal 0.8 feet is limestone: light gray, fine- to coarse-grained; *Angulotreta tetonensis, Billingsella perfecta, Taenicephalus gallupensis, T. shumardi,* Crinoid columnals	7.8	78.7
Parabolinoides Subzone		
Limestone: light gray, weathers gray, slightly glauconitic, silty coquinite of brachiopods; *Angulotreta tetonensis, Billingsella perfecta, Ceratreta hebes, Eoorthis remnicha, Orygmaspis llanoensis, Parabolinoides cordillerensis, P. hebe*	1.5	77.2
Elvinia Zone		
Covered: probably shale or shaly limestone, with two 0.5-foot beds of limestone-pebble conglomerate: gray, fine-grained, with brownish-gray pebbles, silty; *Linnarssonella girtyi,* at 67.8 and 72.7 feet	9.4	67.8
Dry Creek Member—67.8 feet thick		
Covered: green fissile shale and brownish-gray, thin-bedded, calcareous siltstone	67.8	0
Pilgrim Formation		
Limestone: top of Pilgrim Limestone datum for measurements		

Gallup Creek Section (GC)

Section measured near head of southernmost fork of Gallup Creek, in canyon immediately north of Morrison Canyon, Bridger Mountains, SW.1/4sec. 13, T. 3 N., R. 5 E., Gallatin County, Montana. This is northernmost section measured in Bridgers. Strike and dip: N. 2° E., 72° W. (beds overturned). (Map by McMannis, 1955)

DEVONIAN SYSTEM

	Bed thickness in feet	Feet above base
Jefferson Formation—not measured		
Limestone: dusky brown, weathers gray, forms traceable gray ledge ..		204.4
Maywood unit—65 feet thick		
Covered: by rubble of pink and yellow limestone and dolomite, thin-bedded, platy	65.0	139.4

CAMBRIAN SYSTEM

Snowy Range Formation—139.4 feet thick
Sage Member—76.4 feet thick

FRANCONIAN STAGE

	Bed thickness in feet	Feet above base
Idahoia Zone		
Idahoia wisconsensis Subzone		
Limestone: gray, fine-grained, thin-bedded, shaly, glauconitic; *Lingulella desiderata, Sinuella vaticina, Drumaspis briscoensis, Idahoia wisconsensis,* Phosphatic balls, *Ptychaspis granulosa*	2.1	137.3
Idahoia wyomingensis Subzone		
Limestone: light gray, fine-grained, medium-bedded, slightly glauconitic, in 1–2-foot beds alternating with similarly thick beds of shaly, crinkly limestone; *Angulotreta vescula, Billingsella perfecta, Sinuella vaticina, Drumaspis briscoensis, Idahoia wyomingensis, Pseudagnostus josephus.* Lowermost beds have *Angulotreta vescula, Billingsella perfecta, Sinuella vaticina, Idahoia wyomingensis, Pseudagnostus sentosus, Ptychaspis granulosa, Saratogia fria, S. fracida Wilbernia diademata,* Crinoid columnals	14.5	122.8
Taenicephalus Zone		
Limestone: gray, fine-grained, slightly pebbly, slightly silty, in eight 0.5–1.5-foot beds alternating with 1–7-foot intervals covered: probably shale or shaly limestone; *Angulotreta tetonensis, A. vescula, Eoorthis remnicha* var. *A., Huenella texana, Taenicephalus gallupensis, T. gouldi, T. shumardi,* Crinoid columnals	28.6	94.2
Parabolinoides Subzone		
Limestone: gray, medium-grained, dolomitic, slightly silty, slightly glauconitic; *Angulotreta tetonensis, Billingsella perfecta, B. plicatella, Ceratreta hebes, Eoorthis remnicha, E. remnicha* var. *A., Lingulella desiderata, Kendallina eryon, Orygmaspis firma, O. llanoensis, Parabolinoides contractus, P. cordillerensis, Taenicephalus gallupensis, T. shumardi, Wilbernia halli,* Pelmatozoan calyx	4.6	89.6
Elvinia Zone		
Irvingella major Zonule		
Limestone-pebble conglomerate: gray, medium-grained, slightly glauconitic, top 3 feet covered; *Linarssonella girtyi, Comanchia lippa, Irvingella major*	3.8	85.8
Base of *Irvingella major* Zonule		
Limestone and limestone-pebble conglomerate: gray, medium-grained silty, glauconitic, pebbles slightly weathered, in 0.5–1.5-foot beds alternating with 0.5–2.0-foot intervals covered: probably shale or shaly		

Gallup Creek Section (GC) *Continued*
Cambrian System *Continued*
Franconian Stage *Continued*
Base of *Irvingella major* Zonule *Continued*

	Bed thickness in feet	Feet above base
limestone; *Lingulella desiderata, Linnarssonella girtyi, Burnetiella ectypa, Dellea suada, Westergaardodina tricuspidata*	22.8	63.0
Dry Creek Member—63.0 feet thick		
Covered: green shale and rusty siltstone	63.0	0
Pilgrim Formation		
Limestone: top of Pilgrim Limestone datum for measurements		

Felix Canyon Section (FC)

Section measured just north of Felix Canyon on ridge between Felix and Morrison canyons in Bridger Mountains, SW.1/4sec. 24, T. 3 N., R. 5 E., Gallatin County, Montana. Strike and dip: N. 3° W., 50° W. (overturned). (Map by McMannis, 1955)

DEVONIAN SYSTEM

	Bed thickness in feet	Feet above base
Jefferson Formation—not measured		
Limestone: dusky brown, dolomitic, petroliferous, forms gray ledge ..		251.4
Maywood unit—97.5 feet thick		
Covered: roots of fallen trees expose fragments of yellow, thin-bedded dolomite and limestone	97.5	153.9

CAMBRIAN SYSTEM

Snowy Range Formation—153.9 feet thick
Sage Member—67.9 feet thick

FRANCONIAN STAGE

Idahoia Zone

Idahoia wyomingensis Subzone

Limestone: gray, fine- to medium-grained, thin-bedded, shaly, crinkly, very glauconitic, broken by two 1-foot covered intervals, probably shaly limestone; *Billingsella perfecta,* Phosphatic balls, *Sinuella vaticina, Drumaspis briscoensis, Idahoia wyomingensis, Monocheilus demissus, Pseudagnostus sentosus, Ptychaspis granulosa,* Crinoid columnals	4.0	149.9
Limestone: gray mottled with brownish gray, medium-grained, thin- to medium-bedded, slightly glauconitic, dolomitic, forms ledge; *Angulotreta catheta, Billingsella perfecta, Sinuella vaticina, Croixana bipunctata, Drumaspis briscoensis, Idahoia wisconsensis, I. wyomingensis, Pseudagnostus josephus, P. sentosus, Saratogia carita, S. fracida, S. fria, Wilbernia diademata, W. explanata, Westergaardodina bicuspidata*	8.0	141.9

Taenicephalus Zone

Limestone and limestone-pebble conglomerate: gray, fine-grained, thin-bedded, slightly glauconitic, dolomitic, in 0.1–1-foot beds alternating with 1–8-foot covered intervals: probably shale or shaly limestone; *Angulotreta tetonensis, A. vescula, Billingsella perfecta, B. plicatella, Lingulella desiderata, Kendallina biforota, Pseudagnostus josephus,*

	Bed thickness in feet	Feet above base
Taenicephalus gallupensis, T. shumardi, Wilbernia halli, Crinoid columnals	32.1	109.8
Parabolinoides Subzone		
Limestone-pebble conglomerate: gray, medium-grained, dolomitic, very glauconitic; *Angulotreta tetonensis, Billingsella perfecta, B. plicatella, Pseudodicellomus mosaicus, Lingulella desiderata, Parabolinoides cordillerensis, Taenicephalus gouldi, T. shumardi*	1.2	108.6
Elvinia Zone		
Limestone-pebble conglomerate: greenish gray, slightly glauconitic, silty, medium-grained with small, fine-grained pebbles, in 1–2-foot beds alternating with 2–4-foot covered intervals: probably greenish-gray shale; *Lingulella* sp., *Linnarsonella girtyi, Burnetiella ectypa, Dellea juvenalis, D. saratogensis, D. suada*	22.6	86.0
Dry Creek Member—86 feet thick		
Covered: probably green shale and brown, thin-bedded siltstone, thickness of member only approximate, beds overturned and covered, top and bottom uncertain	86.0	0
Pilgrim Formation		
Limestone: top of Pilgrim Limestone datum for measurements		

Flathead Pass Section (FP)

Section measured in second gully north of Flathead Pass, Bridger Mountains, NW.¼sec. 25, T. 3 N., R. 5 E., Gallatin County, Montana. Strike and dip: N. 15° W., 55° SW. (overturned). (Map by McMannis, 1955)

DEVONIAN SYSTEM

	Bed thickness in feet	Feet above base
Maywood unit—not measured		
Covered: everything covered up to and including base of Jefferson Formation		179.6
CAMBRIAN SYSTEM		
Snowy Range Formation—179.6 feet thick		
Sage Member—71.9 feet thick		
FRANCONIAN STAGE		
Idahoia Zone		
Idahoia wisconsensis Subzone		
Limestone: gray, medium-grained, glauconitic, dolomitic, middle 2.5 feet covered: probably shale or shaly limestone; *Sinuella vaticina, Drumaspis briscoensis, Idahoia wisconsensis, Monocheilus demissus, Pseudagnostus josephus, P. sentosus, Ptychaspis granulosa,* Crinoid columnals	2.9	176.7
Limestone: gray, medium-grained, glauconitic, in 0.5–1-foot beds alternating with 0.5–2-foot beds of limestone and shale, partly covered; *Billingsella perfecta, Sinuella vaticina, Idahoia wyomingensis, Pseudagnostus sentosus, Wilbernia expansa*	18.2	158.5
Taenicephalus Zone		
Covered: probably shale and shaly limestone. At 123.0 feet is a 1-foot bed of limestone-pebble conglomerate; gray, medium-grained, me-		

Flathead Pass Section (FP) *Continued*
Cambrian System *Continued*
Franconian Stage *Continued*
Taenicephalus Zone *Continued*

	Bed thickness in feet	Feet above base
dium-bedded; *Angulotreta tetonensis, A. vescula, Billingsella perfecta, B. plicatella, Huenella texana, Pelagiella primordialis, Taenicephalus gallupensis, T. shumardi,* Crinoid columnals	45.0	113.5
Parabolinoides Subzone		
Limestone-pebble conglomerate: gray, medium-grained, shaly; *Angulotreta tetonensis, Ceratreta hebes, Parabolinoides expansus,* lower foot covered	2.0	111.5
Elvinia Zone		
Limestone: greenish gray, fine-grained, columns of *Collenia magna.* Limestone-pebble conglomerate between columns contains *Pseudodicellomus mosaicus, Lingulella* sp., *Linnarssonella girtyi*	3.8	107.7
Dry Creek Member—107.7 feet thick		
Limestone-pebble conglomerate: brownish gray, medium-grained, slightly glauconitic, silty, pebbles weathered, poorly sorted, in 0.2–2.0-foot beds alternating with 1–10-foot covered intervals; *Linnarssonella girtyi, Burnetiella ectypa, Bynumina terrenda, Dellea suada, Kindbladia wichitaensis*	19.7	88.0
Covered: shale, greenish gray, calcareous, with a few thin beds of siltstone, brownish gray, dolomitic	88.0	0
Pilgrim Formation		
Limestone: top of Pilgrim Limestone datum for measurements		

Johnson Canyon Section (JC)

Section measured near head of Mill Creek, up-ridge from mine in Johnson Canyon, about half way between "Peak North of Ross" and Flathead Pass, Bridger Mountains, NW.¼sec. 5, T. 2 N., R 6 E., Gallatin County, Montana. Strike and dip: N. 40° W., 65° NE. (Map by McMannis, 1955)

DEVONIAN SYSTEM

	Bed thickness in feet	Feet above base
Jefferson Formation—3 feet measured		
Limestone: dusky brown, weathers gray, dolomitic, petroliferous, forms small ledge	3.0	194.0
Maywood unit—49.0 feet thick		
Covered: probably thin-bedded limestone and dolomite, yellow and red in lower half, brown and petroliferous near top	49.0	145.0

CAMBRIAN SYSTEM

Snowy Range Formation—145 feet thick
Sage Member—86.6 feet thick

FRANCONIAN STAGE

Idahoia Zone
Idahoia serapio Subzone

Mostly covered: probably shale or shaly limestone. Top 3 feet has beds of limestone-pebble conglomerate: light gray, medium- to coarse-

	Bed thickness in feet	Feet above base
grained, pebbles limonitic, weathered, matrix fresh, glauconitic; Linguloid fragments	21.6	123.4
Idahoia wisconsensis Subzone		
Limestone: gray, alternating fine- and medium-grained, thin-bedded, shaly, crinkly bedded, alternating with intervals of shale or covered; *Lingulella desiderata, Sinuella vaticina, Ptychaspis granulosa*	14.8	108.6
Idahoia wyomingensis Subzone		
Limestone: alternating beds brownish gray, medium-grained, slightly glauconitic, with darker gray, finer-grained, forms thick ledge; *Pseudodicellomus mosaicus, Lingulella desiderata, Sinuella vaticina, Idahoia wyomingensis, Pseudagnostus josephus, P. sentosus, Saratogia fria*	16.0	92.6
Taenicephalus Zone		
Mostly covered: shale and shaly limestone, with thin beds of limestone and limestone-pebble conglomerate: gray, medium-grained, pebbles fine-grained, randomly oriented; *Angulotreta vescula*	20.6	72.0
Parabolinoides Subzone		
Limestone: gray, coarse-grained, medium-bedded, glauconitic, dolomitic, silty, chiefly fossil-fragment coquinite; *Angulotreta tetonensis A. vescula, Billingsella perfecta, B. plicatella, Ceratreta hebes, Eoorthis remnicha, E. remnicha* var. *A., Huenella abnormis, Orygmaspis firma, Parabolinoides cordillerensis, P. hebe, Taenicephalus gallupensis, T. gouldi, T. shumardi, Wilbernia halli*	3.9	68.1
Elvinia Zone		
Limestone-pebble conglomerate and covered intervals: former light gray, medium- to coarse-grained, very silty, pebbles poorly sorted, above fine-grained, greenish-gray columns of *Collenia magna,* not as columnar as elsewhere; *Linnarssonella girtyi, Ocnerorthis monticola*	9.7	58.4
Dry Creek Member—58.4 feet thick		
Covered: shale, greenish gray, fissile and crumbly, with thin beds of brownish-gray, irregularly bedded siltstone. Thin bed near top is limestone-pebble conglomerate: brownish gray, medium-grained, silty, pebbles poorly sorted; *Linnarssonella girtyi*	58.4	0
Pilgrim Formation		
Limestone: top of Pilgrim Limestone datum for measurements		

Bighorn Lake Section (BL)

Section measured below peak just south of peak that rises directly above Bighorn Lake, Bridger Mountains, SW.1/4sec. 16, T. 2 N., R. 6 E., Gallatin County, Montana. Strike and dip: N. 5° W., 61° N. (Map by McMannis, 1955)

CAMBRIAN SYSTEM

	Bed thickness in feet	Feet above base
Snowy Range Formation—52.9 feet measured		
Sage Member—not measured		
FRANCONIAN STAGE		
Elvinia Zone		
Limestone: fine-grained, columns of *Collenia magna*		52.9
Dry Creek Member—52.9 feet thick		

Bighorn Lake Section (BL) *Continued*
Cambrian System *Continued*
Franconian Stage *Continued*
Elvinia Zone *Continued*

	Bed thickness in feet	Feet above base
Limestone: greenish gray, shaly, lumpy, and limestone-pebble conglomerate: gray, medium-grained, silty, with flat limonitic pebbles, in five thin beds; *Linnarssonella girtyi, Dellea* sp., *Kindbladia wichitaensis*	5.2	47.7
Shale: greenish gray, fissile to lumpy. Lower third has thin beds of siltstone: brown, thinly laminated, irregularly bedded, calcareous	44.9	2.8

DRESBACHIAN STAGE

Aphelaspis Zone

Shale: greenish gray, fissile, calcareous, typical of Dry Creek shale, top 0.3 feet is limestone-pebble conglomerate: gray, silty, large and small pebbles; *Lingulella* sp., *Micromitra modesta, Aphelaspis* sp.	2.8	0

Pilgrim Formation
Limestone: top of Pilgrim Limestone datum for measurements

Bill Smith Creek Section (BC)

Section measured about midway between sections at Bighorn Lake and Sacajawea Peak, Bridger Mountains, in center of sec. 21, T. 2 N., R. 6 E., Gallatin County, Montana. Strike and dip: N. 35° W., 55° NE. (Map by McMannis, 1955)

DEVONIAN SYSTEM

	Bed thickness in feet	Feet above base
Jefferson Formation—2.3 feet measured		
Limestone: dusky brown, weathers gray, forms ledge	2.3	244.4
Maywood unit—33.5 feet thick		
Limestone: light brown, finely laminated, dolomitic, top 13 feet petroliferous, bottom 19 feet covered	33.5	210.9

CAMBRIAN SYSTEM

Snowy Range Formation—211.1 feet thick
Grove Creek Member—5.7 feet thick

TREMPEALEAUAN STAGE

Illaenurus Zone

Limestone: gray, fine-grained, hard, thin-bedded, slightly glauconitic, top foot mottled with yellow, middle foot covered; near base are *Finkelnburgia osceola,* Gastropod fragments, *Hyolithes primordialis, Bynumiella typicalis, Eurekia binodosa, Homagnostus* sp., *Illaenurus truncatus, Rasettia snowyensis*	5.7	205.2
Sage Member—159.1 feet thick		
Limestone: purplish gray, fine- to medium-grained, thin-bedded, irregularly bedded, glauconitic, dolomitic, pebbly, top 9.5 feet and bottom 4.5 feet covered; *Multivasculatus ovatus, Angulotreta catheta,* Gastropod columellae, *Homagnostus* sp., *Illaenurus quadratus, I. sinclairensis* and *I. truncatus*	18.9	186.3

FRANCONIAN STAGE

Prosaukia Zone ?

	Bed thickness in feet	Feet above base
Limestone: dark gray, medium-grained, thick-bedded, with unidentifiable trilobite and brachiopod fragments, alternating with covered, probably shale	20.3	166.0
Idahoia Zone *Idahoia serapio* Subzone		
Limestone: gray, medium-grained, pebbly, glauconitic, with large and small brown pebbles, beds 1–2 feet thick, with two 3-foot covered intervals, top 34.5 feet covered; *Angulotreta vescula, Billingsella perfecta, Lytospira* sp., *Sinuella vaticina, Idahoia serapio, Maladia americana, Pinctus ? pullus, Pseudagnostus josephus*	45.7	120.5
Idahoia wisconsensis Subzone		
Limestone: gray, medium-grained, thin-bedded, slightly glauconitic, in 0.5–1.0-foot beds alternating with 2–3-foot covered; shaly lumpy limestone; *Angulotreta vescula, Billingsella perfecta, B. plicatella, Pseudodicellomus mosaicus, Lingulella desiderata,* Phosphatic balls, *Sinuella vaticina, Drumaspis briscoensis, Ellipsocephaloides silvestris, Idahoia wisconsensis, Monocheilus demissus, Pseudagnostus sentosus, Ptychaspis granulosa, Wilbernia pero*	11.4	109.1
Idahoia wyomingensis Subzone		
Limestone: brownish gray, some beds gray, fine- to medium-grained, irregular, glauconitic, dolomitic, forms ledge; *Billingsella perfecta, Pseudodicellomus mosaicus,* Linguloid fragments, *Sinuella vaticina, Croixana bipunctata, Idahoia wyomingensis, Pseudagnostus sentosus, Saratogia carita, S. fria, Wilbernia diademata, Westergaardodina bicuspidata*	9.6	99.5
Taenicephalus Zone		
Limestone: gray, medium- to coarse-grained, silty, glauconitic, in 0.3–2.0-foot beds alternating with 0.5–2.5-foot covered intervals of shale or shaly limestone; *Angulotreta tetonensis, A. vescula, Billingsella perfecta, B. plicatella, Ceratreta hebes, Pseudodicellomus mosaicus, Lingulella desiderata, Pelagiella primordialis, Maustonia nasuta, Taenicephalus gallupensis, T. shumardi,* Crinoid columnals	26.7	72.8
Parabolinoides Subzone		
Limestone: gray, mottled with brown, pebbly, glauconitic, limonitic, lower half covered; *Angulotreta tetonensis, Billingsella perfecta, B. plicatella, Ceratreta hebes, Pseudodicellomus mosaicus, Eoorthis remnicha, Huenella texana, Orygmaspis llanoensis, Parabolinoides contractus, P. cordillerensis, P. expansus, Taenicephalus gallupensis, T. shumardi,* Crinoid columnals	7.0	65.8
Elvinia Zone		
Limestone: greenish gray, fine-grained, top 2 feet bedded, lower 17.5 feet columns of *Collenia magna;* pebbly matrix has *Linnarssonella girtyi, Burnetiella ectypa, Dellea juvenalis, D. saratogensis, D. suada, Pseudodicellomus mosaicus, Kyphocephalus* ? sp., *Pseudagnostus sentosus, Pterocephalia sanctisabae*	19.5	46.3

Bill Smith Creek Section (BC) *Continued*
Cambrian System *Continued*
Franconian Stage *Continued*
Elvinia Zone *Continued*

	Bed thickness in feet	Feet above base
Dry Creek Member—46.3 feet thick		
Covered: float indicates greenish-gray shale with thin beds of brown calcareous siltstone	46.0	0.3
DRESBACHIAN STAGE		
Aphelaspis Zone		
Limestone-pebble conglomerate: brownish gray, matrix medium- to coarse-grained, pebbles fine-grained, rounded, poorly sorted, *Dytremacephalus* ? sp.	0.3	0
Pilgrim Formation		
Limestone: top of Pilgrim Limestone datum for measurements		

Sacajawea Peak Section (SP)

Section measured at top of cirque wall just north of Sacajawea Peak, near end of switchback trail from Fairy Lake campground, Bridger Mountains, NW.1/4sec. 27, T. 2 N., R. 6 E., Gallatin County, Montana. Strike and dip: N. 20° W., 65° E. (Map by McMannis, 1955)

DEVONIAN SYSTEM

	Bed thickness in feet	Feet above base
Jefferson Formation—1 foot measured		
Limestone: dusky brown, weathers gray, petroliferous, forms ledge	1.0	295.7
Maywood unit—112.2 feet thick		
Limestone and dolomite: dusky red and light yellow, platy, silty, top 10 feet petroliferous, mostly covered, forms rubbly slope	112.2	183.5
CAMBRIAN SYSTEM		
Snowy Range Formation—183.5 feet thick		
Sage Member—97.5 feet thick		
FRANCONIAN STAGE		
Idahoia Zone		
Idahoia serapio Subzone		
Limestone: brownish gray, weathers gray, medium- to coarse-grained, pebbly, slightly glauconitic, dolomitic, in 0.3–2.0-foot beds with 4–6-foot covered intervals; *Angulotreta vescula, Billingsella perfecta, Pseudodicellomus mosaicus, Lytospira* ? sp., *Drumaspis briscoensis D. idahoensis, Idahoia serapio, I. wisconsensis, Maladia americana, Monocheilus demissus, Pseudagnostus sentosus, Ptychaspis granulosa, Wilbernia expansa*	22.5	161.0
Idahoia wisconsensis Subzone		
Limestone: gray, fine-grained, thin-bedded, dolomitic, some light gray and medium-grained, shale breaks between limestones, unit forms top of ledge; *Billingsella perfecta, Sinuella vaticina, Drumaspis brisco-*		

	Bed thickness in feet	Feet above base
ensis, *Idahoia wisconsensis, I. wyomingensis, Maladia americana, Monocheilus demissus, Pseudagnostus sentosus, Wilbernia diademata*	5.0	156.0
Idahoia wyomingensis Subzone		
Limestone: brownish gray, weathers gray and brown mottled, medium-grained, thin-bedded, some pebbles, slightly glauconitic, base of ledge at 146.6 feet; *Angulotreta vescula, Billingsella perfecta, Pseudodicellomus mosaicus, Lingulella desiderata, Lytospira* ? sp., Phosphatic balls, *Sinuella vaticina, Idahoia wyomingensis, Pseudagnostus sentosus, Saratogia carita, S. fracida, S. fria, Wilbernia expansa, Westergaardodina* sp.	11.7	144.3
Taenicephalus Zone		
Limestone-pebble conglomerate: gray to brownish gray, alternating fine- and medium-grained, thin-bedded, glauconitic, pebbles small, top 22 feet mostly covered; *Angulotreta tetonensis, A. vescula, Billingsella perfecta, B. plicatella, Ceratreta hebes, Pseudodicellomus mosaicus, Eoorthis remnicha, E. remnicha* var. *A., Huenella abnormis, Lingulella desiderata, Pelagiella primordialis, Kendallina eryon, Maustonia nasuta, Taenicephalus gallupensis, T. shumardi,* Crinoid columnals	26.9	117.4
Parabolinoides Subzone		
Limestone: gray, medium- to coarse-grained, thin-bedded, sporadically pebbly, glauconitic, very fossiliferous, some beds shaly and lumpy; *Angulotreta tetonensis, Billingsella perfecta, B. plicatella, Ceratreta hebes, Pseudodicellomus mosaicus, Eoorthis remnicha, Huenella abnormis, Pelagiella primordialis, Orygmaspis firma, Parabolinoides hebe, Pseudagnostus sentosus, Taenicephalus gallupensis, T. gouldi, T. shumardi, Wilbernia halli,* Crinoid columnals	7.5	109.9
Elvinia Zone		
Camaraspis Subzone		
Limestone-pebble conglomerate: gray, matrix medium-grained, silty, pebbles fine-grained, flat; *Linnarssonella girtyi, Sulcocephalus* sp., *Burnetiella ectypa, Camaraspis convexa, Dellea saratogensis, D. suada, Elvinia roemeri, Pseudagnostus sentosus*	2.6	108.6
Base of *Camaraspis* Zone		
Limestone: fine-grained, greenish gray, columns of *Collenia magna,* pebbly matrix between columns, top of bioherm irregular	21.3	86.0
Dry Creek Member—86 feet thick		
Covered: float indicates shale: green, fissile, calcareous, with thin beds of thin-bedded, brown siltstone	86.0	0
Pilgrim Formation		
Limestone: top of Pilgrim Limestone datum for measurements		

Ross Peak Section (RP)

Section measured at head of Ross Creek, between Ross and Sacajawea peaks, about 1 mile northwest of Ross Peak, Bridger Mountains, NW.1/4sec. 3, T. 1 N., R. 6 E., Gallatin County, Montana. Strike and dip: N. 20° E., 50° E. (Map by McMannis, 1955)

Ross Peak Section (RP) *Continued*

DEVONIAN SYSTEM	Bed thickness in feet	Feet above base
Jefferson Formation—1.5 feet measured		
Limestone: gray, alternating fine- and medium-grained beds, forms ledge	1.5	272.6
Maywood unit—16 feet thick		
Limestone: dusky brown, medium-grained, thin-bedded, petroliferous	16.0	256.6
CAMBRIAN SYSTEM		
Snowy Range Formation—256.6 feet thick		
Grove Creek Member—41.5 feet thick		
PROBABLY TREMPEALEAUAN STAGE		
Limestone: orange yellow, some purplish gray, finely laminated but weathers massive, some beds crinkly, shaly, no fossils	41.5	215.1
Sage Member—157.6 feet thick		
Limestone: purplish gray, fine-grained, dolomitic, pebbly, alternating with shaly limestone and dusky-red and greenish-gray fissile shale	15.0	200.1
PROBABLY FRANCONIAN STAGE		
Limestone-pebble conglomerate: medium-grained, dolomitic, pebbles well rounded, alternating with dark-gray, shaly, crinkly, bedded limestone; *Angulotreta catheta*, Linguloid fragments, *Westergaardodina bicuspidata*	13.0	187.1
Probably *Idahoia serapio* Subzone of *Idahoia* Zone		
Covered: float indicates shale with beds of shaly limestone	39.0	148.1
Idahoia wisconsensis Subzone		
Limestone: light gray, fine- to medium-grained, crinkly bedded, shaly, slightly glauconitic; *Sinuella vaticina, Idahoia wisconsensis, Monocheilus demissus, Pseudagnostus josephus, P. sentosus, Ptychaspis granulosa,* Crinoid columnals	3.5	144.6
Idahoia wyomingensis Subzone		
Limestone: gray, medium- to coarse-grained, thick-bedded, glauconitic, some pebbly, some shaly; *Billingsella perfecta, Pseudodicellomus mosaicus,* Phosphatic balls, *Sinuella vaticina, Drumaspis briscoensis, Idahoia wyomingensis, Maladia americana, Pseudagnostus josephus, P. sentosus, Ptychaspis granulosa, Saratogia fracida, S. fria,* Crinoid columnals	22.9	121.7
Covered: probably chiefly shale with thin beds of shaly limestone. Half foot at base is limestone: gray, fine-grained with lenses coarser-grained; *Billingsella perfecta, Sinuella vaticina, Drumaspis briscoensis, Idahoia wyomingensis, Maladia americana, Pseudagnostus sentosus*	27.4	94.3
Limestone: gray, fine-grained, glauconitic, some pebbles, forms top of ledge; *Angulotreta vescula, Billingsella perfecta, Pseudodicellomus mosaicus,* Linguloid fragments, Phosphatic balls, *Sinuella vaticina, Drumaspis briscoensis, Idahoia wisconsensis, I. wyomingensis, Pseudagnostus sentosus, Saratogia carita, S. fracida, Wilbernia* sp.	9.4	84.9

Probable top of *Taenicephalus* Zone

	Bed thickness in feet	Feet above base
Limestone: dark-gray, fine-grained, laminated but weathers massive, slightly pebbly, some beds crinkly, shaly, alternating with covered intervals of shale and shaly limestone	24.7	60.2
Parabolinoides Subzone		
Limestone: gray, fine-grained, pebbly; *Angulotreta tetonensis, Ceratreta hebes, Maustonia nasuta*	2.7	57.5
Dry Creek Member—57.5 feet thick		
Probably *Elvinia* Zone		
Covered: shale, greenish gray, with thin beds of brownish-gray siltstone	57.5	0
Pilgrim Formation		
Limestone: top of Pilgrim Limestone datum for measurements		

Bridger Peak Section (BP)

Section measured south of Bridger Peak, up Bostwick Creek east of Bostwick Creek fault, Bridger Mountains, NE.¼sec. 2., T. 1 S., R. 6 E., Gallatin County, Montana. Strike and dip: N. 3° E., 65° E. (Map by McMannis, 1955)

DEVONIAN SYSTEM

	Bed thickness in feet	Feet above base
Maywood unit—8 feet measured		
Limestone: partly covered, dusky brown, thin-bedded, petroliferous	8.0	249.1
CAMBRIAN SYSTEM		
Snowy Range Formation—249.1 feet thick		
Grove Creek Member—43.8 feet thick		
TREMPEALEAUAN STAGE		
Illaenurus Zone		
Dolomite and limestone: greenish gray, coarse-grained, glauconitic, calcareous, in 1-foot beds alternating with 1–10-foot covered intervals	34.9	214.2
Limestone and dolomite; fine- and medium-grained, forms small ledge, *Angulotreta catheta*	6.3	207.9
PROBABLY FRANCONIAN STAGE		
Limestone: shaly, crinkly, and dolomite: grayish blue and brownish gray, thick-bedded, hard	2.6	205.3
Sage Member—130.3 feet thick		
Covered: probably shale and shaly limestone with half a foot near base limestone: gray, fine-grained, pebbly	11.0	194.3
Idahoia Zone		
Idahoia serapio Subzone		
Limestone: gray, fine- to medium-grained, dolomitic, some pebbly, in 1–2-foot beds alternating with thicker, covered intervals; *Angulotreta vescula, Sinuella vaticina, Drumaspis idahoensis, Idahoia serapio, Maladia americana, Pseudagnostus sentosus*	33.1	161.2

Bridger Peak Section (BP) *Continued*
Cambrian System *Continued*
Probably Franconian Stage *Continued*

	Bed thickness in feet	Feet above base
Idahoia wisconsensis Subzone		
Limestone: gray, fine-grained, medium-bedded, slightly pebbly, dolomitic; *Sinuella vaticina, Drumaspis idahoensis, Idahoia wisconsensis*	4.4	156.8
Idahoia wyomingensis Subzone		
Limestone: gray to grayish blue, fine-grained, dolomitic, thin-bedded, shaly, crinkly, in 1.5-foot beds alternating with 1.5–3.0-foot covered intervals: probably shaly, crinkly bedded limestone	15.0	141.8
Limestone: brownish gray, alternating beds fine- and medium-grained, slightly glauconitic, dolomitic, slightly pebbly, forms 10-foot ledge; *Billingsella perfecta,* Linguloid fragments, Phosphatic balls, *Sinuella vaticina*	10.0	131.8
Limestone: brownish gray, medium-grained undulating bedding surfaces, slightly glauconitic, in half-foot beds alternating with thicker, covered intervals: probably shaly, crinkly bedded limestone; Linguloid fragment, *Sinuella vaticina*	8.0	123.8
Taenicephalus Zone		
Mostly covered: probably shaly limestone, some thin beds of limestone-pebble conglomerate: brownish gray, commonly dolomitic, with green pebbles; *Angulotreta tetonensis, A. vescula, Billingsella perfecta, B. plicatella, Ceratreta hebes, Pseudodicellomus mosaicus, Eoorthis remnicha, E. remnicha* var. *A., Huenella abnormis, Lingulella desiderata, Orygmaspis firma, O. llanoensis, Parabolinoides hebe, Taenicephalus shumardi, Wilbernia halli,* Crinoid columnals	21.1	102.7
Parabolinoides Subzone		
Limestone-pebble conglomerate: bluish gray, dolomitic, large pebbles, medium- to coarse-grained matrix, alternating with thin beds of limestone: brownish gray, fine-grained, thin-bedded; *Angulotreta tetonensis, A. vescula, Billingsella perfecta, B. plicatella, Ceratreta hebes, Eoorthis remnicha, E. remnicha* var. *A., Huenella abnormis, Pseudodicellomus mosaicus, Orygmaspis firma, O. llanoensis, Parabolinoides hebe, Taenicephalus shumardi, Wilbernia halli,* Crinoid columnals	5.4	97.3
Elvinia Zone		
Limestone-pebble conglomerate: medium-grained, silty matrix, pebbles brown, poorly sorted, fine-grained, in 0.5–1.5-foot covered intervals: probably shaly limestone; *Linnarssonella girtyi*	6.8	90.5
Limestone: greenish gray, fine-grained, stylolitic columns of *Collenia magna,* with matrix of limestone-pebble conglomerate between columns	15.5	75.0
Dry Creek Member—75 feet thick		
Mostly covered: shale, greenish gray, fissile, with thin beds of brownish-gray siltstone. Top 12 feet has beds of limestone and limestone-pebble conglomerate	75.0	0
Pilgrim Formation		
Limestone: top of Pilgrim Limestone datum for measurements		

Baldy Mountain Section (BM)

Section measured just southwest of Baldy Mountain, near head of Sypes Canyon, Bridger Mountains, SW.¼sec. 15, T. 1 S., R. 6 E., Gallatin County, Montana, reached best by walking up Middle Cottonwood Creek, then south along strike to head of Sypes Canyon. Strike and dip: N. 36° E., 87° E. (Map by McMannis, 1955)

DEVONIAN SYSTEM

	Bed thickness in feet	Feet above base
Jefferson Formation—4 feet measured		
Limestone: dusky brown, dolomitic, petroliferous, weathers to gray ledge	4.0	388.7
Maywood unit—63 feet thick		
Limestone: dusky brown, medium-grained, thin-bedded, petroliferous, lower 49 feet covered by rubble of dolomite: brownish yellow, calcareous, thin-bedded, slightly arenaceous	63.0	325.7

CAMBRIAN SYSTEM

Snowy Range Formation—325.7 feet thick
Grove Creek Member—23.6 feet thick

TREMPEALEAUAN STAGE

Illaenurus Zone

Limestone: yellowish brown, finely laminated, cherty, slightly glauconitic, dolomitic, arenaceous, in 2–4-foot beds; *Multivasculatus ovatus, Angulotreta catheta,* Linguloid fragments	23.6	302.1
Sage Member—216.1 feet thick		
Limestone: brownish gray, medium-grained, medium-bedded, dolomitic, glauconitic, one 3.5-foot bed of greenish-gray calcareous shale; *Angulotreta catheta, Finkelnburgia osceola, Illaenurus quadratus* ?, *Stenopilus* ? sp.	13.6	288.5
Limestone: gray, fine-grained, with lenses medium-grained, dolomitic, slightly glauconitic, in 2–5-foot beds alternating with similarly thick beds of greenish-gray shale; *Angulotreta catheta,* Gastropod columellae, *Illaenurus quadratus, I. sinclairensis, Monocheilus* cf. *M. truncatus*	25.8	262.7
Limestone: gray, fine-grained, dolomitic, in 0.5–2-foot beds alternating with 2–6-foot beds of greenish-gray shale; *Angulotreta catheta, Dikelocephalus* sp., *Idiomesus* sp., *Pseudagnostus* cf. *P. laevis, Rasettia snowyensis*	16.2	246.5

FRANCONIAN STAGE

Prosaukia Zone

Limestone: gray, fine- to medium-grained, dolomitic, in 0.5–1.0-foot beds alternating with greenish-gray fissile shale in 1–5-foot beds, partly covered; *Angulotreta catheta, Pseudodicellomus mosaicus, Lingulella desiderata, Lytospira* ? sp., *Ellipsocephaloides silvestris, Prosaukia* sp., *Ptychaspis* cf. *P. miniscaensis,* Crinoid columnals	47.7	198.8

Idahoia Zone

Idahoia serapio Subzone

Limestone: gray, medium-grained, some beds glauconitic, in 0.5–2-foot beds alternating with 0.5–4-foot beds, covered, and beds of greenish-gray, crinkly bedded shaly limestone; *Angulotreta catheta, Pseudodicellomus mosaicus, Sinuella vaticina, Drumaspis briscoensis, D. idahoensis, Ellipsocephaloides silvestris, Idahoia serapio, Pseudagnostus sentosus, Ptychaspis granulosa, Stigmacephaloides curvabilis, Wilbernia* sp., Crinoid columnals (star-shaped)	41.9	156.9

Baldy Mountain Section (BM) *Continued*
Cambrian System *Continued*
Franconian Stage *Continued*

	Bed thickness in feet	Feet above base
Idahoia wisconsensis Subzone		
Limestone: brownish gray, medium-grained, medium-bedded, pebbly, dolomitic, alternating with unfossiliferous, shaly, crinkly bedded limestone; *Angulotreta vescula, Lingulella desiderata, Sinuella vaticina,* Aglaspid fragments, *Drumaspis briscoensis, Idahoia wisconsensis, I. serapio, Maladia americana, Monocheilus demissus, Pseudagnostus sentosus, Westergaardodina* sp.	8.8	148.1
Idahoia wyomingensis Subzone		
Limestone: brownish gray, medium-grained, pebbly, dolomitic; *Angulotreta vescula, Lytospira* ? sp., *Sinuella vaticina, Idahoia wyomingensis, Pseudagnostus sentosus, Ptychaspis granulosa, Saratogia fracida, Wilbernia* sp., Crinoid columnals	16.5	131.6
Taenicephalus Zone		
Limestone-pebble conglomerate: gray mottled with brownish gray, fine- and medium-grained, glauconitic, dolomitic, in 0.5–3.5-foot beds alternating with slightly thicker, covered intervals; *Angulotreta tetonensis, A. vescula, Billingsella perfecta, B. plicatella, Ceratreta hebes,* in basal 8 feet	35.4	96.2
Limestone: gray, coarse-grained, pebbly, glauconitic, lower half foot covered; *Angulotreta tetonensis, Billingsella perfecta, B. plicatella, Ceratreta hebes, Eoorthis remnicha, E. remnicha* var. *A., Lingulella desiderata, Parabolinoides* sp. (pygidium), *Taenicephalus gallupensis, T. gouldi, T. shumardi,* Crinoid columnals	4.2	92.0
Elvinia Zone		
Limestone and limestone-pebble conglomerate: greenish gray, fine-grained, dolomitic, in thin beds alternating with thin, covered intervals; *Linnarssonella girtyi, Burnetiella ectypa,* basal 2.5 feet is columnar *Collenia magna*	6.0	86.0
Dry Creek Member—86 feet thick		
Limestone-pebble conglomerate: slightly glauconitic, dolomitic, gives way laterally to fine-grained, algal-appearing but noncolumnar limestone; *Linnarssonella girtyi*	3.5	82.5
Shale: partly covered, green, fissile, calcareous, with thin beds of siltstone: brownish gray, calcareous, dolomitic	82.0	0.5
Limestone-pebble conglomerate: pebbles flat, edges with limonite	0.5	0
Pilgrim Formation		
Limestone: top of Pilgrim Limestone datum for measurements		

Mount Ellis Section (ME)

Section measured about 1 mile northwest of Mount Ellis, near head of south fork of Limestone Creek, sec. 10, T. 3 S., R. 6 E., Gallatin County, Montana. Beds are overturned and badly faulted; dip is 42° W. at bottom of section, 75° W. at top. Measurements probably are inaccurate, but sequence of beds is correct. (Maps by U.S. Forest Service, 1947, Gallatin National Forest, West Half; U.S. Geological Survey Folio No. 1, 1894, Livingstone quadrangle, Montana)

Devonian System

	Bed thickness in feet	Feet above base
Maywood unit—46 feet thick		
Partly covered: rubble of red and yellow platy dolomite and limestone	23.0	77.6
Dolomite and limestone: moderate yellow, fine- to medium-grained, thin- to medium-bedded, transition zone between Maywood and Snowy Range: slightly glauconitic, fine-grained limestone at base, grading upward to nonglauconitic, medium-grained dolomite	23.0	54.6

Cambrian System

Snowy Range Formation—54.6 feet measured
Grove Creek Member—25.6 feet thick

TREMPEALEAUAN STAGE

Illaenurus Zone

Limestone: gray, fine- to medium-grained, thin-bedded, shaly, slightly glauconitic, slightly dolomitic, lower 4 feet covered by rubble from nearby fault; *Multivasculatus ovatus, Finkelnburgia osceola,* Gastropod columellae, Phosphatic balls, *Bynumina* sp., *Eurekia binodosa, Illaenurus quadratus, I. sinclairensis*	14.2	40.4
Limestone: pinkish gray to brownish gray, medium-grained, dolomitic, limonitic, shaly, in 0.5–1.0-foot beds alternating with similarly thick beds of limestone: gray, fine-grained, shaly, crinkly bedded; *Multivasculatus ovatus, Angulotreta catheta, Finkelnburgia osceola, Briscoia dalyi, Eurekia binodosa, Illaenurus quadratus,* Saukid sp.	11.4	29.0
Sage Member—29 feet measured		
Limestone: brownish gray, pale reddish in lower part, fine-grained, shaly, crinkly bedded, stylolitic, some pebbles; *Multivasculatus ovatus, Angulotreta catheta*	12.6	16.4
Covered: rubble of limestone and soil; fault here cuts out remainder of Sage Member and all of Dry Creek Member	16.4	0
Pilgrim Limestone		
Limestone: top of Pilgrim Limestone datum for measurements		

Flying "D" Ranch Section (FD)

Section measured on small fault block of Snowy Range, Maywood, and Jefferson on Flying "D" Ranch, southwest of Gallatin Gateway, sec. 11, T. 3 S., R. 3 E., Gallatin County, Montana. (Maps by U.S. Forest Service, 1947; U.S. Geological Survey Folio No. 24, 1894)

Devonian System

	Bed thickness in feet	Feet above base
Jefferson Formation—2.7 feet measured		
Dolomite: dusky brown, petroliferous (no prominent ledge here)	2.7	123.9
Maywood unit—45.7 feet thick		
Dolomite: yellowish gray, medium- to coarse-grained, medium-bedded, shaly	24.9	99.0
Dolomite: yellowish gray, medium- to coarse-grained, calcareous,		

Flying "D" Ranch Section (FD) *Continued*
Devonian System *Continued*

	Bed thickness in feet	Feet above base
cherty, vuggy, medium- to thick-bedded, unfossiliferous. External appearance is that of Sage Member but it has been dolomitized, destroying glauconite, fossils, pebbles; probably weathered in post-Cambrian, pre-Late Devonian	20.8	78.2

CAMBRIAN SYSTEM

Snowy Range Formation—78.2 feet thick
Sage Member—63.2 feet thick

FRANCONIAN STAGE

Covered: probably shale and shaly, crinkly bedded limestone; included with Sage because it weathers differently from overlying Maywood	52.3	25.9
Taenicephalus Zone (Top probably in covered interval above)		
Limestone-pebble conglomerate: gray, medium-grained, thin-bedded, dolomitic, shaly; *Angulotreta vescula*	0.3	25.6
Parabolinoides Subzone		
Mostly covered: probably shale and shaly limestone. Lower half foot is limestone-pebble conglomerate: gray, medium- to coarse-grained, thin-bedded, shaly, dolomitic, slightly glauconitic; *Angulotreta tetonensis, Billingsella perfecta, B. plicatella, Ceratreta hebes, Pseudodicellomus mosaicus, Eoorthis remnicha, Pellagiella primordialis, Parabolinoides expansus, Kendallina biforota, K. eryon,* Pelmatozoan calyx	10.6	15.0
Dry Creek Member—15 feet thick		
Elvinia Zone		
Shale: greenish gray, fissile and crumbly, calcareous, with thin beds of grayish-brown, calcareous, dolomitic siltstone	15.0	0
Pilgrim Formation		
Limestone: top of Pilgrim Limestone datum for measurements		

Squaw Creek Section (SC)

Section measured on south-facing slope of Storm Castle Mountain, near mouth of Squaw Creek where it enters Gallatin River from east, NW.1/4sec. 34, T. 4 S., R. 4 E., Gallatin County, Montana. This is near Hanson's (1952, p. 37) Squaw Creek Section No. 21. Strike and dip: N. 35° W., 17° NE. (Map by U.S. Forest Service, 1947)

DEVONIAN SYSTEM

	Bed thickness in feet	Feet above base
Jefferson Formation—2 feet measured		
Limestone: brownish black, medium-bedded, petroliferous odor	2.0	92.1
Maywood unit—32.2 feet thick		
Dolomite: dark gray, weathers to light gray and yellowish gray, medium- to thick-bedded, top 6 feet petroliferous, stands up as resistant ledge resembling Maywood dolomite at Section FD	32.2	59.9

CAMBRIAN SYSTEM

	Bed thickness in feet	Feet above base
Snowy Range Formation—59.9 feet thick		
Sage Member—26 feet thick		
FRANCONIAN STAGE		
Taenicephalus Zone		
Limestone: dark gray, medium-grained, thin- to thick-bedded, very dolomitic, vuggy, pyritic, some beds pebbly; *Angulotreta tetonensis, A. vescula, Billingsella perfecta, Lingulella perattenuata, Taenicephalus shumardi,* Crinoid columnals	6.4	53.5
Parabolinoides Subzone		
Limestone: dark gray, medium- to coarse-grained, thin-bedded, limonitic, glauconitic, very dolomitic, alternating with thin, covered intervals: probably shale and shaly limestone; *Angulotreta tetonensis, A. vescula, Billingsella perfecta, B. plicatella, Ceratreta hebes, Pseudodicellomus mosaicus, Eoorthis remnicha, E. remnicha* var. *A., Huenella texana, Lingulella perattenuata, Kendallina eryon, Maustonia nasuta, Orygmaspis firma, Parabolinoides contractus, P. cordillerensis, P. hebe, Taenicephalus shumardi*	14.9	38.6
Elvinia Zone		
Limestone-pebble conglomerate: dark gray, medium-grained, thick-bedded, slightly glauconitic, very dolomitic, top 3 feet covered: probably shale	4.7	33.9
Dry Creek Member—33.9 feet thick		
Mostly covered: green shale. Basal foot limestone-pebble conglomerate: gray, medium-grained, medium-bedded, slightly glauconitic, dolomitic, very silty; *Linnarssonella girtyi, Burnetiella ectypa, Pterocephalia sanctisabae*	6.9	27.0
Shale: greenish gray, fissile and crumbly, calcareous, some beds covered, also thin beds of siltstone: rusty brown, thin-bedded, dolomitic, platy (2.5-foot sill of andesite porphyry at 15.8 feet)	27.0	0
Pilgrim Formation		
Limestone: top of Pilgrim Limestone datum for measurements		

Crowfoot Ridge Section (CF)

Section measured on northwest spur of Crowfoot Ridge, northwestern corner of Yellowstone National Park, Wyoming, in the Gallatin Mountains, about 5.5 miles east of West Gallatin Road (U.S. Highway 191). It can be reached by trails along Gallatin River or Grayling Creek (*see* Weed, 1899, Pl. 10; U.S. Geological Survey, 1930, map of Yellowstone National Park). This is section measured by Weed (1899, p. 6–8, Pl. 2) and Deiss (1936, p. 1318–1325, Fig. 10). Dip: 30° N.

Fossiliferous Snowy Range Formation is capped by high cliff of hard white dolomite. Weed and Deiss assigned dolomite to Jefferson Formation. Basal 23 feet of Jefferson has gross appearance of underlying fossiliferous limestone but is hard, unfossiliferous dolomite. Twenty-three feet above base of dolomite is an obvious change in bedding and weathering characteristics. Basal 23 feet probably was part of Snowy Range Formation, later dolomitized along with Jefferson Formation; its top may be original boundary between Jefferson and Snowy Range. Elsewhere (*e.g.,* Sections FD, SC) dolomitized Snowy Range rock is assigned to Maywood unit, but here it so closely resembles Jefferson except in bedding that it is assigned to Jefferson.

Crowfoot Ridge Section (CF) *Continued*

DEVONIAN SYSTEM

	Bed thickness in feet	Feet above base
Jefferson Formation—not measured		
Dolomite: grayish pink to moderate red, medium- to coarse-grained, thick-bedded, vertically jointed, stands up as cliff		103.7
(*Altered Maywood unit* ?)—23 feet thick		
Dolomite: white to light gray, fine-grained, evenly bedded, alternating with coarser-grained, crinkly bedded, unfossiliferous, hard, forms base of Jefferson cliff; lithically like overlying Jefferson; bedding resembles underlying Snowy Range	23.0	80.7
CAMBRIAN SYSTEM		
Snowy Range Formation—80.7 feet thick		
Sage Member—65.2 feet thick		
FRANCONIAN STAGE		
Taenicephalus Zone		
Limestone: gray, fine- to coarse-grained, flaggy, in 1–2-foot beds, glauconitic, dolomitic, alternating with similarly thick beds of shaly, crinkly bedded limestone; *Angulotreta vescula, Billingsella perfecta, Pseudodicellomus mosaicus, Lingulella desiderata, Pelagiella primordialis, Maustonia nasuta, Orygmaspis firma, O. llanoensis, Taenicephalus gallupensis, T. shumardi,* Phosphatic balls	19.7	61.0
Parabolinoides Subzone		
Limestone: gray, flaggy, slightly dolomitic, slightly pebbly, in 1–3.5-foot beds with a few thin shale breaks; *Angulotreta tetonensis, A. vescula, Billingsella perfecta, B. plicatella, Ceratreta hebes, Pseudodicellomus mosaicus, Eoorthis remnicha, Lingulella perattenuata, Orygmaspis firma, O. llanoensis, Parabolinoides cordillerensis, P. expansus, P. hebe, Wilbernia halli,* Crinoid columnals	27.7	33.3
Elvinia Zone		
Camaraspis Subzone		
Limestone: gray and brownish gray, medium- to coarse-grained, thin-bedded, slightly glauconitic, silty, with one thin shale break; *Lingulella perattenuata, Linnarssonella girtyi, Ocnerorthis monticola, Camaraspis convexa, Dellea saratogensis*	4.1	29.2
Base of *Camaraspis* Subzone		
Shale: grayish green, with pods and thin beds of limestone: slightly glauconitic, slightly silty; *Linnarssonalla girtyi, Dellea suada, Pseudagnostus sentosus,* Crinoid columnals	8.7	20.5
Limestone: gray, thin-bedded, fine-grained, slightly glauconitic, silty, slightly pebbly; *Linnarssonella girtyi, Burnetiella ectypa, Bynumina terrenda, Dellea* sp., Crinoid columnals	5.0	15.5
Dry Creek Member—15.5 feet thick		
Shale: grayish green with thin beds of purple and brownish gray, middle has thin beds of limestone: brownish to greenish gray, wavy-bedded, may be rippled	15.5	0
Pilgrim Formation		
Limestone: top of Pilgrim Limestone datum for measurements		

Mill Creek Section (MC)

Section measured at type locality of Snowy Range Formation on south slope of Castle Rock, just above Mill Creek, SE.¼sec. 13, T. 6 S., R. 9 E., Park County, Montana. (Map by Wilson, 1936, M.A. thesis, Montana State Univ.). Dip: 15° NE. Type locality of Snowy Range Formation designated by Dorf and Lochman (1940, p. 545–547; Pl. 2, figs. 1–2).

	Bed thickness in feet	Feet above base
DEVONIAN SYSTEM		
Jefferson Formation—5.3 feet measured		
Limestone: sugary-grained, forms high cliff		313.6
Covered: probably shale, forms deep recess at base of cliff above Snowy Range Formation	5.3	308.3
CAMBRIAN SYSTEM		
Snowy Range Formation—308.3 feet thick		
Grove Creek Member—13.8 feet thick		
TREMPEALEAUAN STAGE		
Illaenurus Zone		
Dolomite: dark yellowish orange, hard, interbedded with thin beds of dolomitic shale and limestone	13.8	294.5
Sage Member—189.1 feet thick		
Partly covered: probably shale or shaly limestone, in 5–10-foot intervals, with 1–4-foot beds of limestone: gray, coarse-grained, glauconitic, some algal beds; *Tetonophycus blackwelderi*. Limestones have *Multivasculatus ovatus, Angulotreta catheta, Pseudodicellomus mosaicus, Finkelnburgia osceola, Eurekia binodosa, Geragnostus ? insolitus, Illaenurus montanensis, I. sinclairensis, Rasettia snowyensis,* Crinoid columnals	56.3	238.2
FRANCONIAN STAGE (?)		
(Probably *Prosaukia* Zone)		
Mostly covered: probably shale and shaly limestone, 2 feet near top limestone: gray, fine- to coarse-grained, thin-bedded, slightly dolomitic	52.2	186.0
Idahoia Zone		
Idahoia serapio Subzone		
Limestone: gray, coarse-grained, very dolomitic, fossils at top, middle covered: shale or shaly limestone; *Angulotreta catheta, A. vescula, Pseudodicellomus mosaicus, Sinuella vaticina, Drumaspis idahoensis, Idahoia serapio, I. wisconsensis, Maladia americana, Pseudagnostus josephus, P. sentosus, Ptychaspis granulosa, Wilbernia pero*	8.0	178.0
Idahoia wisconsensis Subzone		
Covered: probably shale or shaly limestone, has thin beds of limestone: gray, coarse-grained, glauconitic, silty, dolomitic; Aglaspid fragments, *Angulotreta catheta, Billingsella perfecta, Pseudodicellomus mosaicus, Sinuella vaticina, Drumaspis briscoensis, Idahoia wisconsensis, Maladia americana, Pseudagnostus josephus, P. sentosus, Ptychaspis granulosa, Saratogia fracida, S. fria, Wilbernia pero*	9.0	169.0

Mill Creek Section (MC) *Continued*
Cambrian System *Continued*
Franconian Stage *Continued*

Idahoia wyomingensis Subzone

	Bed thickness in feet	Feet above base
Limestone and limestone-pebble conglomerate: gray, fine-grained, medium- to thick-bedded, glauconitic, slightly dolomitic, forms ledge; *Billingsella perfecta, Pseudodicellomus mosaicus,* Linguloid fragments, Phosphatic balls, *Sinuella vaticina, Drumaspis briscoensis, Idahoia wyomingensis, Maladia americana, Pseudagnostus josephus, P. sentosus, Saratogia carita, S. fracida, S. fria, Wilbernia diademata, W. pero,* Crinoid calyx and columnals	15.1	153.9
Taenicephalus Zone (Top of zone probably within covered interval)		
Covered: by float of shale and limestone. Basal 1.5 feet is limestone-pebble conglomerate: gray, dolomitic; *Angulotreta vescula, Pseudodicellomus mosaicus, Lingulella perattenuata*	36.6	117.3
Parabolinoides Subzone		
Limestone and limestone-pebble conglomerate: gray, coarse-grained, slightly glauconitic, thin-bedded; *Angulotreta tetonensis, Billingsella perfecta, B. plicatella, Ceratreta hebes, Pseudodicellomus mosaicus, Eoorthis remnicha, E. remnicha* var. *A., Kendallina eryon, Parabolinoides contractus, P. cordillerensis, Taenicephalus shumardi, Wilbernia halli,* Crinoid columnals	3.1	114.2
Elvinia Zone / *Camaraspis* Subzone / *Irvingella major* Zonule		
Limestone: gray, fine-grained, clayey, crinkly bedded, slightly pebbly; *Pseudodicellomus mosaicus,* Linguloid fragments, *Comanchia lippa, Irvingella major, Parabolinoides hebe*	2.5	111.7
Base of *Irvingella major* Zonule		
Limestone: greenish gray, fine-grained, slightly dolomitic, algal; *Collenia magna,* partly columnar, partly bedded, matrix has *Angulotreta glabra, Pseudodicellomus mosaicus, Linnarssonella girtyi, Deadwoodia duris, Housia vacuna, Kindbladia* sp. (top 5 feet covered)	6.3	105.4
Dry Creek Member—105.4 feet thick		
Limestone: gray, coarse-grained, slightly pebbly, slightly glauconitic, top crinkly bedded and shaly; *Camaraspis convexa,* Crinoid columnals	1.0	104.4
Base of *Camaraspis* Subzone		
Covered: probably grayish-green fissile shale. Three thin beds of limestone-pebble conglomerate: gray with green pebbles, crinkly bedded, matrix fresh but pebbles weathered, *Linnarssonella girtyi*	6.9	97.5
Shale: grayish green and dusky purple, beds just above sill are baked and blackened	28.5	69.0
(Dacite: sill of irregular thickness averaging about 60 feet; not included in measurements of formation)		
Shale: grayish green, fissile, with many thin beds of siltstone: brownish gray, dolomitic, platy, top 60 feet partly covered	69.9	0
Pilgrim Formation		
Limestone: top of Pilgrim Limestone datum for measurements		

Wyoming Creek Section (YO)

Section measured in Wyoming Creek, just south of Silver Gate, on the Montana-Wyoming state border. Creek flows from sec. 18, T. 58 N., R. 108 W., Park County, Wyoming, into sec. 34, T. 9 S., R. 14 E., Park County, Montana. Measured section probably on Wyoming side of border, just west of Republic Peak (Map by U.S. Forest Service, 1947). Locality reached by crossing bridge at Silver Gate, Montana, heading south across Soda Butte Creek, keeping to left along creek to sign with arrow pointing way to "Falls": waterfall in Wyoming Creek where Pilgrim Limestone forms cliff just below Snowy Range Formation. Dry Creek Member measured in bed of main stream just above falls, remainder of formation measured in small tributary branching to left a few years above top of falls. Dip: 15°, component in direction of small tributary 10° SE.

Ordovician System

	Bed thickness in feet	Feet above base
Bighorn Formation—4.5 feet measured		
Dolomite: gray, medium- to coarse-grained, petroliferous, directly overlain by Tertiary pyroclastic breccia	4.5	287.7

Cambrian System

Snowy Range Formation—287.7 feet thick
Grove Creek Member—19.4 feet thick

TREMPEALEAUAN STAGE

Illaenurus Zone

Limestone: fine-grained, algal: *Tetonophycus blackwelderi* with layers of medium-grained dolomite, lenses of coarse-grained limestone, fossiliferous, much pyrite, alternating with shale: dusky blue, hard, calcareous, blocky, approaches being shaly limestone, has limestone pods, unfossiliferous; *Lingulella desiderata, Eurekia binodosa, Geragnostus ? insolitus, Rasettia snowyensis,* Crinoid columnals	19.4	268.3
Sage Member—219.5 feet thick		
Limestone: beds of *Tetonophycus blackwelderi* and nonalgal limestone alternating with grayish-green shale containing limestone pods; *Angulotreta catheta, Pseudodicellomus mosaicus,* Phosphatic brachiopod fragments, *Illaenurus sinclairensis*	35.5	232.8
Shale: mostly covered, pale green, with pods and thin stringers of limestone	22.5	210.3
Limestone: fine-grained, greenish gray, chiefly beds of *Tetonophycus blackwelderi,* some grayish-green shale with limestone pods; *Angulotreta catheta,* Linguloid fragments	16.2	194.1

FRANCONIAN STAGE

Prosaukia Zone ?

Limestone and limestone-pebble conglomerate: greenish gray, dolomitic, slightly glauconitic, pebbles rimmed with limonitic stain, few beds of fine-grained, nonpebbly limestone, alternating with slightly thicker intervals of shale: grayish green, with pods and stringers of limestone; *Angulotreta catheta, Pseudodicellomus mosaicus*	21.3	172.8

Wyoming Creek Section (YO) *Continued*
Cambrian System *Continued*
Franconian Stage *Continued*

	Bed thickness in feet	Feet above base
Idahoia Zone *Idahoia serapio* Subzone		
Limestone and limestone-pebble conglomerate: greenish gray, slightly dolomitic, slightly glauconitic, some algal pebbles, alternating with shale: grayish green, with limestone pods and stringers, one 5-inch bed of *Tetonophycus blackwelderi* at 166.6 feet; *Angulotreta vescula, Pseudodicellomus mosaicus, Lingulella* sp., *Lytospira* ? sp., *Maladia americana*	23.7	149.1
Idahoia wisconsensis Subzone		
Limestone and limestone-pebble conglomerate: in half-foot beds, greenish gray, very dolomitic, slightly glauconitic, and shale: in 0.5–2-foot beds, grayish green, with limestone pods; *Angulotreta vescula, Pseudodicellomus mosaicus, Lingulella desiderata, Sinuella vaticina,* Aglaspid fragments, *Idahoia wisconsensis, Pseudagnostus sentosus, Ptychaspis granulosa,* Phosphatic balls	13.4	135.7
Idahoia wyomingensis Subzone		
Limestone: greenish gray, fine-grained, crinkly bedded, clayey, forms ledge; *Billingsella perfecta, Pseudodicellomus mosaicus, Sinuella vaticina, Idahoia wyomingensis, Pseudagnostus sentosus, Wilbernia diademata,* Crinoid columnals, *Westergaardodina bicuspidata*	13.4	122.3
Taenicephalus Zone		
Limestone: greenish gray, commonly fine-grained, shaly, crinkly bedded, some slightly pebbly, coarse-grained, glauconitic, several beds of shale with pods of limestone; *Angulotreta vescula,* Linguloid fragments	30.3	92.0
Limestone: greenish gray, coarse-grained, unevenly bedded, perhaps rippled, alternating with grayish-green shale with limestone pods, top half mostly covered; *Angulotreta tetonensis, A. vescula, Billingsella perfecta, B. plicatella, Pseudodicellomus mosaicus,* Linguloid fragments, *Orygmaspis llanoensis, Taenicephalus gouldi,* Crinoid columnals	10.9	81.1
Parabolinoides Subzone		
Limestone: greenish gray, coarse-grained, dolomitic, some beds pebbly, some algal (?); *Angulotreta tetonensis, A. vescula, Billingsella perfecta, B. plicatella, Ceratreta hebes, Pseudodicellomus mosaicus, Eoorthis remnicha, Lingulella desiderata, L. perattenuata, Otusia sandbergi, Kendallina eryon, Maustonia nasuta, Orygmaspis firma, Parabolinoides contractus, P. cordillerensis, P. hebe, Taenicephalus gouldi, Wilbernia halli,* Crinoid columnals	7.2	73.9
Elvinia Zone *Camaraspis* Subzone *Irvingella major* Zonule		
Limestone: some pebbly, some crinkly bedded and shaly; lens has *Pseudodicellomus mosaicus, Huenella texana* var. *fortis, Comanchia lippa, Irvingella major, Kiowaia* cf. *K. timberensis,* Crinoid columnals	4.5	69.4
Base of *Irvingella major* Zonule		
Shale: grayish green, pods of limestone; lens 1 foot above base has *Linnarssonella girtyi, Camaraspis convexa, Pseudagnostus sentosus*	3.5	65.9

Base of *Camaraspis* Subzone

	Bed thickness in feet	Feet above base
(Limestone: greenish gray, fine-grained, columnar, *Collenia magna* discontinuous here; description below refers to beds butting against 11.8-foot-thick bioherm.)		
Limestone: greenish gray, fine-grained, clayey, crinkly bedded, with lenses of algal debris eroded from adjacent bioherm. Beds lie against bioherm, basal beds below major part, contain small algal "heads," *Angulotreta glabra, Linnarssonella girtyi*	17.1	48.8
Dry Creek Member—48.8 feet thick		
Limestone: fine-grained, pebbly, silty, some beds look algal but are bedded, not columnar, few intervals of grayish-green shale with limestone pods; *Angulotreta glabra, Lingulella perattenuata, Linnarssonella girtyi*	6.8	42.0
Shale: grayish green and dusky purple, with thin beds of brownish-gray, platy siltstone with *Linnarssonella girtyi* (top 14 feet covered)	42.0	0
Pilgrim Formation		
Limestone: top of Pilgrim Limestone datum for measurements		

Upper Wyoming Creek Section (UYO)

Location same as Wyoming Creek section, but farther up creek on small tributary branching to right, where only upper part of formation is exposed. Beds can be correlated from Wyoming Creek section; measurements in Upper Wyoming Creek section are calculated from base of Wyoming Creek section.

ORDOVICIAN SYSTEM

	Bed thickness in feet	Feet above base
Bighorn Formation—6 feet thick		
Dolomite: yellowish gray, petroliferous, overlain by Tertiary pyroclastic breccia	6.0	290.2
CAMBRIAN SYSTEM		
Snowy Range Formation—290.2 feet thick		
Grove Creek Member—26.2 feet thick		
TREMPEALEAUAN STAGE		
Illaenurus Zone		
Limestone: medium-grained, very dolomitic, pyritic, slightly pebbly, and shale: bluish gray, very dolomitic, hard, blocky; *Finkelnburgia osceola, Eurekia binodosa, Rasettia snowyensis, Stenopilus* ? sp.	23.6	266.6
Shale: dusky blue, very dolomitic, hard, blocky, base is limestone-pebble conglomerate: bluish gray, dolomitic	2.6	264.0
Sage Member—47.2 feet measured		
Limestone and shale: partly covered, alternating beds of algal limestone with pebbles at base (*Tetonophycus blackwelderi*) and dark-green fissile shale	28.3	235.7
Mostly covered: probably shale and shaly limestone, at base is lens of limestone: gray, medium-grained; *Angulotreta catheta, Briscoia dalyi*	18.9	216.8
Partly covered: not measured (thickness calculated by correlation with Wyoming Creek section) to top of Pilgrim Limestone	216.8	0

Fox Creek Section (FOX)

Section measured along Fox Creek, sec. 25, T. 58 N., R. 108 W., Park County, Wyoming. Locality reached by following Fox Creek (identified by sign on Highway 12) up slope of Index Peak. Snowy Range Formation best exposed along tributary entering main stream from left. Section also measured by Hanson (1952, p. 39–40). Dip: about 1°–2° SW.

ORDOVICIAN SYSTEM	Bed thickness in feet	Feet above base
Bighorn Formation—not measured		
Dolomite: yellow, sugary-grained		277.3
CAMBRIAN SYSTEM		
Snowy Range Formation—277.3 feet thick		
Grove Creek Member—22.9 feet thick		
TREMPEALEAUAN STAGE		
Illaenurus Zone		
Limestone and dolomite: bluish gray and dark orange, medium-bedded, forms ledge, coarse-grained, many beds of limestone-pebble conglomerate, edgewise conglomerate, and slump structures, also *Tetonophycus blackwelderi:* gray, fine-grained. Fossils are Linguloid fragments, Crinoid columnals	22.9	254.4
Sage Member—215.3 feet thick		
Limestone-pebble conglomerate: gray, thin-bedded, dolomitic, some beds *Tetonophycus blackwelderi* and shale: grayish green, with pods of light-gray shaly, fine-grained limestone; *Multivasculatus ovatus, Angulotreta catheta, Pseudodicellomus mosaicus,* Linguloid fragments, *Illaenurus quadratus*	18.7	235.7
Limestone-pebble conglomerate: gray, medium-grained, medium-bedded, in 1–3-foot beds alternating with similarly thick beds of shale: grayish green, with thin stringers of fossiliferous dolomitic limestone; several have structure of *Tetonophycus blackwelderi.* Fossils are *Angulotreta catheta, Pseudodicellomus mosaicus, Lingulella desiderata, Dikelocephalus* sp.	33.2	202.5
Shale: grayish green, with limestone pods and thin stringers of limestone, in 1–4-foot beds of limestone: greenish gray, with 0.2–0.5-foot beds of limestone: greenish gray, dolomitic, slightly glauconitic, slightly pebbly; *Pseudodicellomus mosaicus,* Linguloid fragments, fragments of *Briscoia dalyi*	19.9	182.6
FRANCONIAN STAGE		
Prosaukia Zone (?)		
Limestone-pebble conglomerate: greenish gray, slightly dolomitic, slightly glauconitic, in 0.5–2-foot beds, some with small pebbles, some with cobbles, alternating with shale: grayish green, with limestone pods, dolomitic, in 1–3-foot beds; *Angulotreta vescula, Pseudodicellomus mosaicus, Lingulella desiderata,* Phosphatic balls, *Sinuella vaticina, Westergaardodina* sp.	40.8	141.9

Idahoia Zone
Idahoia serapio Subzone

	Bed thickness in feet	Feet above base
Limestone: greenish gray, medium-grained, pebbly, dolomitic, glauconitic, fossiliferous, in 0.5–2-foot beds alternating with 2–3-foot beds of shale: grayish green, few limestone pods; *Pseudodicellomus mosaicus, Lingulella desiderata,* Phosphatic balls, *Sinuella vaticina, Idahoia serapio, Maladia americana, Pseudagnostus josephus, Westergaardodina bicuspidata*	23.2	118.7
Idahoia wisconsensis Subzone (?)		
Shale: grayish green, with many pods and stringers of limestone, alternating with limestone: gray, fine-grained, thin-bedded, slightly pebbly, slightly silty; *Pseudodicellomus mosaicus,* Linguloid fragments, Aglaspid fragments, Trilobite spines, Crinoid columnals	6.7	112.0
Idahoia wyomingensis Subzone (?)		
Limestone: greenish gray, fine-grained, thin-bedded, crinkly bedded, very clayey, slightly dolomitic, alternating with similarly thin beds of shale: grayish green, with limestone pods; *Angulotreta vescula, Billingsella perfecta, Pseudodicellomus mosaicus,* Trilobite fragments, *Westergaardodina bicuspidata*	23.1	88.9
Taenicephalus Zone		
Limestone-pebble conglomerate: greenish gray, medium-grained, slightly dolomitic, and shale: grayish green, soft, crumbly, with cobble-size lenses and pebbles of bedded limestone, fine-grained; *Angulotreta tetonensis, A. vescula, Billingsella perfecta, Pseudodicellomus mosaicus, Lingulella* sp., *Orygmaspis firma, Taenicephalus shumardi,* Crinoid columnals	22.4	66.5
Parabolinoides Subzone		
Limestone and limestone-pebble conglomerate: greenish gray, coarse-grained, large pebbles, top few inches is brachiopod coquinite; *Angulotreta tetonensis, Ceratreta hebes, Eoorthis remnicha, Orygmaspis llanoensis, Parabolinoides contractus, P. cordillerensis, P. hebe,* Crinoid calyx and columnals	3.5	63.0
Elvinia Zone		
Limestone: greenish gray, slightly dolomitic, slightly pebbly, in 0.5–1-foot beds alternating with somewhat thicker beds of shale: grayish green, calcareous, hard, crinkly bedded, limestone pods; *Lingulella perattenuata, Linnarssonella girtyi,* Crinoid columnals	11.7	51.3
(Limestone: grayish green, fine-grained, columns of *Collenia magna* 9.5 feet thick but discontinuous. Descriptions below refer to beds lying against bioherm.)		
Limestone: greenish gray, pebbly, dolomitic, thickens toward bioherm, with intercalated beds of shale: grayish green, calcareous, basal bed has small algal heads separate from main bioherm; *Linnarssonella girtyi, Dellea,* cf. *D. saratogensis*	12.2	39.1
Dry Creek Member—39.1 feet thick		
Shale: grayish green, fissile, alternating with limestone-pebble conglomerate: greenish gray, coarse-grained, with two types of pebbles:		

Fox Creek Section (FOX) *Continued*
Cambrian System *Continued*
Franconian Stage *Continued*
Elvinia Zone *Continued*

	Bed thickness in feet	Feet above base
(1) weathered, with brachiopods, (2) unweathered, unfossiliferous. Matrix has *Linnarssonella girtyi*	12.9	26.2
Shale: dusky purple and grayish green, fissile, with thin beds of brownish-gray calcareous siltstone; *Linnarssonella girtyi, Micromitra modesta* (at top of unit 3.5-foot andesite sill, not included in footages) ..	22.6	3.6

DRESBACHIAN STAGE

Dunderbergia Zone

Limestone: gray, silty (almost siltstone), lenses into shale, *Apsotreta expansa,* basal 3.5 feet is shale: partly covered, green with bands of dusky purple	3.6	0

Pilgrim Formation
Limestone: top of Pilgrim Limestone datum for measurements

Upper Fox Creek Section (UFOX)

Locality same as Fox Creek section, but farther upstream across small fault that repeats upper part of Sage Member and entire Grove Creek Member. Beds of this repeated part of section could not be correlated exactly with those below, so datum of measurement is top of Grove Creek Member in Fox Creek section. Dip above fault: 15° S.

ORDOVICIAN SYSTEM

	Bed thickness in feet	Feet above base
Bighorn Formation—not measured		
Dolomite: pale yellowish orange, medium-grained, big included slabs of limestone-pebble conglomerate: fault breccia from Heart Mountain thrust		70.4

CAMBRIAN SYSTEM

Snowy Range Formation—70.4 feet measured
Grove Creek Member—13.9 feet thick

TREMPEALEAUAN STAGE

Illaenurus Zone

Limestone: dark yellowish orange to gray, thin-bedded, fine-grained, discontinuous mounds of *Tetonophycus blackwelderi,* dolomitic, and shale: greenish gray, calcareous, silty, thickness varying because of downward-slumping limestone beds	13.9	56.5
Sage Member—56.5 feet measured		
Shale: grayish green, with pods and stringers of limestone, dolomitic, fossiliferous lens with *Lingulella desiderata,* Aglaspid fragments, *Briscoia dalyi, Bynumina* sp., *Illaenurus quadratus, I. sinclairensis,* alternating with limestone and limestone-pebble conglomerate: gray, coarse-grained, very dolomitic, prominent mounds of *Tetonophycus blackwelderi, Angulotreta catheta, Lingulella desiderata*	20.0	36.5
Limestone-pebble and boulder conglomerate: greenish gray, dolomitic,		

	Bed thickness in feet	Feet above base
boulders made of pebble conglomerate, alternating with shale: grayish green, few limestone pods; *Angulotreta catheta*	10.5	26.0
Covered: across series of small faults that repeat section	26.0	0
Grove Creek Member		
Limestone and dolomite: top of ledge of Grove Creek Member in Section FOX datum for measurements		

Beartooth Butte Section (BB)

Section measured on southeast side of Beartooth Butte, near northeasternmost extremity of exposure of Snowy Range Formation, approximately same section as measured by Hanson (1952, p. 41), sec. 31, T. 58 N., R. 105 W., Park County, Wyoming.

This locality was visited twice: once in early summer when formation was covered by snow; once later in summer when formation was covered by mud. Access is difficult, involving a 2-hour climb either by way of Beartooth Lake or from the end of the road at Clay Butte. Only in exceptionally dry years are the rocks sufficiently exposed for collecting.

Ordovician System

	Bed thickness in feet	Feet above base
Bighorn Formation—not measured		
Dolomite: yellow, medium-grained		328.5

Cambrian System

	Bed thickness in feet	Feet above base
Snowy Range Formation—328.5 feet thick		
Grove Creek Member—20 ? feet thick		
Covered: greenish mud from melting snow. Thickness estimated to be about same as at Section KZ	20.0	308.5
Sage Member—259 feet thick		
Covered: probably shale and shaly limestone	190.0	118.5
FRANCONIAN STAGE		
Idahoia Zone		
Limestone: greenish gray, fine-grained, crinkly bedded, very clayey, glauconitic, dolomitic; *Pseudodicellomus mosaicus, Sinuella vaticina,* Crinoid columnals	5.5	113.0
Taenicephalus Zone		
Covered: by mud from melting snow. Top of *Taenicephalus* Zone unknown: presence indicated by species in float; *Billingsella perfecta, B. plicatella, Ceratreta hebes, Eoorthis remnicha, E. remnicha* var. *A., Otusia sandbergi, Orygmaspis firma, Parabolinoides cordillerensis.* Basal foot of unit is fine-grained columnar *Collenia magna* with pebbly matrix containing *Irvingella major*	58.0	55.0
Elvinia Zone		
Limestone: greenish gray, fine-grained, columns of *Collenia magna* with interstitial conglomerate; *Lingulella desiderata, Burnetiella ectypa, Cheilocephalus* sp., *Deadwoodia duris, Dellea butlerensis*	5.5	49.5

Beartooth Butte Section (BB) *Continued*
Cambrian System *Continued*
Franconian Stage *Continued*
Elvinia Zone *Continued*

	Bed thickness in feet	Feet above base
Dry Creek Member—49.5 feet thick		
Shale: grayish green and dusky purple, thin beds of brown siltstone, interval mostly covered	49.5	0
Pilgrim Formation		
Limestone: approximate top of Pilgrim Limestone datum for measurements		

K-Z Ranch Section (KZ)

Section measured on west end of Cathedral Cliff above K-Z Ranch. Entrance to ranch is from Yellowstone-Cody road. Section is east of Crandal Ranger Station of Shoshone National Forest, south of Beartooth Butte and Table Mountain, just west of Swamp Lake section (SL) in south wall of Clark Fork Canyon, near line between secs. 14 and 15, T. 56 N., R. 106 W., Park County, Wyoming. (Map by U.S. Forest Service, 1941, Shoshone National Forest)

ORDOVICIAN SYSTEM

	Bed thickness in feet	Feet above base
Bighorn Formation—not measured		
Dolomite: dusky yellow, sugary-textured		28.2
Snowy Range Formation—28.2 feet measured		
Grove Creek Member—21.1 feet thick		
TREMPEALEAUAN STAGE		
Limestone-pebble conglomerate: dusky yellow, dolomitic, pyritic, pebbles green and yellow, oriented edgewise, alternating with beds of dolomite: dusky yellow, with lenses of limestone and spherulites of marcasite, also beds of shale: brownish gray, weathers greenish gray, hard, calcareous, dolomitic, slightly glauconitic, very silty; top foot has *Apheoorthis* sp., Graptolite fragments, *Problematicum*	13.6	14.6
Limestone: greenish gray, weathers yellow, beds of *Tetonophycus blackwelderi*, fine-grained, base pebbly, top rounded, slightly arenaceous, and dolomite: greenish gray, weathers dusky yellow, medium-grained	7.5	7.1
Sage Member—7.1 feet measured		
Limestone-pebble conglomerate: gray, mottled and streaked by dusky-yellow dolomite, matrix medium- to coarse-grained, pebbles randomly oriented, alternating with shale: grayish green, fissile, soft; *Pseudodicellomus mosaicus, Lingulella desiderata*	7.1	0
Covered: most of Sage Member covered; better exposed about 1 mile east at Swamp Lake		

Swamp Lake Section (SL)

Section measured at east end of Cathedral Cliffs just above Swamp Lake, directly in line with Beartooth Butte and Table Mountain, south of both, in sec. 14, T. 56 N., R. 106 W., Park County, Wyoming; reached from K-Z Ranch off Yellowstone-Cody road. Best access is about ½ mile into ranch from road, where boulder train covers part of steep cliff in Pilgrim Limestone. Section is in first permanent stream west, where running water keeps rocks exposed. Dip: 1°–2° N. (Map by U.S. Forest Service, 1941)

ORDOVICIAN SYSTEM

	Bed thickness in feet	Feet above base
Bighorn Formation—9 feet measured		
Dolomite: dusky yellow, mottled, coarse-grained, hard, slightly arenaceous, with included blocks containing trilobite fragments: fault breccia between Snowy Range and Bighorn, forms top of ledge most of which is of Grove Creek Member	9.0	293.0

CAMBRIAN SYSTEM

Snowy Range Formation—292.9 feet thick
Grove Creek Member—16.9 feet thick

TREMPEALEAUAN STAGE

Illaenurus Zone

Limestone: dark bluish gray, fine- to medium-grained, hard, very dolomitic, clayey, few beds of limestone-pebble conglomerate, forms ledge; *Callograptus staufferi*	16.9	276.1
Sage Member—232.2 feet thick		
Limestone and shale: beds of *Tetonophycus blackwelderi* about 1.5 feet thick, pebbly at base, fine-grained, nonpebbly in upper part of each bed, dolomitic, alternating with equally thick beds of shale: grayish green, soft, fissile; *Angulotreta catheta, Pseudodicellomus mosaicus,* Linguloid fragments, Crinoid columnals, *Callograptus staufferi*	27.0	249.1
Limestone: beds of *Tetonophycus blackwelderi,* top with concentric growth structures, sides showing laminae, dolomitic, in 1–2-foot beds alternating with equally thick beds of shale: grayish green, calcareous, few pods and stringers of limestone; Linguloid fragments	17.4	231.7
Shale: grayish green with many limestone pods, alternating with limestone: gray, medium-grained, evenly bedded, dolomitic, slightly glauconitic; *Pseudodicellomus mosaicus,* Linguloid fragments	11.7	220.0

FRANCONIAN STAGE (?)

(*Prosaukia* Zone probably lies within covered interval.)

Covered: probably green shale and clayey limestone. Basal 3 feet is limestone-pebble conglomerate: dolomitic, pebbles weathered but matrix fresh	48.5	171.5

Idahoia Zone (?)

Predominantly covered: probably green, fissile shale, a few protruding thin limestone beds	32.8	138.7
Limestone: greenish gray, slightly pebbly, very dolomitic, glauconitic, 0.5–1.5-foot beds alternating with somewhat thicker beds of shale with limestone pods; *Angulotreta vescula, Pseudodicellomus mosaicus,* Linguloid fragments, Phosphatic balls, *Sinuella vaticina,* Crinoid columnals, *Westergaardodina bicuspidata*	30.5	108.2

Taenicephalus Zone

Limestone: gray, thin-bedded, fine- to coarse-grained, some pebbles, slightly dolomitic, pyritic, in 1–3-foot beds alternating with thicker intervals of shale: grayish green, fissile, limestone pods, some beds covered; *Angulotreta tetonensis, Billingsella perfecta, Pseudodicellomus mosaicus, Lingulella desiderata,* Crinoid columnals	25.7	82.5

Swamp Lake Section (SL) *Continued*
Cambrian System *Continued*
Franconian Stage (?) *Continued*

Parabolinoides Subzone	Bed thickness in feet	Feet above base
Limestone: gray, coarse-grained, dolomitic, very fossiliferous; *Angulotreta tetonensis, A. vescula, Billingsella perfecta, B. plicatella, Ceratreta hebes, Pseudodicellomus mosaicus, Eoorthis remnicha, E. remnicha* var. *A.*, *Lingulella* sp., *Kendallina eryon, Maustonia nasuta, Orygmaspis firma, O. llanoensis, Parabolinoides contractus, P. cordillerensis, P. expansus, P. hebe, Taenicephalus shumardi,* Crinoid columnals	2.7	79.8
Limestone-pebble conglomerate: gray, dolomitic, many large pebbles, alternating with shale: grayish green, lenses of limestone with *Angulotreta tetonensis, Ceratreta hebes, Lingulella perattenuata, Otusia sandbergi,* Crinoid columnals	3.0	76.8
Elvinia Zone		
Shale: grayish green, mostly covered, capped by thin bed of limestone-pebble conglomerate: gray, dolomitic, slightly arenaceous, Linguloid fragments, Crinoid columnals	6.2	70.6
(Limestone: greenish gray, fine-grained bioherm of columnar *Collenia magna,* divided into three layers, each about 5 feet high with pebbly limestone between, total thickness about 19 feet. Bioherm discontinuous; measurements and descriptions below are those of beds lying against it. Pebbly matrix has *Hyolithes primordialis, Dellea butlerensis, D. Suada, Housia vacuna*)		
Shale: grayish green, with pods and beds of limestone; one slightly dolomitic lens crowded with *Pseudodicellomus mosaicus, Linnarssonella girtyi*	19.2	51.4
Limestone: greenish gray, fine-grained, clayey, some crinkly bedded, several small heads of *Collenia magna,* lies below main mass of bioherm; *Angulotreta glabra, Pseudodicellomus mosaicus,* Linguloid fragments, *Linnarssonella girtyi*	7.5	43.9
Dry Creek Member—43.9 feet thick		
Shale: dusky green and dusky purple, with few thin layers of brown, platy siltstone; top 10 feet covered	43.9	0
Pilgrim Formation		
Limestone: top of Pilgrim Limestone datum for measurements		

North Grove Creek Section (GR)

Section measured at type locality of Grove Creek Member, at North Grove Creek, east of Red Lodge, NW.1/4sec. 36, T. 8 S., R. 20 E., Carbon County, Montana. Dip: 35°E. (*see* Dorf and Lochman, 1940, p. 543, Pl. 1, figs. 1–2)

ORDOVICIAN SYSTEM	Bed thickness in feet	Feet above base
Bighorn Formation—not measured		
Dolomite: dark yellowish orange, arenaceous		245.2
CAMBRIAN SYSTEM		
Snowy Range Formation—245.2 feet measured		
Grove Creek Member—48 feet thick		

TREMPEALEAUAN STAGE

Illaenurus Zone

	Bed thickness in feet	Feet above base
Limestone and shale: yellowish green, thin-bedded, some pebbles	12.4	232.8
Predominantly covered: probably yellowish-green shale, has one 3-foot bed of limestone-pebble conglomerate	22.0	210.8
Limestone and limestone-pebble conglomerate: yellowish green, weathers rusty brown, thin-bedded, clayey, dolomitic, *Finkelnburgia osceola,* alternating with shale: yellowish green, calcareous	13.6	197.2
Sage Member—197.2 feet thick		
FRANCONIAN STAGE (?)		
(*Prosaukia* Zone and most of *Idahoia* Zone covered)		
Covered: probably shale and clayey crinkly limestone	100.0	97.2
Predominantly covered: probably shale and clayey limestone: top is 6 inches of limestone-pebble conglomerate: greenish gray, mainly pebbles with little matrix, very dolomitic, slightly glauconitic, Trilobite spines, Crinoid columnals	8.9	88.3
Taenicephalus Zone		
Limestone: brownish gray, fine-grained, thin-bedded, very dolomitic, some pebbly beds, alternating with intervals of covered: probably shale or clayey limestone; *Angulotreta vescula, Billingsella perfecta, Pseudodicellomus mosaicus, Lingulella* sp., *Kendallina eryon*	11.2	77.1
Parabolinoides Subzone		
Limestone: brownish gray, fine-grained, thin-bedded, very dolomitic; *Angulotreta tetonensis, Pseudodicellomus mosaicus, Huenella texana, Pseudagnostus sentosus, Taenicephalus shumardi*	10.5	66.6
Covered: greenish-gray shale and thin-bedded, clayey, crinkly bedded limestone	39.3	27.3
Elvinia Zone		
Limestone: gray, medium-grained, thin-bedded, dolomitic; *Pseudodicellomus mosaicus, Lingulella* sp., *Linnarssonella girtyi, Westergaardodina* sp., alternating with somewhat thicker, covered intervals: probably green shale and clayey limestone	11.3	16.0
Limestone-pebble conglomerate: dolomitic; *Pseudodicellomus mosaicus, Linnarssonella girtyi, Sulcocephalus* sp., *Burnetiella ectypa, Camaraspis berkeyi, C. convexa, Dokimocephalus intermedius, Elvinia roemeri*	8.3	7.7
Limestone: greenish-gray, fine-grained columns of *Collenia magna,* top of bioherm irregular, with beds of limestone-pebble conglomerate above and below columns	7.7	0
Dry Creek Member—not measured		
Covered: probably green shale and thin beds of brown siltstone		

Yogo Gulch Section (YG)

Section measured by Deiss (1936, p. 1283–1286, Fig. 4) and Sloss and Laird (1947, p. 1415; p. 1414, Fig. 4, section 4), referred to by Weed (1900, p. 286) and Lochman and Duncan (1944, p. 9), in Yogo Gulch near mouth of Bear Creek, Little Belt Mountains, Montana; according to Deiss it is in SE.¼sec. 1, T. 13, N., R. 10 E., Judith Basin County. Beds that Deiss assigned to the Pilgrim Limestone and some of those that he assigned to "Dry Creek Shale" (basal 31 feet) now are referred to as the Sage Member of the Snowy Range Formation. Likewise, beds that Sloss and Laird assigned to the "Dry Creek Shale" belong to the

Yogo Gulch Section (YG) *Continued*

Sage Member (Lochman-Balk, 1955, personal written communication). Their "Basal Devonian unit" and "Beds of undetermined age" belong to the Maywood unit (Lochman, 1950b, p. 2213).

Dr. Lochman provided collections of Franconian fossils from Yogo Gulch. Descriptions by Deiss are combined here with descriptions and measurements by Sloss and Laird (1947, p. 1415). Lochman's collections are numbered to fit Deiss' published section; these are fitted into Sloss and Laird's measured section and assigned member names in accordance with modern usage. In the following composite section descriptions are directly quoted from published references or based upon study of hand specimens in Lochman's collection.

DEVONIAN SYSTEM

	Bed thickness in feet	Feet above base
Maywood unit—48 feet thick		
Limestone: "yellowish brown, slightly argillaceous, dolomitic" (Sloss and Laird, 1947, p. 1415)	8.0	79.0
Shale and dolomite: "yellow-brown and dark gray-brown dolomitic shale interbedded with fine- to medium-saccharoidal dolomite" (Sloss and Laird, 1947), top 10 feet petroliferous (Deiss, 1936, p. 1283)	30.0	49.0
"Mudstone: salmon-colored with yellow-green spots, interbedded with brick-red. Scattered round sand grains and trace of glauconite".... basal 8 feet is shale, maroon, fissile, slightly dolomitic (Sloss and Laird, 1947, p. 1415)	18.0	31.0
CAMBRIAN SYSTEM		
Snowy Range Formation—31 feet thick		
Sage Member—27 feet thick		
FRANCONIAN STAGE		
Taenicephalus Zone		
"Shale: red and green, micaceous, fissile; with 2-inch beds of dense to finely crystalline limestone bearing trilobite fragments" (Sloss and Laird, 1947, p. 1415). Limestone portions of collections 39/1, 3.2., 3.3, and 39/1 + 3 of Lochman; *Pseudodicellomus mosaicus, Maustonia nasuta, Parabolinoides contractus, P. cordillerensis, P. expansus, P. hebe,* and many meraspid molts of indeterminable species of *Parabolinoides*	3.0	28.0
"Shale: very finely micaceous and silty, green at base, grading to red at top" (Sloss and Laird, 1947, p. 1415). Shale part of Lochman's collections 39/1, 3.2, and 3.3; *Eoorthis remnicha, Parabolinoides contractus, P. cordillerensis, P. hebe,* meraspids	6.0	22.0
Elvinia Zone		
Limestone and limestone-pebble conglomerate: "light gray, dense .... flat pebbles of dense gray limestone with few of red argillaceous limestone" (Sloss and Laird, 1947, p. 1415), moderately dolomitic; Lochman's collections 3.4a, 3.5, *Linnarssonella girtyi, Sulcocephalus granulosus, Burnetiella* sp. (free checks), *Dellea juvenalis,* Crinoid columnals	18.0	4.0
Dry Creek Member (?)—4 feet thick		
"Shale: altered to argillite by andesite sill; phosphatic brachiopods" (Sloss and Laird, 1947, p. 1415). Brachiopods probably are *Linnarssonella girtyi*	4.0	0
"Andesite" (Sloss and Laird, 1947, p. 1415): sill, top of sill datum for measurements		

BIOSTRATIGRAPHY

GENERAL STATEMENT

The Snowy Range Formation of southwestern Montana and northwestern Wyoming contains faunas of the three standard stages of the Croixan Series (Howell and others, 1944). These are, in ascending order, the Dresbachian, Franconian, and Trempealeauan stages of the Upper Cambrian.

Two zonations are presented in this paper (Pl. 4). One is similar to that of the standard zonation of the Cambrian Correlation Chart and is based on ranges of genera and species of trilobites. The other is based entirely on ranges of genera and species of brachiopods. The major framework of the brachiopod zonation is the distribution of small, phosphatic, inarticulate brachiopods that are obtained by dissolving limestone samples in acetic or formic acid.

Use of zonal terms in this paper is similar to that of Bell, Feniak, and Kurtz (1952); Berg (1953); and Bell, Berg, and Nelson (1956), with a few modifications. *Local range* is similar to the term *teilzone* as used by Moore (1955, p. 551, 563), an informal designation for the local stratigraphic span of any genus or species. Here, *local* means those parts of southwestern Montana and northwestern Wyoming which contain the faunas of the Snowy Range Formation of this study. Other zonal units are defined somewhat arbitrarily by formal recognition of certain ranges or groups of ranges. *Zone* is the fundamental biostratigraphic unit; each is named for a characteristic genus or species but need not coincide entirely with the local range of that genus or species. The Franconian Stage of this study is divisible into four zones that happen to be more or less equal in thickness and in number of species; only the *Prosaukia* Zone has few species, but its inferred thickness is comparable to that of the other three zones. Zones are subdivided into subzones, and they in turn are subdivided into zonules. The term *fauna* is used for the constituent genera and/or species of any biostratigraphic unit.

TRILOBITE ZONATION

General statement. Trilobite zones recognized in this paper are locally applicable to the Montana-Wyoming area. They differ somewhat from the zones on the Cambrian Correlation Chart (Howell and others, 1944) and from local zones used in other parts of the United States, but wherever possible, equivalence of Montana-Wyoming zones with those of the Chart or of other areas is stated.

The *Aphelaspis* Zone of the Dresbachian Stage and the *Elvinia* Zone of the Franconian Stage are the only two zones used as they appear on the Cambrian Correlation Chart. The fauna of the *Aphelaspis* Zone in the Snowy Range Formation is too poorly known for definite assignment either to the

Dunderbergia Zone (Palmer, 1960; Lochman-Balk and Wilson, 1958) or to the equivalent of the *Aphelaspis* Zone as used in Texas.

Shaw (1954) proposed *Taenicephalus* Zone for the Wyoming equivalent of part of the *Conaspis* Zone of the Correlation Chart and *Idahoia* Zone for the *Ptychaspis* Subzone of the Chart. These names, useful and applicable in Montana as well as in Wyoming, are here preferred to the standard names.

The *Prosaukia* Subzone of the Cambrian Correlation Chart is treated as a separate zone of the Franconian, occupying the strata between the *Idahoia* Zone and the base of the Trempealeauan Stage. This interval is sparsely fossiliferous (commonly shaly or covered), and only a few species suggest the presence of a *Prosaukia* Zone.

The late Franconian *Briscoia* Zone of the Correlation Chart is not recognized in this paper. Specimens identified as *Briscoia dalyi* are very rare and occur with species of genera thought to be diagnostic of the Trempealeauan Stage. These findings are in accord with recent developments in the Croixan type area where use of the *Briscoia* Zone has been abandoned (Raasch, 1951; Bell and others, 1956).

Few Saukid trilobites were recovered from Trempealeauan rocks of the Snowy Range Formation. The most abundant Trempealeauan trilobite genus is *Illaenurus,* and therefore a local *Illaenurus* Zone is proposed for part of the *Saukia* Zone (Raasch, 1951, p. 114, Fig. 14; Berg and others, 1956, p. 18) in the Montana-Wyoming area. The *Illaenurus* Zone cannot be subdivided on the basis of available evidence; probably it approximates the lower Trempealeauan *Dikelocephalus postrectus, Rasettia* (*i.e., Platycolpus*), and upper *Dikelocephalus* subzones of the upper Mississippi Valley (Berg and others, 1956, p. 18–19) and the Lower Trempealeauan of Texas.

No Ordovician fossils were obtained from the Snowy Range Formation in the area investigated.

Dresbachian Stage. The Dresbachian Stage is represented in the Snowy Range Formation only by the upper part of its topmost zone, the *Aphelaspis* Zone. Dresbachian species have been found at three localities: Bill Smith Creek, Bridger Lake, and Fox Creek. Shaw (1956, p. 48–49) reports an *Aphelaspis* fauna from the Dry Creek Shale at Steele Butte, Wyoming.

APHELASPIS ZONE: The fauna of the *Aphelaspis* Zone consists of the following species: (*see also* Pl. 4)

Brachiopoda
Lingulella sp.
Micromitra modesta
Trilobita
Aphelaspis sp.
Dytremacephalus ? sp.

Shaw found the following species at Steele Butte:

Gastropoda
Hypseloconus simplex simplex Lochman
Hypseloconus simplex erectus Shaw

Trilobita
Aphelaspis walcotti Resser
Cheilocephalus delandi Shaw
Raaschella occidentalis Lochman

Prior to Shaw's discovery of an *Aphelaspis* fauna in the Dry Creek, the *Aphelaspis* Zone was thought to be confined to the Pilgrim Limestone or its equivalent below the base of the Dry Creek Shale (Dorf and Lochman, 1940, p. 547–550; Shaw, 1954). Now more species are known from the part of the *Aphelaspis* Zone in the Dry Creek Shale than from the part in the Pilgrim Limestone (Lochman and Duncan, 1944, p. 21). The top of the zone and the boundary between the Dresbachian and Franconian stages probably should be drawn somewhere in the lower third of the Dry Creek Member, but evidence is lacking at most localities because fossils are not preserved in the shale or the lowermost siltstone beds of the Dry Creek. Trilobites and calcareous brachiopods are preserved only in a few lenses of limestone or limestone-pebble conglomerate.

The lithic change between the Pilgrim Limestone and the Dry Creek Shale is the most widespread and abrupt in the entire Cambrian sequence of this area (Lochman-Balk, 1956b, p. 620), but the fauna of the *Aphelaspis* Zone spans this boundary and continues from the upper part of the Pilgrim into the lower part of the Dry Creek.

DUNDERBERGIA ZONE: Many specimens of the brachiopod *Apsotreta expansa* were found in siltstone beds near the base of the Dry Creek Member at Fox Creek. Palmer (1955a, p. 716, 771) considers this species to be characteristic of the "post-*Aphelaspis*" Zone of central Texas. This zone has been named the *Dunderbergia* Zone (Lochman-Balk and Wilson, 1958; Palmer, 1960). Its presence suggests that the species listed in the *Aphelaspis* Zone may belong instead to the *Dunderbergia* Zone, and that the characteristic species of the *Aphelaspis* Zone proper will be found biostratigraphically lower, in the Pilgrim Limestone.

Franconian Stage. The Franconian Stage is represented in the Snowy Range Formation by all zones that are recognized currently in the Croixan type area (Bell and others, 1956, p. 430–435; Berg and others, 1956, p. 15–18). The *Elvinia* Zone occurs at the base, represented by 26 trilobite species, six brachiopod species, and one mollusk. Above the *Elvinia* Zone the *Taenicephalus* Zone (Shaw, 1954; Shaw and DeLand, 1955) contains 17 trilobite species, 13 brachiopod species, one mollusk and one sponge species. In number of individuals per species the *Taenicephalus* Zone is the most populous zone in the Snowy Range Formation. It is overlain by the *Idahoia* Zone (Shaw, 1954; Shaw and DeLand, 1955), which contains 21 trilobite species, six brachiopod species, three mollusk species, and one sponge species. The uppermost zone of the Franconian Stage is called the *Prosaukia* Zone (Moore, 1955), poorly represented by only three trilobite species, two brachiopod species, and a doubtful mollusk.

ELVINIA ZONE: The fauna of the *Elvinia* Zone consists of the following species (*see also* Pl. 4):

Brachiopoda
- *Angulotreta glabra*
- *Pseudodicellomus mosaicus*
- *Lingulella desiderata*
- *Lingulella perattenuata*
- *Linnarssonella girtyi*
- *Ocenerorthis monticola*

Mollusca
- *Hyolithes primordialis*

Trilobita
- *Sulcocephalus granulosus*
- *Sulcocephalus* sp.
- *Burnetiella ectypa*
- *Bynumina terrenda*
- *Camaraspis berkeyi*
- *Camaraspis convexa*
- *Cheilocephalus* sp.
- *Comanchia lippa*
- *Deadwoodia duris*
- *Dellea butlerensis*
- *Dellea juvenalis*
- *Dellea saratogensis*
- *Dellea snoburgensis*
- *Dellea suada*
- *Dokimocephalus intermedius*
- *Elvinia roemeri*
- *Homagnostus* cf. *H. tumidosus*
- *Housia vacuna*
- *Irvingella major*
- *Irvingella (Parairvingella) eurekensis*
- *Kindbladia* cf. *K. wichitaensis*
- *Kyphocephalus bridgerensis*
- *Kyphocephalus* ? sp.
- *Pinctus* ? *artus*
- *Pseudagnostus sentosus*
- *Pterocephalia sanctisabae*

DeLand and Shaw (1956, p. 545) report a trilobite fauna from the *Elvinia* Zone in western Wyoming consisting of the following species:

- *Apachia convexa* DeLand
- *Burnetiella alta* (Resser)
- *Camaraspis plana* Frederickson
- *Cliffia latagenae* (Wilson)
- *Deadwoodia duris* (Walcott)
- *Dellea* cf. *D. butlerensis* Frederickson
- *Dellea saginata* DeLand
- *Dellea suada* (Walcott) ?
- *Elvinia* sp.
- *Housia vacuna* (Walcott)
- *Iddingsia occidentalis* DeLand and Shaw
- *Irvingella* aff. *I. flohri* Resser
- *Xenocheilos* cf. *X. spineum* Wilson

The *Elvinia* Zone is present in most exposures of the Snowy Range Formation (Pls. 1–3); it has been found at 26 localities in addition to Shaw and DeLand's localities in western Wyoming. It is not particularly well represented at most of these localities; however, its presence is indicated by a few characteristic species such as *Linnarssonella girtyi, Burnetiella ectypa,* and species of *Dellea.* The zone occupies all of the Dry Creek Member above the *Aphelaspis* or *Dunderbergia* Zone at the base and extends into the lower fourth of the Sage Member. The bioherm of *Collenia magna* that marks the base of the Sage Member is in the *Elvinia* Zone; the top of the zone commonly is 3–5 feet above the top of the bioherm.

CAMARASPIS SUBZONE: Species of *Camaraspis* have been found only near the top of the *Elvinia* Zone in about one-third of the localities studied. Segregation of these species is considered consistent enough to warrant proposal of a *Camaraspis* Subzone for the Snowy Range Formation. Nowhere has a specimen of *Camaraspis* been found lower than 10 feet below the top of the *Elvinia* Zone.

Apparently *Camaraspis* occurs throughout the *Elvinia* Zone in Minnesota and Wisconsin (Twenhofel, Raasch, and Thwaites, 1935; Stauffer, Schwartz, and Thiel, 1939; Nelson, 1951; Bell and others, 1952), Texas (Wilson, 1949), and in Oklahoma (Frederickson, 1949). It is present in the upper two thirds of the *Elvinia* Zone in the central Appalachians (Wilson, 1951, p. 618, Table 1), but its occurrence there is too sporadic for establishment of a subzone.

IRVINGELLA MAJOR ZONULE: The top of the *Elvinia* Zone in many parts of the United States is characterized by a suite of species that many authors (*see* Wilson and Frederickson, 1950) segregate into a zone or zonule called the *Irvingella major* Zone. The species commonly associated with *Irvingella major* are *Comanchia amplooculata, Kiowaia timberensis,* and *Sulcocephalus candidus.*

Dorf and Lochman (1940, p. 545, 547) and Lochman and Duncan (1944, p. 2, 13) state that in Montana and Wyoming the *Irvingella major* faunule is associated with the columnar limestone of *Collenia magna* at the base of the Sage Member. Data here support the findings of Wilson (Wilson and Frederickson, 1950, p. 898–899) that the *I. major* faunule (*i.e., I. major* and associates, not *I. major* alone) does not occur in the columnar limestone but above it. Wilson reports *I. major* without its characteristic associates in the columnar limestone and throughout a thickness of 10 feet of rock above it. In this study it has been found only in a few feet of rock at the top of the *Elvinia* Zone or in the base of the *Taenicephalus* Zone.

The *Irvingella major* faunule occurs sporadically in the top of the *Elvinia* Zone in the Snowy Range Formation, but where present its few species are represented by abundant cranidia. A species from the *Taenicephalus* Zone (*Parabolinoides hebe*) occurs in the *I. major* Zonule at MC 111.7, suggesting that the separation between the *I. major* faunule and the fauna of the *Taenicephalus* Zone is not as complete as implied by Wilson and Frederickson (1950, p. 899–900). A similar situation was reported by Raasch (1939, p. 34) and Berg (1953, p. 556) in the upper Mississippi Valley.

The *Irvingella major* Zonule originally was termed the *"Ptychopleurites"* Zone (Wilson and Frederickson, 1950, p. 892–893). Frederickson (*in* Wilson and Frederickson, 1950, p. 901) considered *"P." amplooculata* of the *"Ptychopleurites"* Zone to be generically different from Kobayashi's type specimens of *Ptychopleurites,* and he named the new genus *Comanchia.* Wilson and Frederickson (1950, p. 893) renamed the zone for *Irvingella major,* stating that "Although the assemblage includes a species assigned in the past to *Ptychopleurites* Kobayashi 1936, it is better characterized by numerous trilobites belonging to species of *Irvingella.*" Their chart (p. 894, Table 1) shows that *I. major* is not confined to the zone but that *Comanchia* is. Now that the name *Berkeia* has been suppressed in favor of *Sulcocephalus, Comanchia* is the only genus confined to the zone. In the Snowy Range Formation *C. lippa* is more than four times as abundant in the *I. major* Zonule than *I. major.* The current name for the zone is retained here because of its frequent and familiar usage.

TAENICEPHALUS ZONE: The fauna of the *Taenicephalus* Zone consists of the following species (*see also* Pl. 4):

Porifera
- *Multivasculatus ovatus*

Brachiopoda
- *Angulotreta tetonensis*
- *Angulotreta vescula*
- *Billingsella perfecta*
- *Billingsella plicatella*
- *Ceratreta hebes*
- *Pseudodicellomus mosaicus*
- *Eoorthis remnicha*
- *Huenella abnormis*
- *Huenella texana*
- *Lingulella desiderata*
- *Lingulella perattenuata*
- *Otusia sandbergi*

Gastropoda
- *Pelagiella primordialis*

Trilobita
- *Bemaspis gouldi*
- *Croixana bipunctata*
- *Irvingella major*
- *Maustonia nasuta*
- *Orygmaspis firma*
- *Orygmaspis llanoensis*
- *Parabolinoides contractus*
- *Parabolinoides cordillerensis*
- *Parabolinoides expansus*
- *Parabolinoides hebe*
- *Pseudagnostus josephus*
- *Pseudagnostus sentosus*
- *Kendallina biforota*
- *Kendallina eryon*
- *Taenicephalus gallupensis*
- *Taenicephalus shumardi*
- *Wilbernia halli*

DeLand and Shaw (1956, p. 545) report only *Taenicephalus shumardi* (identified by them as *T. cordillerensis* Miller) from this zone.

The *Taenicephalus* Zone is the most fossiliferous in the Snowy Range Formation. It occurs entirely within the Sage Member, extending from 3 to 5 feet above the *Collenia magna* columnar limestone to near the base of the persistent ledge of brownish-gray limestone just below the middle of the member. The base of the zone normally is marked by a bed of brachiopod coquinite that contains species of *Angulotreta, Billingsella, Ceratreta, Eoorthis,* and *Otusia.* At a few localities this bed occurs a few feet above the first occurrence of species that characterize the *Taenicephalus* Zone.

The lower part of the zone is very fossiliferous, but the number of specimens decreases upward; few are found just below the ledge that contains the lower *Idahoia* Zone. The paucity of specimens in the upper part of the zone is the result of increasing amounts of shale and shaly limestone in that part of the section. Fossils are very rare in the shale beds, and at many localities shale tends to cover the few thin limestone beds present.

PARABOLINOIDES SUBZONE: Species of *Parabolinoides* at most localities are confined to the basal 5 feet of the *Taenicephalus* Zone. The segregation is so consistent that a *Parabolinoides* Subzone can be defined as the part of the local range of *Parabolinoides* within the *Taenicephalus* Zone. This definition excludes from the *Parabolinoides* Subzone a few occurrences of *Parabolinoides* with the *Irvingella major* faunule in the top of the *Elvinia* Zone.

Species that are confined to the *Parabolinoides* Subzone are the trilobites:

- *Parabolinoides contractus*
- *Parabolinoides cordillerensis*
- *Parabolinoides expansus*
- *Parabolinoides hebe*

Several brachiopod species attain epiboles in the *Parabolinoides* Subzone but range slightly above it at a few localities. They are:

Billingsella plicatella	*Huenella abnormis*
Ceratreta hebes	*Huenella texana*
Eoorthis remnicha	*Otusia sandbergi*

The *Parabolinoides* Subzone of Montana and Wyoming corresponds very nearly to the *Eoorthis* Subzone of the upper Mississippi Valley (Berg, 1953, p. 556, Table 1) and Oklahoma (Frederickson, 1949, p. 343, Table 1). It includes the epibole of *Eoorthis* in Montana and Wyoming as well, but the name *Parabolinoides* is preferred for this subzone in the interest of consistent nomenclature that employs only trilobite names. The *Parabolinoides* Subzone of Montana and Wyoming differs from its near equivalents in other regions by containing most of the species of the *Taenicephalus* Zone. The *Eoorthis* Subzone of the upper Mississippi Valley, Texas, and Oklahoma occurs within the *Conaspis* Zone of those areas, below and separate from the local ranges of *Taenicephalus* and several other genera of the *Taenicephalus* Subzone.

IDAHOIA ZONE: The fauna of the *Idahoia* Zone consists of the following species (*see also* Pl. 4):

Porifera
- *Multivasculatus ovatus*

Brachiopoda
- *Angulotreta catheta*
- *Angulotreta vescula*
- *Billingsella perfecta*
- *Billingsella plicatella*
- *Lingulella desiderata*
- *Pseudodicellomus mosaicus*

Mollusca incertae sedis
- *Hyolithes primordialis*

Gastropoda
- *Lytospira* ? sp.
- *Sinuella vaticina*

Trilobita
- *Croixana bipunctata*
- *Drumaspis briscoensis*
- *Drumaspis idahoensis*
- *Ellipsocephaloides silvestris*
- *Idahoia serapio*
- *Idahoia wisconsensis*
- *Idahoia wyomingensis*
- *Maladia americana*
- *Monocheilus demissus*
- *Pinctus* ? *pullus*
- *Pseudagnostus josephus*
- *Pseudagnostus sentosus*
- *Ptychaspis granulosa*
- *Saratogia carita*
- *Saratogia fracida*
- *Saratogia fria*
- *Stigmacephaloides curvabilis*
- *Wilbernia diademata*
- *Wilbernia expansa*
- *Wilbernia explanata*
- *Wilbernia pero*

The *Idahoia* Zone is confined to the Sage Member of the Snowy Range Formation. It extends from near the base of the brownish-gray ledge near the middle of the member to an indefinite horizon 50–70 feet above the top of the ledge. The upper part of the *Idahoia* Zone at many localities is truncated by the Maywood unit.

This zone lies within the lower two thirds of the *Ptychaspis-Prosaukia* Zone of the standard system of subdivision for the Franconian Stage (Howell and others, 1944; Bell and others, 1952). It does not include the ranges of species of *Prosaukia* or of *Ptychaspis miniscaensis;* these and a few other species comprise the *Prosaukia* Zone, which is treated separately in Montana and Wyoming.

The *Idahoia* Zone could be subdivided in several different ways. It can be divided into two unequal parts on the basis of the local ranges of its two species of *Drumaspis*. The local range of *D. briscoensis* occupies the lower two thirds to three fourths of the zone; that of *D. idahoensis* occupies the remainder. Another acceptable system of subdivision of the *Idahoia* Zone involves the local ranges of *Saratogia* and its species (Pl. 4). The lower half of the zone contains *Saratogia;* the upper half does not. The range of *Saratogia* can be subdivided into two subequal parts, with *S. carita* and *S. fracida* in the lower half and *S. fria* in the upper half. Subdivision of the zone on the basis of the ranges of species of *Idahoia* is adopted here because such a system is applicable in other areas. *Idahoia* is a common genus in the Franconian of Texas (Bell and Ellinwood, 1962) and of the upper Mississippi Valley (Bell and others, 1952; Grant, 1962). The *Ptychaspis* Subzone of the *Ptychaspis-Prosaukia* Zone in the upper Mississippi Valley includes two zonules: *Ptychaspis granulosa* near the base; and *P. striata* near the top. These two zonules correspond exactly to zonules based on species of *Idahoia* in the same region (Grant, 1962). There, the *P. granulosa* Zonule coincides with the range of *Idahoia wisconsensis,* and the *P. striata* Zonule coincides with the range of *I. serapio.*

The most abundant and diagnostic fossil of the *Idahoia* Zone is the small gastropod *Sinuella vaticina,* which is restricted to the zone. Its range coincides only with the *Ptychaspis* Subzone of the standard section. In the absence of other fossils it is possible to draw boundaries consistent with those of the *Idahoia* Zone on the basis of the presence of *S. vaticina.*

IDAHOIA WYOMINGENSIS SUBZONE: The lowermost subzone of the *Idahoia* Zone is characterized by *I. wyomingensis.* This subzone occupies almost the entire thickness of the brownish-gray ledge near the middle of the Sage Member. Locally the base of the subzone lies below the base of the ledge, or the top of the subzone may lie above the top of the ledge, but normally, the major part of the subzone is within the ledge. A few species are confined to the *I. wyomingensis* Subzone; they are the trilobites:

Saratogia carita	*Wilbernia diademata*
Saratogia fracida	*Wilbernia explanata*

Saratogia fria normally occurs in the upper part of the *Idahoia wyomingensis* Subzone, but a few specimens occur in the lower part of the overlying *I. wisconsensis* Subzone. At most localities *I. wyomingensis* is confined to the *I. wyomingensis* Subzone, but a few isolated specimens may be found in the basal *I. wisconsensis* Subzone. The top of the *I. wyomingensis* Subzone is the highest occurrence of abundant *I. wyomingensis.* At a few localities single specimens of *I. wisconsensis* were found in the upper third of the *I. wyomingensis* Subzone, with abundant *I. wyomingensis* above it; such isolated specimens are not considered in drawing the top of the *I. wyomingensis* Subzone.

IDAHOIA WISCONSENSIS SUBZONE: This is the thinnest of the three subzones of the *Idahoia* Zone. Its base is above the highest occurrence of abundant *I. wyomingensis* and below the lowest appearance of abundant *I. wisconsensis.* Its top is the lowest appearance of *I. serapio,* no matter how abundant, provided that succeeding beds also carry *I. serapio.* At Baldy Mountain a specimen of *I. serapio* was found near the base of the *I. wisconsensis* Subzone, but higher beds have abundant *I. wisconsensis* without *I. serapio.* Elsewhere the lowest appearance of *I. serapio* marks the base of the *I. serapio* Subzone and the top of the *I. wisconsensis* Subzone.

The *Idahoia wisconsensis* Subzone extends from near the top of the brownish-gray ledge in the middle of the Sage Member to about 5–10 feet above the ledge. At a few localities it occupies the top 5 feet of the ledge. No species is confined exclusively to the *Idahoia wisconsensis* Subzone; its fauna contains species from the underlying *I. wyomingensis* Subzone and the overlying *I. serapio* Subzone.

IDAHOIA SERAPIO SUBZONE: The base of the *Idahoia serapio* Subzone lies at the lowest occurrence of *I. serapio,* except where an isolated specimen occurs low in the range of *I. wisconsensis.* The subzone occurs in the middle or upper part of the Sage Member, but the top of the subzone (and the top of the *Idahoia* Zone) is ill-defined. Fossils are rare immediately above the *Idahoia* Zone, and a sharp upper boundary cannot be recognized. The rock is relatively barren of fossils up to the base of the Trempealeauan Stage, and much of it is shaly and covered.

No species is confined exclusively to the *Idahoia serapio* Subzone, although several are so nearly confined to it as to be considered diagnostic of the subzone. These are the trilobites:

Drumaspis idahoensis
Idahoia serapio
Maladia americana
Pinctus ? pullus

PROSAUKIA ZONE: The *Prosaukia* Zone of Montana and Wyoming occupies the strata between the top of the *Idahoia* Zone and the base of the Trempealeauan Stage. This interval is sparsely fossiliferous, but the genera are those that occur in the *Prosaukia* Subzone of the upper Mississippi Valley (Bell and others, 1952, p. 177, Table 1). The *Prosaukia* Zone extends from just above the middle of the Sage Member through most of the upper part, lying wholly within the Sage Member at all localities except at Bridger Peak where the top of the zone is in the base of the Grove Creek Member. Boundaries of the *Prosaukia* Zone are not sharp; its thickness averages about 40 feet.

The following species occur in the *Prosaukia* Zone:

Brachiopoda
Angulotreta catheta
Pseudodicellomus mosaicus
Gastropoda
Lytospira ? sp.
Trilobita
Ellipsocephaloides silvestris
Prosaukia sp.
Ptychaspis cf. *P. miniscaensis*

Trempealeauan Stage. The lower part of the Trempealeauan Stage is represented in the Snowy Range Formation by a single zone, the *Illaenurus* Zone. This zone contains 16 species of trilobites, five brachiopod species, one graptolite species, and one sponge species. It occurs where the Grove Creek Member is present, although it is not confined wholly to that member.

ILLAENURUS ZONE: The fauna of the *Illaenurus* Zone consists of the following species:

Porifera
- *Multivasculatus ovatus*

Brachiopoda
- *Angulotreta catheta*
- *Apheoorthis* sp.
- *Finkelnburgia osceola*
- *Lingulella desiderata*
- *Pseudodicellomus mosaicus*

Trilobita
- *Briscoia dalyi*
- *Bynumiella typicalis*
- *Bynumina* sp.
- *Dikelocephalus* sp.
- *Eurekia binodosa*
- *Geragnostus* ? *insolitus*
- *Homagnostus* sp.
- *Idiomesus* sp.
- *Illaenurus montanensis*
- *Illaenurus quadratus*
- *Illaenurus sinclairensis*
- *Illaenurus truncatus*
- *Monocheilus* cf. *M. truncatus*
- *Pseudagnostus* cf *P. laevis*
- *Rasettia snowyensis*
- *Stenopilus* ? sp.

Graptolithina
- *Callograptus staufferi*

The *Illaenurus* Zone occupies all the Trempealeauan present in the Snowy Range Formation here. Its base at most localities is in the upper part of the Sage Member as much as 70 feet below the base of the Grove Creek Member, but at Bridger Peak its base is in the lower Grove Creek Member. The zone extends through the Grove Creek Member to the base of the overlying Maywood unit or Bighorn Formation.

Illaenurus Zone is a local name used in Montana and Wyoming to correspond to part of the *Saukia* Zone of the Croixan type area (Raasch, 1951, p. 149). Its most probable correlation with local zonation elsewhere is with the *Dikelocephalus postrectus, Rasettia,* and upper *Dikelocephalus* subzones of the upper Mississippi Valley (Howell and others, 1956) and the Lower Trempealeauan of Texas (Bell and Ellinwood, 1962).

BRACHIOPOD ZONATION

General statement. All but two of the brachiopod zones proposed here for the Montana-Wyoming area are new. Only the *Eoörthis* Subzone and *Apostreta expansa* Zone have been recognized formally elsewhere (Howell and others, 1944; Palmer, 1955a). The brachiopod zones are based primarily on ranges of genera and species of phosphatic inarticulate brachiopods. They appear to be valid in southwestern Montana and northwestern Wyoming, but their applicability elsewhere is unknown.

Stage boundaries within the Croixan Series have been established on the basis of ranges of trilobites and are irrelevant in terms of brachiopod zonation. The Dresbachian-Franconian boundary falls between the local ranges of *Apsotreta expansa* and *Linnarssonella girtyi,* two closely related species (*see* discussion of *A. expansa*). The Franconian-Trempealeauan boundary falls in the middle of the *Angulotreta catheta* Zone. If stage boundaries were to be established using brachiopods instead of trilobites, the top of the Dresbachian probably would be the top of the range of *Linnarssonella girtyi,* including the present *Elvinia* Zone. The top of the Franconian might be placed at the lowest occurrence of *Angulotreta catheta,* in the middle of the *Idahoia serapio* Subzone. The base of the Ordovician could be placed at the lowest occurrence of *Finkelnburgia* or of *Apheoorthis,* both of which continue into the Ordovician as presently defined. This is not to suggest that the subdivision of the Croixan or the Cambro-Ordovician boundary be modified, but merely to emphasize disparity between boundaries based on animals of different phyla.

Brachiopod Stage 1 (equivalent to Dresbachian Stage). The uppermost part of the Dresbachian Stage in the Snowy Range Formation is represented by diagnostic brachiopods only at Fox Creek, although typical Dresbachian trilobites indicate its presence at Bill Smith Creek and Bighorn Lake.

APSOTRETA EXPANSA ZONE: Siltstone beds near the base of the Dry Creek Member at Fox Creek contain abundant specimens of *Apsotreta expansa.* The species was first described in Texas where it occurs abundantly in the "post-*Aphelaspis*" Zone (Palmer, 1955a), now termed the *Dunderbergia* Zone (Lochman-Balk and Wilson, 1958). Palmer (1955a, p. 716) established for central Texas an *Apsotreta expansa* Zone characterized by *A. expansa* and some linguloid brachiopods. At Fox Creek the valves of *A. expansa* closely resemble *Linnarssonella girtyi* of the immediately superjacent *Linnarssonella* Zone (*i.e., Elvinia* Zone). Possibly the *A. expansa* Zone of Montana-Wyoming is the correlative of the *A. expansa* Zone of Texas, but more collecting is needed to determine whether or not *A. expansa* in Montana and Wyoming occurs with *Aphelaspis* Zone or *Dunderbergia* Zone trilobites. Several samples of limestone from the *Aphelaspis* Zone of the Snowy Range Formation at Bill Smith Creek and Bighorn Lake were dissolved in acid, but no valves of *A. expansa* were found in the residues.

Brachiopod Stage 2 (equivalent to part of Franconian Stage). The Franconian Stage is represented in the Snowy Range Formation by all or part of four brachiopod zones (Pl. 4). The *Linnarssonella* Zone at the base is equivalent to the *Elvinia* Zone. It is overlain by the *Angulotreta tetonensis* Zone, which corresponds to the *Taenicephalus* Zone of the local trilobite-based nomenclature. Above the *A. tetonensis* Zone is the *A. vescula* Zone, which extends from the top of the *Taenicephalus* Zone into the middle of the *Idahoia serapio* Subzone. This is followed by the Franconian part of the *A. catheta* Zone, which is equivalent to the upper half of the *I. serapio* Subzone and the entire *Prosaukia* Zone. The top of the Franconian Stage falls below the base of the *Finkelnburgia* Subzone of the *A. catheta* Zone.

LINNARSSONELLA ZONE: The *Linnarssonella* Zone is equivalent to the

Elvinia Zone of the standard Franconian sequence (Howell and others, 1944). It extends from low in the Dry Creek Member to near the base of the *Ceratreta-Eoorthis* bed that lies several feet above the top of the *Collenia magna* bioherm of the Sage Member. *Linnarssonella girtyi,* the most abundant and characteristic species of the zone, has never been found associated with brachiopods or trilobites of the overlying zone. The faunal change is complete and sharp, at places occurring within a vertical distance of only a few inches. Specimens of *Ocnerorthis monticola* were collected near the top of the *Linnarssonella* Zone at Sections HH, JC, and CF. The species is rare but apparently occurs at a consistent biostratigraphic level (Bell, 1941, p. 253; 1956, oral communication). Available evidence (*see also* Lochman and Hu, 1960, p. 815) indicates that species of *Ocnerorthis* occur in the *Elvinia* Zone, with *O. monticola* in the upper part of the *Camaraspis* Subzone, immediately below the top of the *Elvinia* or *Linnarssonella* Zone. More occurrences of species of *Ocnerorthis* must be recorded before their ranges can be established.

ANGULOTRETA TETONENSIS ZONE: The *Angulotreta tetonensis* Zone is defined by the local range of *A. tetonensis.* The base of the zone coincides with the base of the *Taenicephalus* Zone; it falls below the bed of brachiopod coquinite that contains abundant valves of species of *Billingsella, Ceratreta,* and *Eoorthis.* The top of the zone is the highest occurrence of *A. tetonensis.* This species is very abundant in the lower part of the zone, moderately common in the middle, but rare in the upper part, so the upper boundary of the zone is not sharp. No specimen of *A. tetonensis* has been found above the level of the top of the *Taenicephalus* Zone; therefore, the *A. tetonensis* Zone may be equivalent to the *Taenicephalus* Zone.

CERATRETA-EOORTHIS SUBZONE: The lower 5–10 feet of the *Angulotreta tetonensis* Zone contains several distinctive brachiopod species. Within this interval is a 1–2-foot bed of brachiopod coquinite that contains the epiboles of *Angulotreta tetonensis, A. vescula, Billingsella perfecta, B. plicatella, Ceratreta hebes, Eoorthis remnicha, Huenella abnormis, H. texana,* and *Otusia sandbergi.* Only *A. tetonensis, A. vescula,* and *B. perfecta* range more than a few feet above the coquinite; the other species are confined to the lower part of the *A. tetonensis* Zone and constitute the diagnostic fauna of the *Ceratreta-Eoorthis* Subzone.

The *Ceratreta-Eoorthis* Subzone corresponds rather closely to the *Parabolinoides* Subzone of the trilobite zonation but ranges slightly higher at some localities. It is the faunal correlative of the *Eoorthis* Subzone and lower part of the *Parabolinoides-Orygmaspis* Subzone of Texas (Ellinwood, 1953, Ph.D. thesis, Univ. Minnesota), of the *Eoorthis* Subzone and lower part of *Taenicephalus* Subzone of Oklahoma (Frederickson, 1949, p. 343, Table 1), and the upper Mississippi Valley (Berg, 1953, p. 556, Table 1; Berg and others, 1956, p. 17).

ANGULOTRETA VESCULA ZONE: The *Angulotreta vescula* Zone is not defined by the entire range of *A. vescula* because part of that range lies in the *A.*

tetonensis Zone. Instead it is defined by the presence of *A. vescula* in the absence of *A. tetonensis* from the zone below and of *A. catheta* from the zone above. With this definition both the upper and lower boundaries of the *A. vescula* Zone are necessarily indefinite. *A. vescula* attains its epibole in the *Ceratreta-Eoorthis* Subzone although it is moderately common throughout the *A. tetonensis* and *A. vescula* zones. It is rare in the lower part of the *A. catheta* Zone and extends only a few feet into that zone. The base of the *A. vescula* Zone is drawn at the highest occurrence of *A. tetonensis,* perhaps coinciding with the top of the *Taenicephalus* Zone and the base of the *Idahoia* Zone. The top of the *A. vescula* Zone falls below the lowest occurrence of *A. catheta,* which commonly appears in the middle or lower part of the *Idahoia serapio* Subzone.

The *Angulotreta vescula* Zone occupies the greater part of the *Idahoia* Zone; its faunal list includes all species present in the *Idahoia* Zone. Like the *Idahoia* Zone, the limits of the *A. vescula* Zone can be approximated fairly closely, even in the absence of *A. vescula,* by the presence of the abundant small gastropod *Sinuella vaticina.*

Brachiopod Stage 3 (equivalent to upper part of Franconian Stage and lower part of Trempealeauan Stage). The upper part of the Franconian Stage (Bell and others, 1956) and the part of the Trempealeauan Stage present in the Snowy Range Formation are represented by the *Angulotreta catheta* Zone. The approximate level of the Franconian-Trempealeauan boundary is marked by the base of the *Finkelnburgia* Subzone of the *A. catheta* Zone.

ANGULOTRETA CATHETA ZONE: The *Angulotreta catheta* Zone occupies the part of the Franconian Stage above the *A. vescula* Zone and the entire Trempealeauan Stage; it is defined as the range of *A. catheta.* The base of the zone is the lowest occurrence of *A. catheta,* which commonly appears in the lower or middle part of the *Idahoia serapio* Subzone. The position of the top of the zone is unknown; the zone extends to the top of the Snowy Range Formation.

The fauna of the *Angulotreta catheta* Zone includes species of the *Idahoia serapio* Subzone and the *Prosaukia* Zone of the Franconian Stage and the *Illaenurus* Zone of the Trempealeauan. *A. catheta* is moderately common to rare throughout the zone; it is the only species that spans the zone and is confined to it.

FINKELNBURGIA OSCEOLA SUBZONE: At most localities where Trempealeauan rock is present, *Finkelnburgia osceola* is found in the upper half of the *Angulotreta catheta* Zone. The *Finkelnburgia osceola* Subzone is the local range of *F. osceola.* Its base coincides closely with the base of the Trempealeauan *Illaenurus* Zone, and its fauna is that of the *Illaenurus* Zone. The top of the *F. osceola* Subzone is unknown; at most localities the subzone extends to the top of the Snowy Range Formation. *F. osceola* is known only from the Trempealeauan (Ulrich and Cooper, 1938, p. 140), but other species of *Finkelnburgia* have been found in the Lower Ordovician (Ulrich and Cooper, 1938, p. 132; Young, 1956, p. 1165–1167).

Near the top of the Grove Creek Member, at the section behind K-Z Ranch, a specimen of *Apheoorthis* sp. was found associated with Trempealeauan graptolites. The genus *Apheoorthis* is considered by Ulrich and Cooper (1938, p. 79) to be the latest Cambrian and earliest Ordovician.

SYSTEMATIC PALEONTOLOGY: CROIXAN FAUNAS

Phyla represented in the Snowy Range Formation are arranged according to the conventional biologic classification given by Shrock and Twenhofel (1953). Authority for arrangement of lower taxa within each phylum is cited below.

Porifera. Classification of the one species of sponge is that of de Laubenfels (1955).

Brachiopoda. This phylum is represented by 20 species in 14 genera. The number of species is second only to that of the trilobites. Genera are arranged by superfamily following Cooper (*in* Shimer and Shrock, 1944, p. 277–365). Within each superfamily genera are arranged alphabetically, as are species within each genus.

Mollusca. Four genera of gastropods, each with one species, comprise the molluscan fauna of the Snowy Range Formation. They are classified according to Shrock and Twenhofel (1953).

Arthropoda. This phylum is represented in the Snowy Range Formation by 18 families, 48 genera, and 80 species of trilobites, and a few merostome fragments that have been identified as aglaspids. Discussions of trilobites are grouped according to families, which are arranged alphabetically. Within each family, genera and species are arranged alphabetically. Assignment of trilobite genera to families follows the Treatise on Invertebrate Paleontology (Harrington and others, 1959). Definitions of morphologic terms can be found in the same volume (p. 042–047; glossary, p. 0117–0126).

Measurements of parts of the cranidium follow the suggestions of Frederickson (1949, p. 342), except that measurement of width of the fixed cheek is made immediately anterior or posterior to the palpebral lobe, unless otherwise stated. Where adequate descriptions are available in recent literature, only the characteristic features by which a species can be recognized are mentioned here; where large collections have been available, descriptions may be amplified and variation discussed.

Echinodermata. "Crinoid" columnals and fragmentary calyces are classified as Pelmatozoan fragments.

Chordata (?). Classification of Graptolithina follows Bulman (1955).

Conodonts. These are classified according to the arrangement by Müller (1959).

Problematica and calcareous algae. These have no supergeneric classification; they are described at the end of the section on systematic paleontology.

Locality designations. Occurrences of each species are listed in biostratigraphic order according to local zonation following the species description. Each listing contains the initials of the locality and a number that corresponds to footage above the base of the section. Localities are given in the following order, with these abbreviations:

HA to HK—localities in the Horseshoe Hills, listed alphabetically from west to east (Fig. 1).

GC to ME—localities in the Bridger Mountains listed in order from north to south along the strike of the range: GC–Gallup Creek; FC–Felix Canyon; FP—Flathead Pass; JC—Johnson Canyon; BL—Bighorn Lake; BC—Bill Smith Creek; SP–Sacajawea Peak; RP–Ross Peak; BP–Bridger Peak; BM–Baldy Mountain; ME–Mount Ellis.

FD to SL—localities south and east of the Bridger Mountains, listed approximately in northwest to southeast direction: FD–Flying "D" Ranch; SC–Storm Castle Mountain on Squaw Creek; CF–Crowfoot Ridge; MC–Mill Creek; YO–Wyoming Creek; UYO–Upper Wyoming Creek; FOX–Fox Creek; UFOX–Upper Fox Creek; BB–Beartooth Butte; KZ–K bar Z Ranch; GR–North Grove Creek; SL–Swamp Lake.

Collections provided by C. Lochman—NG–Nixon Gulch (same locality as HG); DC–Dry Creek; YG–Yogo Gulch.

Phylum PORIFERA Grant, 1872
Class HYALOSPONGEA Vosmaer, 1886
Order LYSSAKIDA Zittel, 1877
Family MULTIVASCULATIDAE de Laubenfels, 1955
Genus *Multivasculatus* Howell and Van Houten, 1940
Multivasculatus ovatus Howell and Van Houten
(Pl. 15, figs. 29, 32)

Multivasculatus ovatus HOWELL and VAN HOUTEN, 1940, p. 1–8, Pl. 1, figs. 1–3, Pl. 2, figs. 1–2, Pl. 3, figs. 1–4; SHIMER and SHROCK, 1944, p. 55, Pl. 16, figs. 37–38; DE LAUBENFELS, 1955, p. 377, Fig. 59, 5a–b; LOCHMAN, 1949, p. 37
Protospongia ? sp. undet. LOCHMAN, 1950a, p. 328–329, Pl. 46, fig. 18

REMARKS: This species is represented by many siliceous monaxial and hexaxial spicules. Monaxons are straight, unmarked, and slightly tapered. Rays of hexaxons meet at right angles and normally are tapered. In many, one ray is longer than others, not tapered, and marked by tiny papillae on the surface.

Lochman (1950a) described and figured hexaxial spicules from the Little Rocky Mountains that occupy the same biostratigraphic position as do most of these. She assigned them tentatively to *Protospongia,* stating that this is the only described genus with similar spicules. De Laubenfels (1955, p. E68–E69) says that protospongid spicules normally are tetraxons, never hexaxons, and therefore Lochman's specimens may belong to a species of *Multivasculatus,* possibly *M. ovatus* Howell and Van Houten.

OCCURRENCE: Spicules of *Multivasculatus ovatus* are very rare in the *Taenicephalus* Zone at SC 52.3, 54.9; CF 53.1, and in the *Idahoia wyomingensis* Subzone at HD 121.1; HI 111.8. They are abundant in the Trempealeauan at BC 192.6, 196.0; BM 305.4, 307.7, 309.9, 316.5; ME 28.1, 31.1, 33, 36.1, 47.6; MC 238.2, 240.1, 248.7, 283.5; FOX 242.7. Where abundant, this species is a good indicator of the Trempealeauan. Not more than two spicules appeared in any insoluble residue from the Franconian.

Phylum BRACHIOPODA Cuvier, 1805
Class INARTICULATA Huxley, 1869
Order ATREMATA Beecher, 1891
Superfamily OBOLACEA Schuchert, 1896
Genus *Pseudodicellomus* Bell, 1962
Pseudodicellomus mosaicus (Bell)
(Pl. 9, figs. 17–18, 20, 23)

Dicellomus nanus (Meek and Hayden). WALCOTT, 1912a (part), Pl. 53, figs. 3, 3c–d
Dicellomus mosaica BELL, 1941, p. 216–218, Pl. 29, figs. 4–9
Pseudodicellomus mosaicus (Bell). BELL, *in* BELL and ELLINWOOD, 1962, p. 407, Pl. 60, figs. 1–7

REMARKS: This species is characterized by its thick, *Dicellomus*-like shell with pitted outer surface but impunctate inner layers. Many specimens are merely exfoliated outer layers, appearing in acetic acid residues, identified primarily by pitted surfaces (visible under magnification of ×36–×48. No well-preserved interiors are present.

Pseudodicellomus mosaicus, type species of the genus, to date is its only species. According to Bell (Bell and Ellinwood, 1962), it differs from species of *Dicellomus* in its very thick, impunctate inner-shell layers but resembles them in shape and pattern of muscle marks.

Bell finds the species confined to the post-*Elvinia* Zone Franconian of Central Texas, a similar range of significant abundance as in the area under study; a few scattered fragments have been found in the *Elvinia* Zone.

OCCURRENCE: *Pseudodicellomus mosaicus* is very rare in the *Elvinia* Zone at GC 77.8; BC 63.8; MC 105.4; GR 10.7, 11.9, 15.9, 21.7; SL 43.9, 64.7, 70.1. It is common in the *Taenicephalus* Zone at HB 73.8; HD 84.1, 95.3; HF 14.6, 14.8, 15.5, 15.6; HG 47.7, 51, 63.5; HH 72.3, 74.3; HI 67.7, 69.5; HK 72.7, 86.5; GC 93.5; FC 108.6; FP 107.7; BC 69.3, 73.3; SP 111.9, 112.4, 117.4, 112.3; BP 98.7; FD 15.3; SC 40.1, 42.7, 43.8, 50.7; CF 34, 56.2, 59.7, 62.3, 65.6, 72.8, 74, 77; MC 111.7, 116.4, 117.1; YO 69.4, 73.9, 78.1, 84.3; FOX 73.5; GR 66.6, 77.1, 78.1, 88.1; SL 81.1, 81.5, 93.1. It is common in the *Idahoia* Zone at HD 117.9, 127.6, 130.6, 141.1, 146.2, 150.6; HG 77.3, 81.3; HH 100.5, 116.4, 128.8; HI 99.8, 111.8, 124.3; HK 109.1; GC 133; FC 143.2; JC 103.6; 106.6; BC 103.6, 106.4, 109.9; SP 146.6, 181.5; RP 84.9, 134.7, 136.7; BM 166.3, 182.1; MC 164.4, 170.6, 179.8, 185.3; YO 125.9, 128.4, 135.7, 143.4, 144.1, 146.7, 147.5, 157.1, 159.5; FOX 94.2, 98.4, 103.4, 106.1, 111.9, 113.1, 113.7, 116.6, 117.6, 118.6, 123.2, 124.2, 132, 133.2, 133.7, 135.9, 138.3; BB 117.3; SL 101, 108.2, 108.9, 109.4, 114.4, 120.5, 123, 238.1.

It is common in the *Prosaukia* Zone at BM 225.5; YO 172.8, 175.7; FOX 177.1, 178.3 and in the Trempealeauan at MC 238.2, 285.5; YO 233.8; 182.6, 187.6, 198.7, 199.9, 201.9, 202.4, 204.7, 210.7, 218.9, 220.9, 222.9, 230.9, 238.1, 254.3; SL 225.4, 249.1.

Genus *Lingulella* Salter, 1866
Lingulella desiderata (Walcott)
(Pl. 9, figs. 7, 11, 15)

Obolus (*Lingulella*) *desideratus* WALCOTT, 1898b, p. 399–400; WALCOTT (*in* HAGUE AND OTHERS, 1899, p. 445–446, Pl. 60, fig. 2 [not fig. 2a, referred to *Obolus rotundatus* by Walcott, 1912a, p. 492])
Lingulella desiderata (Walcott). WALCOTT, 1912a, p. 492–494, Pl. 20, figs. 4, 4a–c, 5, 5a–j; ULRICH and COOPER, 1938, p. 48

DESCRIPTION: Species small, subovate, with regular growth lines, fine radial ornamentation. Both valves moderately convex; pedicle valve slightly longer, bluntly pointed at beak; brachial valve subelliptical. Pedical valve with triangular, flat propareas bordering shallow, troughlike pedicle groove. Brachial valve has narrow interarea at beak; valves otherwise quite featureless, smooth, with no known diagnostic characteristics.

REMARKS: Walcott (1899, p. 445; 1912a, p. 493) identified this form in the Upper Cambrian at Crowfoot Ridge, Yellowstone National Park, and on the north side of the Gallatin

Valley, localities which span much of the area from which the present specimens were collected and provide the basis for recognition of the species. Not enough of the morphology of the species is known to distinguish it clearly from similar linguloid brachiopods from other areas or in rocks of other ages.

This species is distinguished from *L. perattenuata,* with which it occurs, by its somewhat thicker shell and more ovate, less elongate valves. Normally it is larger than *L. perattenuata.*

OCCURRENCE: *Lingulella desiderata* is sporadic throughout the Franconian and Trempealeauan. It is probably more abundant than is indicated by the following listing because many fragments have been identified merely as "linguloid fragments" and not assigned to either of the two species of *Lingulella* recognized here. It occurs in the *Elvinia* Zone at HG 36; GC 68.2; BB 49.5; in the *Taenicephalus* Zone at HD 85–88, 95.3; HF 14.6; HG 63.5; GC 92.6; FC 108.6, 131.2; BC 73.3, 74.3; SP 117.4, 118.4; BP 97.3; BM 92.7; CF 79.7; YO 75.7, in the *Idahoia* Zone at BH 77.8; HD 112.1; HH 127.1, 132.8; GC 137.3; JC 103.6, 109.4; BC 109.9; SP 144.3; BM 153.9; YO 135.7, 147.5; FOX 133.2; SL 93.1; in the *Prosaukia* Zone at BM 215.8; FOX 163.1, 175.3; and in the Trempealeauan at FOX 230.9; UFOX 55; KZ 4.6.

Lingulella perattenuata (Whitfield)
(Pl. 9, figs. 30, 33)

Lingulepis perattenuatus WHITFIELD, 1877, p. 9; WHITFIELD, 1880, p. 337, Pl. 2, figs. 7–9
Lingulella perattenuata (Whitfield). WALCOTT, 1912a, p. 523–524, Pl. 21, figs. 1, 1a–i (synonymy to date)

DESCRIPTION: Shell thin, elongate oval, ornamented by concentric growth lines, faint radial lines, very fine irregular lines and depressions. Prominent visceral cavity extending posteriorly from beak of pedicle valve, as illustrated by Walcott (1912, Pl. 21, fig. 1e).

REMARKS: *L. perattenuata* differs from *L. desiderata* by its normally smaller and thinner valves that are narrower and more accuminate. It is not distinctive enough to be distinguished with certainty from similar species, except when considered in terms of age and locality.

OCCURRENCE: *L. perattenuata* is common in the lower part of the Franconian. It occurs with *L. desiderata,* but does not extend as high in the section. It has been found in the *Elvinia* Zone at HA 13.6; CF 31.6; YO 44.6; FOX 55.7; in the *Taenicephalus* Zone at HD 84.6; HE 98.6; HF 19; HG 47.7, 51, 65.5; SC 42.7, 43.8, 50.7, 56.7; CF 40; MC 117.9; YO 74.1; SL 76.8.

Order NEOTREMATA Beecher, 1891
Superfamily PATERINACEA Schuchert, 1929
Genus *Micromitra* Meek, 1873
Micromitra modesta (Lochman)
(Pl. 8, figs. 3–4)

Paterina modesta LOCHMAN, 1940, p. 14, Pl. 1, figs. 20–21, 23–24
Micromitra paucicostellae BELL, 1944, p. 144
Micromitra modesta (Lochman). BELL, 1944, p. 144–145, Pl. 18, figs. 1–8, 18–19; LOCHMAN and HU, 1960, p. 820, Pl. 95, figs. 37–40

REMARKS: A few well-preserved brachial valves exhibit the characteristic surface ornamentation of *M. modesta.* This consists of many threadlike circumumbonal fila crossed by radial undulations. Interiors have undulations on the inner surface of the shell and therefore are not true costellae (Bell, 1944, p. 144). Displaying no features other than propareas and a pair of weak callosities on each side of the median line, the interior of this species remains relatively unknown. This is the first record of this species from Franconian rocks.

OCCURRENCE: *Micromitra modesta* is rare in the *Aphelaspis* or *Dunderbergia* Zone at BL 2.5, in the *Elvinia* Zone at FOX 21.7, and in the *Parabolinoides* Subzone of the *Taenicephalus* Zone at HF 14.6; HG 47.7.

Superfamily ACROTRETACEA Schuchert, 1896
Genus *Angulotreta* Palmer, 1955

Angulotreta PALMER, 1955a, p. 769
TYPE SPECIES: *Angulotreta triangularis* PALMER, 1955a, p. 769–770, Pl. 91, figs. 1–6

DESCRIPTION: Shell high, proconical or cataconical, pedicle foramen apical, apical process commonly elongate, pseudointerarea flat to slightly convex, deltoid, without intertrough. Apical pits present or absent: located near apex on lateral or posterior slopes of shell. Brachial valve subcircular possessing slight umbo and narrow propareas. Median septum present or absent: not generically significant.

REMARKS: This genus is distinguished from *Apsotreta* Palmer, *Linnarssonella* Walcott, and *Opisthotreta* Palmer by its proconical or cataconical (not apsoconical) pedicle-valve profile. It is distinguished from *Acrotreta* Kutorga and *Prototreta* Bell by absence of an intertrough in the pseudointerarea of the pedicle valve.

The four species of *Angulotreta* in this collection can be zoned biostratigraphically. *A. glabra* n.sp. is rare and occurs with *Linnarssonella girtyi* Walcott in the *Elvinia* Zone. *A. tetonensis* (Walcott) is abundant in association with *Ceratreta hebes* Bell in the lower part of the *Taenicephalus* Zone, restricted to that zone. *A. vescula* n. sp. is common in the *Taenicephalus* Zone and throughout the *Idahoia* Zone. Isolated specimens have been found in the lower Trempealeauan. *A. catheta* n. sp. is common in the Trempealeauan, but a few specimens have been found high in the *Idahoia* Zone of the Franconian.

Until recently almost all study of phosphatic inarticulate brachiopods was based on external morphology or the fortuitous discovery of an interior or the impression of one. With the advent of acetic and formic acid etching (Bell, 1948), abundant complete specimens have become available for study. Earlier methods of preparation uncovered mainly larger, more obvious specimens on the surface of rock, whereas acid reveals small, frail, and scarce shells. Therefore, the only species here that can be identified definitely with Walcott's species is *A. tetonensis,* the largest and strongest of the Acrotretacea in the Snowy Range Formation.

Angulotreta catheta Grant n.sp.
(Pl. 14, figs. 22–30)

DESCRIPTION: Outline of commissure subcircular; profile of pedicle valve moderately high, proconical to cataconical; apex may or may not overhang pseudointerarea; normally a bulge or irregularity on exterior of shell to accommodate internal apical process; shell thin to moderately thick; apical process moderately developed in apex, including small parts of posterior and anterior slopes, not solely along anterior slope; some specimens with incipient "cone-in-cone" structure around internal pedicle opening; internal pedicle opening wide, straight, parallel to posterior slope of shell, not occupying anterior tube or trough; pedicle opening with ring or collar as internal lining; apical pits lateral to internal pedicle opening, located slightly posterior or slightly anterior to opening.

Brachial valve flatly convex, thin to moderately strong; propareas distinct; median groove shallow; slight callosity on interior near umbo; low median ridge or median callosity commonly present.

HOLOTYPE: UT–12246c, Plate 14, figure 24

ETYMOLOGY: *Catheta,* L., straight, perpendicular; referring to large, straight pedicle opening running along anterior slope, parallel to posterior slope of shell.

REMARKS: This species is characterized by the wide, straight pedicle opening lined by a ring or collar as in *A. postapicalis* Palmer. It differs from that species by absence of a high median septum in the brachial valve. It is distinguished from *A. tetonensis* (Walcott) and *A. microscopica* (Shumard) in Bell and Ellinwood (1962) by the same feature, the much weaker shell structure, the less strongly developed apical process, and by the ring in the pedicle opening. It differs from *A. glabra* n.sp. and *A. vescula* n.sp. by the low median septum in the brachial valve and the ring in the pedicle opening.

OCCURRENCE: *Angulotreta catheta* is rare in the *Idahoia* Zone at FC 144.6; BM 158.8, 181.2;

MC 170.6, 185.3. It is moderately common in the *Prosaukia* Zone at RP 189; BM 200.1, 202.2, 205.6, 209.3, 218.1, 222.7; YO 172.8, 175.7, and common in the Trempealeauan at BC 191.1; BP 207.9; BM 262.1, 284, 296.8, 309.9; ME 28.1, 31.1, 33; MC 238.2, 283.5, 290.5; YO 194.1, 233.8, 240.7; UYO 216.9; FOX 202.4, 204.7, 215.4, 218.9, 220.9, 230.9, 238.1, 242.7; UFOX 35.2, 47.3, 53.1; SL 247.6.

Angulotreta glabra Grant n.sp.
(Pl. 9, figs. 21, 24–25, 27)

DESCRIPTION: Outline subcircular; shell thin to moderately strong; profile of pedicle valve proconical to cataconical with no overhang of apex, but some specimens with concave flexure near base of pseudointerarea; apical pits, when present, posterior to interior pedicle opening.

Brachial valve slightly convex; propareas small but distinct, with very straight interior margin; median groove shallow; muscle scars at anterolateral corners distinct; callosity in beak low, below, and anterior to median groove; no trace of median septum.

HOLOTYPE: UT–12137a, Plate 9, figure 24

ETYMOLOGY: *Glabra,* L., bare, bald, smooth; weak apical process of pedicle valve and lack of median septum in brachial valve give interiors of both valves a bare appearance.

REMARKS: *A. glabra* is characterized by its proconical shape, similar to that of *A. tetonensis,* and weak apical process and posterior apical pits. It differs from *A. tetonensis* and *A. microscopica* (Shumard) by its weak apical process and lack of a median septum; from *A. vescula* by its straight pseudointerarea, profile without overhanging apex, nontroughlike apical process, and subcircular rather than transversely elliptical outline; from *A. catheta* by lack of a ring in the pedicle opening of the pedicle valve and of a median septum in the brachial valve. Lack of a median septum distinguishes it from Palmer's Dresbachian species.

OCCURRENCE: *Angulotreta glabra* occurs only in the *Elvinia* Zone, commonly associated with *Linnarssonella girtyi.* It is rare at SP 86; MC 105.4; YO 43, 44.6, 49.8, 52.3; SL 43.9.

Angulotreta tetonensis (Walcott)
(Pl. 11, figs. 20–21, 23–24)

Acrotreta microscopica tetonensis WALCOTT, 1902, p. 590; WALCOTT, 1912a, p. 694–695, Pl. 67, figs. 3, 3a–d

"Acrotreta" tetonensis Walcott. BELL, 1941, p. 234–235, Pl. 31, figs. 1–9

REMARKS: *A. tetonensis* is recognizable from the description and illustrations by Bell (1941), who studied Walcott's holotype. The species is distinguished from other species of *Angulotreta,* except *A. microscopica* (Shumard), by its robust, high proconical pedicle valve with large, well-developed apical process, usually with "cone-in-cone" structure. It differs from *A. microscopica* by its low median septum in the brachial valve instead of the high, narrow, and normally digitate median septum that characterizes *A. microscopica.*

Abundant complete specimens of this study show no features not described by Bell, but they add to knowledge of the variability of the species. Both valves commonly are thick and strong, but some are thin. The profile of the pedicle valve is proconical or cataconical, normally with no overhang of the apex. The apex of some valves, however, overhangs the pseudointerarea, giving it a concave profile. If the base of the pseudointerarea of these concave specimens is broken, the valve appears low and apsoconical.

A. tetonensis is distinguished from *A. glabra* and *A. vescula* by its thicker shell, stronger apical process with "cone-in-cone" structure in the pedicle valve, and median septum in the brachial valve. Its thicker shell and lack of a ring in the pedicle opening distinguish it from *A. catheta.* The brachial valve of *A. catheta* may possess a weak median septum, which makes it indistinguishable from that of *A. tetonensis;* the brachial valve must be identified by its associated pedicle valve.

OCCURRENCE: *Angulotreta tetonensis* is abundant in the *Taenicephalus* Zone at HB 73.8, 77.8; HC 14.6, 20.5, 26.7; HD 85–88, 90.1, 95.3, 96.3; HE 89.3, 90.8; HF 14.6, 14.8, 15.5, 19;

HG 49, 51, 56; HH 72, 72.3, 77.8, 82.2; HI 67.7, 69.5; HK 77.2, 77.9, 78.7, 86.5; GC 89.6, 92.6, 93.5, 94.2, 98.6; FC 108.6, 109.8, 118.6; FP 112.5, 123; JC 68.1, 69.9; BC 69.3, 74.3, 81.3, 98.6; SP 109.9, 111.9, 112.4, 116.4, 117.4, 118.4, 119.8; RP 57.5; BP 98.7, 102.4, 109.2; BM 92.7, 96.2, 103.2; FD 15.3; SC 38.6, 40.1, 42.7, 47.5, 54.9, 56.7, 58.7; CF 34, 38, 40, 42.4, 43.4, 46.5, 48.1, 49.2, 51.8, 54.5, 56.2, 64.2; MC 117.1; YO 74.1, 75.7, 78.1, 79.7, 83.1, 84.3; FOX 65.4, 66:4; GR 74.1; SL 77.8, 79.8, 80.6, 81.1, 81.5, 93.1.

Angulotreta vescula Grant n.sp.
(Pl. 13, figs. 3, 6–12)

Description: Outline transversely elliptical, widest at posterolateral corners; pedicle valve cataconical with apex overhanging pseudointerarea; foramen precisely apical, pointing posteriorly; internal pedicle opening along low trough in low apical process extending along anterior slope of shell; weak "cone-in-cone" structure developed in apical process of few specimens; apical process expanding anteriorly into low rounded callosity commonly containing secondary opening not connected with internal pedicle opening; apical pits anterior to interior pedicle opening, not developed if apical process is too small to accommodate them; shell normally weak and small; specimens low in range of species moderately robust and as large as *A. tetonensis.*

Brachial valve flatly convex, larger specimens more flattened anteriorly, giving resupinate appearance; propareas small, proportionately very small on larger specimens; no median septum, some specimens with low rounded median callosity.

Holotype: UT–122106, Plate 13, figure 6

Etymology: *Vescula,* L. thin, weak, little. This species normally is smaller and thinner than *A. tetonensis.*

Remarks: *A. vescula* is distinguished from *A. tetonensis* and *A. microscopica* by its smaller and thinner valves, smaller apical process with troughlike internal pedicle opening, wider base of the pseudointerarea which gives the outline its transversely elliptical shape, and overhanging apex with posteriorly oriented foramen. It differs from *A. catheta* by its smaller brachial propareas, absent median septum, and lack of a ring in the pedicle foramen. Its transversely elliptical outline and overhanging apex distinguish it from *A. glabra.* It is distinguished from *A. postapicalis* and *A. triangularis* of the Dresbachian by its thinner shells and lack of a median septum in the brachial valve.

Occurrence: *Angulotreta vescula* is common in the *Taenicephalus* Zone at HC 26.7, 30.6, 32.5; HD 85–88, 95.3, 96.3, 97.9, 102.1; HE 90.8, 92.3, 98.6, 102.1; HF 15.5, 15.6, 19; HH 77.8, 82.2, 89.2, 89.3; HI 67.7; HK 86.5, 90.4, 92.4; GC 94.2, 106.1, 108.2, 109.6; FC 109.8, 118.6, 125.1, 135.4; FP 123; JC 69.6, 81, 83.4; BC 81.3; SP 117.4, 118.4, 119.8, 122.3; BP 102.4, 109.2; BM 103.2, 109.4; SC 40.1, 42.7, 50.7, 52.3, 54.9, 56.7, 58.7; CF 42.4, 43.4, 46.5, 48.1, 51.8, 53.1, 54.5, 56.2, 59.7, 61, 62.3, 67.1, 69.6, 72.8, 74; MC 117.9; YO 78.1, 85, 104.7; FOX 66.4, 70.9, 73.5; GR 88.0 (float); SL 79.8, 81.5. It is common in the *Idahoia wyomingensis* Subzone at HD 115.4; HE 104.8; HI 84.3, 98.1, 102.2, 115.8; GC 125.4, 132.2; SP 144.3, 146.6; RP 84.9; BM 132.9, 140.9; FD 26; FOX 88.8; SL 120.5. It is common in the *Idahoia wisconsensis* Subzone at HD 148.2; BC 109.9, 116.7; BM 150.6; YO 137.7; FOX 94.2, and in the *Idahoia serapio* Subzone at HD 150.6; BC 130.5; SP 181.5; BP 193.3; MC 185.3; YO 157.5, 159.5; and in the *Prosaukia* Zone at FOX 143.5, 178.3.

Genus *Apsotreta* Palmer, 1955
Apsotreta expansa Palmer
(Pl. 8, figs. 5–7)

Apsotreta expansa Palmer, 1955a, p. 770–771, Pl. 90, figs. 6–14; Palmer, *in* Barnes and others, 1959, Pl. 34, figs. 6–8

Description: Shell thick, pedicle valve apsoconical, apical process expanding anteriorly, two distinct nodes on beak of brachial valve, median septum low but strong, propareas flat with grooves very shallow or entirely absent.

REMARKS: The pedicle valve is almost identical to that of *Linnarssonella girtyi,* differing only in possession of a slightly stronger, more anteriorly divergent apical process. The brachial valve differs markedly from that of *L. girtyi* in possession of a median septum and in lack of grooves in the propareas. Specimens of this study can be identified as *A. expansa* on the basis of the median septum of the brachial valve; some have shallow grooves in the propareas, indicating close relationship with *L. girtyi.* These occur just below the first appearance of *L. girtyi.* Among the Acrotretacea, presence or absence of a median septum in the brachial valve has not been regarded as a generic character. However, these specimens, although abundant, all are from one bed at one locality. If more specimens with median septa and shallow grooves in the propareas are found elsewhere, *A. expansa* might be assigned to *Linnarssonella.*

OCCURRENCE: *Apsotreta expansa* is abundant in the top of the *Aphelaspis* Zone at FOX 3.5.

Genus *Ceratreta* Bell, 1941
Ceratreta hebes Bell
(Pl. 11, figs. 11–12, 14–15, 17–18)

Ceratreta hebes BELL, 1941, p. 233–234, Pl. 29, figs. 10–17; BELL and ELLINWOOD, 1962, p. 409, Pl. 61, figs. 10–15

DESCRIPTION: Shell thick, bluntly proconical, foramen slotlike, internal pedicle tube thick, extending along posterior slope of shell. Brachial valve with deep median groove, high median septum that projects into a hornlike process in many specimens, prominent muscle scars at posterolateral corners.

REMARKS: *C. hebes* occurs with or near *Eoorthis remnicha* in the *Parabolinoides* Subzone of the *Taenicephalus* Zone. Normally it is most abundant in a single bed, less abundant or totally absent above and below this bed. It is large and distinctive enough to be identified without the aid of acid etching, and therefore marks a reliable biostratigraphic horizon.

OCCURRENCE: *Ceratreta hebes* is abundant in the lower part of the *Taenicephalus* Zone (*Parabolinoides* Subzone) at HB 73.8, 77.8; HC 14.6; HD 85.1; HE 89.3; HF 14.6, 14.8, 15.5; HG 47.7, 49, 51; HH 72.3; HI 67.7; HK 77.2, 77.9; GC 92.6, 93.5; FC 108.6, 109.8, 125.1, 135.4; FP 112.5; JC 68.1; BC 69.3, 73.3; SP 109.9, 111.9, 112.4, 116.4, 117.4; RP 57.5; BP 98.7; BM 92.7, 96.2; FD 15.3; SC 40.1; CF 48.1; MC 116.4; YO 74.1, 75.7, 78.1; FOX 65.4; BB 56; SL 77.8, 79.8, 80.6, 81.1.

Genus *Linnarssonella* Walcott, 1902
Linnarssonella girtyi Walcott
(Pl. 9, figs. 4, 6, 8–10, 12–14, 16)

Linnarssonella girtyi WALCOTT, 1902, p. 602–603; WALCOTT, 1912a, p. 666–667, Pl. 78, figs. 5, 5a, Pl. 79, figs. 1, 1a–r; SHIMER and SHROCK, 1944, p. 289, Pl. 109, figs. 4–8; BELL and ELLINWOOD, 1962, p. 410, Pl. 61, figs. 4–9

Linnarssonella elongata BELL, 1941, p. 235, figs. 8–10, Pl. 31, figs. 15–19

REMARKS: This distinctive species has been described in detail by Walcott (1912) and Bell (1941). Their specimens appeared on surfaces of rock samples and necessarily were larger, more prominent individuals of the population. Multitudes of complete valves obtained by etching in acids show that *L. "elongata"* is a name applied to the larger, thicker-shelled individuals. All sizes from very tiny and transparent-shelled to large and heavy-shelled occur in etched samples. The large ones are not segregated geographically nor biostratigraphically; therefore, they are considered to be older individuals in the population of *L. girtyi* and not specifically distinct.

L. girtyi is characterized by an apsoconical pedicle valve and posteriorly expanding apical process with trough or tube leading to the internal pedicle opening. The brachial valve has distinct propareas with elongate grooves that parallel the posterior margin of the shell. It has no median septum, but an umbonal callosity below the apical groove.

OCCURRENCE: *Linnarssonella girtyi* is very abundant in the *Elvinia* Zone. It occurs at HA 13.6, 27.6; HC 6.5, 7.8, 10.6; HD 80.4, 82.4, 84.1; HG 36, 45.8, 47.5; HH 51.6, 53.9, 65.9, 68.9, 70.1; HI 61.5; HK 67.8, 72.7; GC 63, 68.2, 79.5, 80.7, 83.1, 85.8; FC 86, 90.3, 93.7, 100.2; FP 88, 90, 95.5, 105.7, 107.7; JC 57, 61.6; BL 47.7; BC 63.8; SP 106, 108.6, 109.1; BP 91.5, 94.1, 95.4; BM 82.5, 88.1, 91.2; SC 27; CF 15.5, 16.5, 19, 20, 21.2, 23.2, 29.2, 31.6; MC 97.5, 105.4; YO 18.5, 43, 44.6, 45.8, 49.8, 52.3, 58.1, 59.6, 60.6, 63.4, 65.9; FOX 9.2, 12.7, 13.9, 21.7, 31.2, 33.8, 34.6, 36.7, 39.1, 46.1, 51.1, 51.2, 53.2, 54.2, 55, 55.7, 57.1; GR 7.7, 10.7, 11.9, 15.9, 19, 21, 21.7, 27.1; SL 43.9, 64.7, 66, 70.1.

Class ARTICULATA Huxley, 1869
Order PROTREMATA Beecher, 1891
Superfamily ORTHACEA Walcott and Schuchert, 1908
Genus *Apheoorthis* Ulrich and Cooper, 1936
Apheoorthis sp.
(Pl. 15, fig. 25)

REMARKS: A fragment of a strongly fascicostate pedicle (?) valve is associated with graptolite fragments and *Problematicum* at the top of the Grove Creek Member. The species is indeterminate, but the strong ribbing indicates that it belongs to *Apheoorthis*.

OCCURRENCE: *Apheoorthis* sp. is very rare in the top of the Trempealeauan. One fragment was found at KZ 26.7.

Genus *Billingsella* Hall, 1892
Billingsella perfecta Ulrich and Cooper
(Pl. 12, fig. 24; Pl. 13, figs. 1–2, 4–5)

Billingsella coloradoensis (Shumard). WALCOTT, 1912a (part), Pl. 85, figs. 1a, 1g, 1l, 1o, 1t, 1w
Billingsella perfecta ULRICH and COOPER, 1936, p. 619; ULRICH and COOPER, 1938, p. 74–75, Pl. 7B, figs. 11–21; BELL, 1941, p. 247, Pl. 35, figs. 1–21
Billingsella radiata BELL, 1941, p. 250, Pl. 36, figs. 6–13

REMARKS: Morphology of *Billingsella perfecta* is well known from descriptions by Ulrich and Cooper (1938, p. 75) and Bell (1941, p. 247). It is distinguished from *B. plicatella* by its much flatter valves and normally finer ornamentation.

Billingsella radiata Bell falls well within the range of variation of the population of *B. perfecta,* without discontinuous characteristics. Bell now agrees (1960, personal communication) that it probably belongs to *B. perfecta.* No separate species with features of *B. radiata* was obtained from the localities where that species was described (Sections CF, BB).

In Montana and Wyoming, *B. perfecta* is present throughout the Franconian Stage above the *Elvinia* Zone.

OCCURRENCE: *Billingsella perfecta* is abundant in the *Taenicephalus* Zone at HB 73.8, 77.8; HC 11.9, 14.6; HD 84.6, 85.1, 85–88, 86.6, 90.1; HE 89.3, 90.8; HF 14.8, 15.5, 15.6; HG 47.7, 49, 51, 63.5, 65.5; HH 72.3, 82.2, 86.8, 89.3; HI 69.5; HK 77.2, 77.9, 78.7; GC 92.6, 93.5, 94.2; FC 108.6, 109.8, 112.5, 131.2; FP 123; JC 68.1, 69.6; BC 69.3, 73.3, 87.1; SP 109.9, 111.9, 112.4, 116.4, 117.4, 118.4, 122.3; BP 97.3, 98.7; BM 92.7, 96.2; FD 15.3; SC 40.1, 42.7, 43.8, 50.7, 56.7; CF 40, 46.5, 48.1, 49.2, 51.8, 56.2, 59.7, 62.3, 64.2, 65.6, 67.1, 69.6, 72.8, 74, 77; MC 116.4, 117.1; YO 73.9, 74.1, 75.7, 78.1, 79.7, 81.1, 84.3; FOX 70.9, 73.5; BB 56; GR 88.1; SL 79.8, 80.6, 81.1, 81.5, 83.1.

It is common in the *Idahoia wyomingensis* Subzone at HD 117.9, 129.4; HG 77.3, 81.3; HH 101.9, 104.9, 116.9; HI 106.5; GC 126.2, 129.6, 135.4; 141.9, 143.2, 143.7, 147.3, 151; FP 167.7; JC 116.2; BC 100, 103.6; SP 146.6, 153; RP 91.1, 94.3, 121.7, 132.2, 134.7, 136.7, 140.1; BP 131.8; MC 164.4, 168; YO 125.9, 127.2, 128.4; FOX 98.4.

It is moderately common in the *Idahoia wisconsensis* Subzone at HD 140.4; HH 128.8; BC 109.9, 116.7; SP 156; MC 170.6, and rare in the *Idahoia serapio* Subzone at HD 148.2; HH 132.8; BC 126.3, 130.5; SP 161, 163, 181.5.

Billingsella plicatella Walcott
(Pl. 11, figs. 22, 25–26)

Billingsella plicatella Walcott, 1905, p. 240; Walcott, 1912a (part), p. 759–760, Pl. 86, figs. 3, 3a–c, 3e–l (not fig. 3d: *Eoorthis* sp.); Bell, 1941, p. 248–250, Pl. 34, figs. 4–12
Billingsella alata Bell, 1941, p. 246, Pl. 34, figs. 1–3
Billingsella exasperata Bell, 1941, p. 246–247, Pl. 34, figs. 13–17

Remarks: *Billingsella plicatella* has been described by Bell (1941, p. 248–250). Present collections do not add to knowledge of morphology of the species but indicate necessity for expansion of the limits of its variability. *B. plicatella* differs from *B. perfecta* primarily by the much greater convexity of its valves and normally by its stronger costation.

Valves of *Billingsella* that have alate cardinal extremities and that fit Bell's (1941, p. 246) description of *B. "alata"* can be culled from populations of *B. perfecta* and *B. plicatella.* The degree of alation ranges continuously from that shown in Bell's illustrations (1941, Pl. 34, figs. 1–3) to a barely visible expansion of the cardinal extremities. As these alate types are not biostratigraphically segregated and can be found in two well-known species, it is deemed best to suppress *B. "alata."* Bell specified that his types are decidedly convex (1941, p. 246), and they are more properly included in *B. plicatella* than in the flat-valved *B. perfecta.*

Detailed stratigraphic collections of topotype material of *B. "exasperata"* show no segregation of these intermediately convex forms. Therefore, they are included in the variable *B. plicatella.*

Except for isolated wanderers, *B. plicatella* occurs with and near *Eoorthis.* Specimens have been found immediately below and above occurrences of *Eoorthis* and associated with it.

Occurrence: *Billingsella plicatella* is common in the *Parabolinoides* Subzone of the *Taenicephalus* Zone at HB 73.8; HC 11.9, 14.6, 30.6; HD 84.6, 85–88; HE 89.3; HF 15.5; HG 47.7, 51; HH 72.3, 74.3; HI 67.7, 69.5; HK 77.9; FC 108.6, 109.8; FP 123; JC 69.6; BC 69.3, 73.3; SP 111.9, 117.4, 118.4; BP 98.7; BM 92.7, 96.2; FD 15.3; SC 40.1, 42.7; CF 41; MC 116.4, 117.1; YO 79.7, 81.1; BB 56; SL 81.1, 81.5.

Isolated valves have been found in the *Idahoia wyomingensis* Subzone at HI 102.2 and in the *I. wisconsensis* Subzone at BC 109.9.

Genus *Eoorthis* Walcott, 1908
Eoorthis remnicha (Winchell)
(Pl. 11, figs. 10, 13; Pl. 12, fig. 27)

Orthis remnicha Winchell, 1886, p. 317, Pl. 2, fig. 7
Eoorthis remnicha (Winchell). Walcott, 1912a, p. 786, Pl. 91, figs. 1, 1a–s; Pl. 92, figs. 2, 2a–d, 3, 3a–e; Bell, 1941, p. 254, Pl. 36, figs. 14–23 (synonymy to date); Lochman and Hu, 1960, p. 810, Pl. 95, figs. 51–53; Bell and Ellinwood, 1962, p. 413, Pl. 63, figs. 10–15

Remarks: *Eoorthis remnicha* is characterized by its relatively large size (larger than *Billingsella* or *Huenella,* with which it occurs), moderate to great convexity, and many strong costae. Brachial valves from Montana and Wyoming are slightly more sulcate than those from Texas. The strong costation resembles that of *Ocnerorthis monticola* Bell, but the costae on that species are rounded in cross section whereas those of *E. remnicha* are angular or multicostellate.

This species is highly variable (Walcott, 1912a, p. 786; Bell, 1941, p. 254). Montana-Wyoming specimens can be separated into two morphologic groups, and in order to distinguish them, the less abundant form is referred to *E. remnicha* var. A.

Specimens of *E. remnicha* occur in shale at Yogo Gulch. They are smaller than typical valves from limestone and flatter. Flatness may be the result of compaction of the shale, but the small size probably is an ecologic effect. These small specimens occur at the same biostratigraphic horizon as the larger valves from limestone.

Occurrence: *Eoorthis remnicha* is common in the *Parabolinoides* Subzone of the *Taenicephalus* Zone. It has been found at HB 73.8; HC 11.9, 14.6; HD 86.6, 90.1; HE 89.3; HF

15.6; HG 47.7, 49, 51; HH 72.3; HI 67.7, 69.5; HK 77.2; GC 92.6; JC 69.6; BC 69.3; SP 109.9, 112.4, 116.4, 117.4; BP 98.7; BM 92.7; FD 15.3; SC 38.6, 40.1, 42.7; CF 34; MC 116.4, 117.1; YO 73.9, 74.1, 78.1, 79.7; FOX 65.4; BB 56; SL 76.8 (float), 76.9, 81.5.

Eoorthis remnicha variety A
(Pl. 11, figs. 16, 19)

REMARKS: *Eoorthis remnicha* variety A is smaller than typical *E. remnicha* and less convex. The major difference is in costation; *E. remnicha* var. A has few, strong costae with weak costellae between them. In Montana and Wyoming this variety occurs in the upper part of the range of the species.

This variety is similar to *Eoorthis indianola* (Walcott), but differs in having stronger costae, weaker costallae, and flatter valves. *E. indianola* occurs most abundantly at the base of the *Eoorthis* Zone in Texas (Bell and Ellinwood, 1962) whereas *E. remnicha* var. A occurs at the top of the *Eoorthis* Zone in Montana and Wyoming.

OCCURRENCE: *Eoorthis remnicha* var. A is moderately common in the upper part of the *Parabolinoides* Subzone of the *Taenicephalus* Zone: HB 73.8, 77.8; HC 14.6; HE 90.8; HF 15.6; HG 51; HH 74.3; HI 67.7; GC 93.5; JC 69.6; SP 117.4; BP 98.7; BM 92.7; SC 40.1; MC 117.1; BB 56; SL 81.5.

Genus *Finkelnburgia* Walcott, 1905
Finkelnburgia osceola (Walcott)
(Pl. 15, fig. 6)

Orthis (Finkelnburgia) osceola WALCOTT, 1905, p. 279
Finkelnburgia osceola (Walcott). WALCOTT, 1912a, p. 795, Pl. 93, figs. 1, 1a–h; ULRICH and COOPER, 1938, p. 140

REMARKS: *Finkelnburgia osceola* is characterized by its small size (largest specimen in present collection 12 mm wide), transverse but nonalate shape, fine to very fine costellae, and moderate convexity. Some valves are sulcate and more coarsely ribbed than others; larger valves are more convex.

These specimens could be placed in several of Ulrich and Cooper's species on the basis of their external morphology. They are assigned to *F. osceola* because they are convex, nonalate, and associated with Trempealeauan trilobites. Similar species of Ulrich and Cooper (1938), *e.g., F. buttsi* (p. 135, Pl. 24E), *F. missouriensis* (p. 139, Pl. 26A) are Ordovician. The only other well-known Cambrian species is *F. finkelnburgi,* the type species, which has strongly alate ventral valves.

OCCURRENCE: *Finkelnburgia osceola* is rare in the Trempealeauan at HJ 262.6; ME 29; ME 48.4; BC 205.5; BM 288.5; MC 293.5x; YO 239.7; UYO 267.6; GR 208.1.

Genus *Ocnerorthis* Bell, 1941
Ocnerorthis monticola Bell
(Pl. 10, fig. 4)

Ocnerorthis monticola BELL, 1941, p. 253–254, Pl. 37, figs. 6–15

REMARKS: Costae, low, rounded, hinge line narrow, biostratigraphic position in *Elvinia* Zone, associated with *Linnarssonella girtyi.* No interiors present, but exteriors closely comparable to Bell's specimens from Crowfoot Ridge. Three of five valves also are from Crowfoot Ridge.

OCCURRENCE: *Ocnerorthis monticola* is rare in the upper part of the *Elvinia* Zone (*Camaraspis* Subzone) at HH 70.1; JC 61.6; CF 29.2.

Genus *Otusia* Walcott, 1905
Otusia sandbergi (Winchell)
(Pl. 10, figs. 16–17)

Orthis sandbergi WINCHELL, 1886, p. 318, Pl. 2, figs. 8–9
Orthis? sandbergi Winchell. WALCOTT, 1899, p. 452, Pl. 61, figs. 2, 2a–d

Billingsella (Otusia) sandbergi (Winchell). WALCOTT, 1905, p. 246–247
Otusia sandbergi (Winchell). WALCOTT, 1912a, p. 769–770, Pl. 93, figs. 4, 4a–d; BELL, 1941, p. 251, Pl. 37, figs. 1–5; LOCHMAN and HU, 1960, p. 810, Pl. 95, figs. 45, 49

DESCRIPTION: Widely alate with moderately sulcate brachial valve, distinct but not strong costae. Brachial interior shows two shallow pallial sinuses, one on each side of sulcus, wide notothyrial cavity, and short brachiophores. One specimen has slight thickening at location of cardinal process; preservation not good enough to prove that *O. sandbergi* possesses cardinal process.

The pedicle valve is poorly known (Walcott, 1912a, p. 770; Bell, 1941, p. 251); no pedicle valves present in this collection.

OCCURRENCE: *Otusia sandbergia* is rare with *Eoorthis* in the *Parabolinoides* Subzone of the *Taenicephalus* Zone at HG 47.7; HH 72.3; YO 73.9; BB 56; SL 76.8 (float).

Superfamily SYNTROPHIACEA Schuchert and Cooper, 1931
Genus *Huenella* Walcott, 1908

TYPE SPECIES: *Syntrophia texana* WALCOTT, 1905, p. 294

REMARKS: Walcott (1912a, p. 806) and Bell (1941, p. 254) pointed out that *Huenella abnormis* intergrades with *H. texana*. They treated the two groups as separate species because "most of the individuals from Montana differ from most of those from Texas" (Bell, 1941, p. 254). However, *H. texana* is more abundant in collections from Montana here than is *H. abnormis*. They are treated separately because the variation is very great, ranging from completely smooth specimens of *H. abnormis* to completely and strongly costate specimens of *H. texana*.

Huenella abnormis (Walcott)
(Pl. 11, figs. 7, 9)

Syntrophia abnormis WALCOTT, 1905, p. 289
Huenella abnormis (Walcott). WALCOTT, 1912a, p. 805, Pl. 103, figs. 2a–m (not fig. 2: *H. texana*); BELL, 1941, p. 254, Pl. 36, figs. 1–3 (synonymy to date); BELL and ELLINWOOD, 1962, p. 415, Pl. 64, figs. 14–17

DESCRIPTION: Fold strong, sulcus costate or nearly smooth, flanks of both valves smooth. This species is one end member of an intergrading population, of which *H. texana* forms the other extreme. Only those specimens with completely smooth flanks are classified as *H. abnormis*.

OCCURRENCE: *Huenella abnormis* is rare in the *Parabolinoides* Subzone of the *Taenicephalus* Zone at HB 77.8; HH 74.3; HI 69.5; JC 69.6; SP 111.9; SP 117.4; BP 98.7.

Huenella texana (Walcott)
(Pl. 11, figs. 6, 8)

Camarella sp. ? SHUMARD, 1861, p. 221
Syntrophia texana WALCOTT, 1905, p. 294
Huenella texana (Walcott). WALCOTT, 1912a, p. 808, Pl. 103, figs. 1, 1a, 1e–i, 2 (1b–d indeterminate, probably *H. abnormis*); SCHUCHERT and COOPER, 1932, p. 159–160; CLOUD and BARNES, 1948, Pl. 38, figs. 39–41; BELL and ELLINWOOD, 1962, p. 415, Pl. 64, figs. 18–20

REMARKS: *Huenella texana* is distinguished by the presence of costae on the flanks of the valves; costae vary from few and weak to many and strong.

OCCURRENCE: *Huenella texana* is moderately common in the *Parabolinoides* Subzone of the *Taenicephalus* Zone at HB 73.8; HD 86.6, 90.1; HE 90.8; HF 15.5; HG 49, 51; GC 94.2; FP 123; BC 69.3; SC 40.1; GR 74.1.

Huenella texana var. *fortis* Grant n.var.
(Pl. 10, fig. 14)

REMARKS: *Huenella texana* var. *fortis* differs from typical *H. texana* in its slightly more alate shape and much stronger costation. Its ribbing is as strong as that of *Eoorthis rem-*

nicha, and with its deep sulcus and wide "wings" it bears superficial resemblance to much younger brachiopods such as species of *Platystrophia.*

This variety has been found only in the *Irvingella major* Zonule at one locality. If further collecting shows it to be more than an abnormal individual, it should be considered a species of *Huenella* separate from *H. texana.*

HOLOTYPE: USNM 142327, Plate 10, figure 14

ETYMOLOGY: *Fortis,* L. strong, referring to strong costation.

OCCURRENCE: *Huenella texana* var. *fortis* is rare in the *Irvingella major* Zonule at the top of the *Elvinia* Zone at YO 69.4.

Phylum MOLLUSCA Cuvier, 1797
Class GASTROPODA Cuvier, 1797
Subclass INCERTAE SEDIS
Genus *Pelagiella* Matthew, 1895
Pelagiella primordialis (Hall)
(Pl. 11, fig. 27)

Platyceras primordialis HALL, 1863, p. 136, Pl. 6, fig. 28; WALCOTT, 1899, p. 453, Pl. 63, fig. 1

REMARKS: This small gastropod has about one and one-half widely expanding whorls. The periphery is sharply rounded; the shell is slightly flattened on one side, making the coiling slightly asymmetrical.

Pelagiella is typically more loosely coiled than *Platyceras;* none of the whorls of *Pelagiella* are in contact, and it has no keel. Franconian specimens conform more closely to the generic characters of *Pelagiella* than to those of *Platyceras.*

OCCURRENCE: *Pelagiella primordialis* is common to rare in the *Taenicephalus* Zone at HD 86.6, 112.1; HE 90.8; HI 69.5; FP 123; BC 73.3; SP 111.9, 117.4; FD 15.3; CF 62.3, 64.2.

Subclass PROSOBRANCHIA Milne-Edwards, 1848
Order ARCHEOGASTROPODA Thiele, 1925
Genus *Sinuella* Knight, 1947
Sinuella vaticina (Hall)
(Pl. 13, figs. 28–30)

Euomphalus ? vaticinus HALL, 1863, p. 136, Pl. 6, fig. 29

DESCRIPTION: Shell small (0.5–2.0 mm diameter), planispiral, with two to four narrowly and evenly expanding whorls in close contact, suture depressed, dorsum gently rounded or flattened, no keel, shoulder slight, aperture asymmetrically oval or subquadrate in cross section.

REMARKS: This species is assigned to *Sinuella* on the basis of its flattened dorsum, which Knight (1947, p. 8) says is the feature that distinguishes this genus from other bellerophont gastropods. *S. vaticina* is distinguished from *S. minuta* Knight, the type species, by its larger size, fewer whorls (up to six in *S. minuta*), and primarily by the flattened but not concave dorsum.

S. vaticina is preserved in the Snowy Range Formation as glauconitized or illitized steinkerns; they are the noticeable and characteristic "little green snails" of the *Idahoia* Zone. Others occur as calcareous shells that may be the original shell, or more probably calcite replacement of original shell material; these are more abundant. Specimens preserved in both ways appear in acetic acid residues.

Lochman and Hu (1959, p. 425) report a similar species (*Anconochilus idahoensis* Lochman and Hu) from the *Ptychaspis* fauna of the Bear River Range, Idaho. *S. vaticina* differs in its flattened or flatly rounded dorsum and greater number of whorls. The two species probably are congeneric, and careful detailed study and comparison are required to determine which generic assignment is correct.

This abundant and biostratigraphically restricted snail is a good indicator of the upper part of the Franconian Stage: it does not occur outside the *Idahoia* Zone. Bell and Ellinwood (1962) report the similar *S. minuta* Knight from the same biostratigraphic level in central Texas.

OCCURRENCE: *Sinuella vaticina* is common throughout the *Idahoia* Zone at HA 45.8; HD 115.4, 116.7, 121.1, 125.1, 127.6, 129.4, 130.6, 131.6, 140.4, 144.2; HE 102.1, 115.4; HG 77.3, 79.3, 81.3; HH 100.5, 103.4, 104.9, 106.4, 124.4; HI 102.2, 106.5, 111.8, 115.8, 121.2; HK 109.1, 111.2, 126.2, 127.5, 132.2, 135.4, 137.3; FC 142.7, 143.2, 143.7, 144.6, 147.3, 148, 151; FP 158.5, 159.9, 167.7, 176.7, 179.5; JC 101.6, 105.1, 106.6, 109.4, 115.2, 120; BC 100, 103.6, 106.4, 109.9, 114.2, 116.7, 120.6; SP 146.6, 150.6, 153.4, 156, 161, 163; RP 84.9, 89.6, 91.1, 92.5, 94.3, 121.7, 132.2, 134.7, 136.7, 139.7, 140.1, 144.6, 146.1; BP 123.8, 138.2, 156.8, 161.2; BM 140.9, 148.1, 150.6, 153.9, 156.9, 158.8, 161.2, 163.8, 166.3, 190.2; MC 155, 158.6, 164.1, 164.4, 170.6, 178, 179.8; YO 122.3, 127.2, 130.2, 135.7, 137.7; FOX 118.6, 163.1; SL 131, 132.4; BB 117.3.

Phosphatic balls
(Pl. 13, figs. 31–32)

REMARKS: Small, irregular, hollow phosphatic balls appear in many acetic acid residues from beds that contain specimens of *Sinuella vaticina*. Possibly they are egg cases from these small gastropods.

The association of phosphatic balls with *Sinuella vaticina* is so consistent that the presence of the balls is as good an indicator of the *Idahoia* Zone as the gastropod itself.

OCCURRENCE: Phosphatic balls are common in the *Idahoia* Zone, associated with *Sinuella vaticina*. No detailed listing of occurrences is given, but their presence is recorded along with that of other fossils in descriptions of measured sections.

Genus *Lytospira* Koken, 1896
Lytospira ? sp.
(Pl. 13, fig. 26)

REMARKS: Small (up to 1 mm), hollow, openly coiled fragments of gastropods resemble species of *Lytospira*. Normally less than one whorl is preserved, but apertures preserved on some specimens display a V-shaped notch. These fragments are too poorly preserved and not sufficiently abundant to warrant more than tentative generic identification.

OCCURRENCE: *Lytospira* ? sp. is rare in the *Idahoia wyomingensis* Subzone at HD 117.9; BC 116.7; SP 144.3; BM 131.6; SL 123; in the *Idahoia serapio* Subzone at HD 148.2; BC 130.5; SP 181.5; YO 170; and in the *Prosaukia* Zone at BM 205.6.

Class INCERTAE SEDIS
Genus *Hyolithes* Eichwald, 1840
Hyolithes primordialis (Hall)
(Pl. 9, fig. 26)

Theca primordialis HALL, 1861, p. 48; HALL, 1862, p. 21, fig. 5
Hyolithes primordialis (Hall). WALCOTT, 1899, p. 454, Pl. 63, figs. 2, 2a (synonymy to date); LOCHMAN, 1940, p. 23, Pl. 2, figs. 8–9 (synonymy to date)

DESCRIPTION: Shell normally one-half inch to 1 inch long, straight-sided, evenly tapered; venter broadly rounded (semicircular), faintly carinate; dorsally flat, gently concave or gently convex, with abruptly rounded edges where dorsal and ventral sides join.

REMARKS: This species has been reported from the Middle Cambrian Flathead Formation in and around Yellowstone Park (Walcott, 1899, p. 454) and from the *Cedaria* and *Crepicephalus* zones of Wisconsin (Shimer and Shrock, 1944, p. 525). It cannot be recognized from illustrations by Hall (1862, Pl. 21, fig. 5; 1863, Pl. 6, figs, 30–31), but Walcott's illustration and description (1899, p. 454, Pl. 63, figs. 2, 2a) make the identification fairly certain.

H. primordialis differs from *H. princeps* Billings (1872; described, illustrated, and compared in Walcott, 1886, p. 135, Pl. 13, figs. 5, 5a, 5b) of the Lower Cambrian chiefly by its smaller size and weaker growth lines that encircle the shell evenly without arching anteriorly over the venter. *H. primordialis* differs from *H. attenuatus* Walcott (1891, p. 269, Pl. 20, figs. 11, 11a) from the Upper Cambrian of Nevada by its larger angle of taper (about 15°, versus less than 10° in *H. attenuatus*) and lack of a narrow longitudinal dorsal groove.

OCCURRENCE: *Hyolithes primordialis* is locally common in the *Elvinia* Zone in the matrix around the columns of *Collenia magna* at HG 36, 79.3; NG 48; SL 65, and in the Trempealeauan at BC 205.5.

Phylum ARTHROPODA Siebold and Stannius, 1845
Class TRILOBITA Walch, 1771
Order AGNOSTIDA Kobayashi, 1935
Family AGNOSTIDAE McCoy, 1849
Genus *Geragnostus* Howell, 1935
Geragnostus ? insolitus Grant n. sp.
(Pl. 15, figs. 9–10, 12)

DESCRIPTION: Cephalon longer than wide; glabella bilobed, with deep dorsal and glabellar furrows, anterior lobe of glabella almost hemispherical, posterior lobe indented by rudimentary furrows; basal glabellar lobes each with prominent node; preglabellar median furrow moderately deep, extending from anterior of glabella to marginal furrow; border unknown.

Pygidium slightly wider than long, very convex; axial lobe narrow, slightly more than two-thirds length of pygidium, slightly constricted at posterior glabellar furrow, giving axial lobe an hourglass shape; posterior axial lobe evenly downsloping posteriorly; axial node on second segment, completely separated from anterior segment by axial furrow extending across axis; anterior axial segment trilobed; pleural lobes steeply downsloping; marginal furrow moderately impressed; border wide, slightly convex; margin with one pair of minute spines.

HOLOTYPE: USNM 142403, Plate 15, figure 10

ETYMOLOGY: *Insolitus*, L., unusual

REMARKS: *Geragnostus* ? *insolitus* differs from species of *Geragnostus* by its complete preglabellar median furrow. The pygidium differs from that of *G. brevis* Palmer in its proportionately shorter, narrower, and less swollen axial lobe.

OCCURRENCE: *Geragnostus* ? *insolitus* is common in the Trempealeauan at MC 293.5; rare at YO 269.3.

Genus *Homagnostus* Howell, 1935
Homagnostus cf. *H. tumidosus* (Hall and Whitfield)
(Pl. 8, fig. 26; Pl. 9, fig. 1)

Agnostus tumidosus HALL and WHITFIELD, 1877, p. 231, Pl. 1, fig. 32; WALCOTT, 1899, p. 455, Pl. 63, figs. 5, 5a
Geragnostus cf. *G. tumidosus* (Hall and Whitfield). PALMER, 1955a, p. 719, Pl. 76, figs. 4, 6
Geragnostus tumidosus (Hall and Whitfield). PALMER, 1955b, p. 89, Pl. 19, figs. 3–4, Pl. 20, figs. 1–3, 12, 15
Homagnostus tumidosus (Hall and Whitfield). PALMER, 1960, p. 63, Pl. 4, figs. 1–2; BELL and ELLINWOOD, 1962, p. 388, Pl. 51, figs. 1–4

REMARKS: A pair of immature pygidia characterized by high convexity and straight-sided axial lobes are assigned tentatively to *H. tumidosus*. The axial node is near the posterior of the axis, but according to Palmer's analysis of the ontogeny of the species, later molts would show the posterior portion of the axis more inflated and elongate, as in typical *H. tumidosus*. These pygidia closely resemble Palmer's illustration of an immature pygidium of *H. tumidosus* (1955b, Pl. 20, fig. 1). A cephalon from YO 65.9 also is assigned to this species on the basis of its incomplete anterior glabellar furrow.

OCCURRENCE: *Homagnostus* cf. *H. tumidosus* is rare in the *Elvinia* Zone at HG 47.5; YO 65.9.

Homagnostus sp.
(Pl. 15, figs. 13–14)

REMARKS: Several pygidia are identified as a species of *Homagnostus* on the basis of the proportionately broad axial lobe, prominent axial node, and pair of small marginal spines.

No cephala were collected, so the species is indeterminate. Pygidia in the Trempealeauan doubtfully belong to *H. tumidosus* (Hall and Whitfield) which normally occurs lower in the section (Palmer, 1955a, 1960).

OCCURRENCE: *Homagnostus* sp. is rare in the Trempealeauan at BG 192.6, 205.5.

Family PSEUDAGNOSTIDAE Whitehouse, 1936
Genus *Pseudagnostus* Jaekel, 1909
Pseudagnostus josephus (Hall)
(Pl. 13, figs. 13–14)

Agnostus josepha HALL, 1863, p. 178, Pl. 6, figs. 54–55
Pseudagnostus josepha (Hall). KOBAYASHI, 1935b, p. 108; NELSON, 1951, p. 776, Pl. 107, fig. 5 (synonymy to date); BELL, FENIAK, and KURTZ, 1952, p. 196, Pl. 32, figs. 4a–b, Pl. 33, fig. 1; WILSON, 1954, p. 284, Pl. 25, figs. 5, 22

REMARKS: *Pseudagnostus josephus* is distinguished by the high relief of its axial features. The posterior glabellar segment is high, and the axial node at the anterior termination of this segment is just a little higher. The anterior of the axial node slopes steeply to the lower and flatter anterior glabellar lobe; the margin of the pygidium is smooth, without spines.

P. josephus is common in the *Conaspis* and *Ptychaspis* zones in Minnesota and Wisconsin (Nelson, 1951, p. 769, 777; Bell, Feniak, and Kurtz, 1952, p. 177, 196–197, Grant, 1962, p. 982, Table 2), as well as in Montana and Wyoming.

OCCURRENCE: *Pseudagnostus josephus* is moderately common in the *Taenicephalus* Zone at HG 63.5, 65.5; FC 131.2; RP 136.7; in the *Idahoia wyomingensis* Subzone at HD 129.4; HG 77.3; HI 115.8; HK 111.2; GC 135.4; FC 143.7, 148.8; JC 103.6; MC 155; in the *Idahoia wisconsensis* Subzone at HH 124.4; FP 176.7; RP 146.1; MC 170.6; and in the *Idahoia serapio* Subzone at HD 146.2; HH 128.8; BC 130.5; MC 178.

Pseudagnostus cf. *P. laevis* Palmer
(Pl. 14, fig. 34–35)

Pseudagnostus laevis PALMER, 1955b, p. 97–98, Pl. 19, figs. 8–9, 11–12

REMARKS: Presence of this species in Montana is indicated by one cranidium and one pygidium. The pygidium is characterized by deep furrows outlining the axial lobe and by two circular muscle scars on the anterior portion of the pseudolobe. Palmer states that the pseudolobe of *P. laevis* is not defined by furrows, but the accessory furrows are present, although weak, on these specimens. Certain identification is impossible because the specimens are exfoliated.

OCCURRENCE: *Pseudagnostus* cf. *P. laevis* is very rare in the Trempealeauan at BM 249.2; YO 240.7.

Pseudagnostus sentosus Grant n.sp.
(Pl. 9, figs. 2–3, 5)

REMARKS: *Pseudagnostus sentosus* is characterized by its shallow cranidial and pygidial furrows that result in relatively smooth shields, and by a pair of minute spines on the margin of the pygidium. It differs from *P. communis* (Hall and Whitfield) by its shallow surface markings although that species has marginal pygidial spines (Palmer, 1955b, p. 94). Both *P. josephus* (Hall) and *P. prolongus* (Hall and Whitfield) have shallow surface markings, but according to Kobayashi (1939, p. 158) *P. josephus* lacks pygidial spines, as does *P. prolongus* according to Palmer (1960, p. 61).

Bell and Ellinwood (1962) recognize a species with characteristics similar to those of *P. sentosus* which they ascribe to *P. communis,* but which occurs in a higher stratigraphic position. *P. sentosus* may be the species referred to by Palmer (1960, p. 61) as the species in the Windfall Formation which has a "cephalon that is indistinguishable from *P. prolongus* but with a pygidium that has marginal spines."

HOLOTYPE: USNM 142284, Plate 9, figure 5

ETYMOLOGY: *Sentosus,* L. thorny: the pygidium has marginal spines.

OCCURRENCE: *Pseudagnostus sentosus* is common in the *Elvinia* Zone at HC 6.5; HG 45.8, 47.5; HH 68.9; BC 63.8; SP 106, 108.6; CF 21.2; YO 65.9; in the *Taenicephalus* Zone at HG 63.5, 65.5; SP 109; GR 74.1; in the *Idahoia wyomingensis* Subzone at KD 125.1, 136.9; HG 77.3, 81.3; HH 104.9, 106.4, 116.4; HI 106.5, 115.8, 121.2; GC 126.2; FC 146.2, 147.3, 151, 167.7; JC 106.6; BC 103.6, 106.4; SP 153.4; RP 89.6, 91.1, 92.5, 94.3, 132.2, 140.1; BM 144.4; MC 155; YO 125.9; in the *Idahoia wisconsensis* Subzone at HD 140.4; HH 124.4; HI 124.3; FP 176.7, 179.5; BC 109.9, 114.2, 116.7; SP 156; RP 144.6, 146.1; BM 150.8, 153.9; MC 170.6; YO 135.7; and in the *Idahoia serapio* Subzone at HD 146.2, 148.2; HH 128.8, 132.8; SP 161, 163; BP 161.2; BM 156.9; MC 185.3.

Order PTYCHOPARIIDA Swinnerton, 1915

Family ANOMOCARIDAE Poulsen, 1927

Genus *Monocheilus* Resser, 1937

Monocheilus demissus Grant n.sp.

(Pl. 14, figs. 10, 14)

DESCRIPTION: Cranidium elongate quadrangular; glabella elongate, slightly tapered; glabellar furrows commonly absent, faint posterior pair visible on some specimens; occipital furrow straight, moderately impressed; occipital ring flat, uniformly wide across axis in most specimens, but slightly produced posteriorly at axis in some; frontal area convex, downsloping; brim convex, downsloping; marginal furrow very shallow, invisible on some specimens; border very narrow, continuing downslope of brim; palpebral lobes long and narrow; fixed cheeks narrow; posterior limbs long and narrow.

Free cheeks as in *M. anatinus* (Hall), illustrated by Bell, Feniak, and Kurtz (1952, Pl. 33, fig. 5b), and *Monocheilus* sp., illustrated by Lochman (1950a, Pl. 46, figs. 8–10). Pygidium unknown.

HOLOTYPE: USNM 142289, Plate 14, figure 10

ETYMOLOGY: *Demissus,* L. drooping; referring to the downsloping frontal area

REMARKS: *Monocheilus demissus* is like *M. anatinus* (Hall) in every feature except the downsloping frontal area, shallow marginal furrow, and tiny border. The frontal area of *M. anatinus* is not divided into brim and border, and although it is convex, it is horizontal, and its posterior junction with the glabella is farther below the anterior crest of the glabella.

OCCURRENCE: *Monocheilus demissus* is rare in the *Idahoia wyomingensis* Subzone at HD 131.6; HI 115.8; FC 151; in the *I. wisconsensis* Subzone at FP 179.5; BC 116.7; SP 156; RP 146.1; BM 150.8; and in the *I. serapio* Subzone at SP 161.

Monocheilus cf. *M. truncatus* Ellinwood

(Pl. 14, fig. 39)

Monocheilus truncatus ELLINWOOD, *in* BELL and ELLINWOOD, 1962, p. 389, Pl. 52, figs. 1–3

REMARKS: Montana specimens are comparable to Ellinwood's types in their quadrate truncate glabellas and long palpebral lobes. Identification is tentative because frontal areas are missing.

OCCURRENCE: *Monocheilus* cf. *M. truncatus* is rare in the Trempealeauan at BM 284.

Family CHEILOCEPHALIDAE Shaw, 1956

Genus *Cheilocephalus* Berkey, 1898

Cheilocephalus sp. undet.

(Pl. 8, fig. 27)

REMARKS: One fragmentary cranidium too poor for specific identification is characterized by a moderately convex and lightly furrowed glabella, very short frontal area, smooth outer surface, and bluntly tapered posterior limb. The posterior limb corresponds in shape to that of the left posterior limb of *C. buttsi* Resser (1942b, Pl. 11, fig. 6), but the specimen here differs from that species in its smooth outer surface.

OCCURRENCE: One cranidium of *Cheilocephalus* sp. was found in the *Elvinia* Zone at BB 49.5.

Family Dikelocephalidae Miller, 1889
Genus *Briscoia* Walcott, 1924
Briscoia dalyi (Walcott)
(Pl. 15, fig. 3–5)

Dikelocephalus ? dalyi Walcott, 1914a, p. 367–368, Pl. 64, figs. 1, 1a (not figs. 2, 4: *Briscoia platyfrons* Ulrich and Resser, 1930; not fig. 5: species unknown according to Ulrich and Resser, 1930, p. 61, footnote)

Briscoia dalyi (Walcott). Ulrich and Resser, 1930, p. 61–62; Kobayashi, 1935a, p. 50–51

Description: Cranidium characterized by convex, anteriorly truncate glabella with tapered sides slightly bowed outward, single pair of glabellar furrows joining on axial line, but not reaching dorsal furrow. Palpebral lobes slightly posterior to midline of glabella; occipital ring widest part of glabella, well defined, flat, uniform in width. Posterior limbs strong and wide, sharply tapered anterior to furrow. Frontal area smoothly convex, about one fourth length of cranidium, on some specimens (*e.g.*, type specimen) possessing faint line marking position of marginal furrow.

Remarks: A pygidium from UYO 216.9 belonging to a species of *Briscoia* on the basis of its straight anterior margin, irregular pleural furrows, and prominent postaxial ridge, is tentatively assigned to *B. dalyi,* although not associated with cranidia of that species.

Briscoia dalyi is distingushed from species of *Dikelocephalus* by its longer, more tapered and truncate glabella, smaller, more anteriorly located palpebral lobes, and its much stronger posterior limbs with the anterior part abruptly tapered. It differs from other species of *Briscoia* by the bowed sides of its glabella and relatively short frontal area.

Occurrence: *Briscoia dalyi* is rare in the lower part of the Trempealeauan. Cranidia have been found at ME 31.1; UFOX 55, pygidia at FOX 183.1; UYO 216.9, and a doubtful free cheek at FOX 183.1.

Genus *Dikelocephalus* Owen, 1852
Dikelocephalus sp. undet.
(Pl. 15, figs. 1–2)

Remarks: One well-preserved cranidium and several fragmentary cranidia and pygidia of a species of *Dikelocephalus* are present in this collection. The cranidium has a convex glabella, large palpebral lobes with strong, arcuate palpebral furrows, a concave brim, and upturned convex border. It resembles *D. "thwaitesi"* or *D. "norwalkensis"* of Ulrich and Resser (1930, p. 52–55, Pl. 21), both of which are considered by Raasch (1951, p. 141) to be synonymous with *D. oweni* Ulrich and Resser. Its closest affinities seem to be with *D. freeburgensis* Feniak (*in* Bell, Feniak, and Kurtz, 1952, p. 195, Pls. 35, 38). It is not assigned even tentatively to any of these species because of the fragmentary nature of the material and the obscure status and definition of species of *Dikelocephalus.*

Occurrence: *Dikelocephalus* sp. is rare in the Trempealeauan. A well-preserved cranidium was found at BM 249.2; fragmentary cranidia and pygidia at BM 249.2; FOX 222.9.

Family Dokimocephalidae Kobayashi, 1935
Genus *Burnetiella* Lochman, 1958
Burnetiella ectypa (Resser)
(Pl. 8, figs. 22, 24)

Burnetia ectypa Resser, 1942b, p. 82, Pl. 17, figs. 30–31

Remarks: This species, originally described from the Honey Creek Formation of Oklahoma, is characterized by its large size, moderately high convex glabella with rather shallow to deep glabellar furrows, elongate and somewhat downsloping frontal area which is slightly convex immediately anterior to the glabella and just behind the anterior margin, and by its granulose outer surface, with rather coarse granules on the glabella and somewhat finer ones on the frontal area. Wilson (1951, p. 625) concluded from statistical considerations that glabellar convexity is not a valid criterion for distinguishing species of *Burnetiella,* and for this reason included *B. ectypa* in the synonymy of *B. urania* (Walcott), the type species.

Glabellar convexity alone is insufficient basis for specific distinctions in this genus; however, in combination with the several other features of *B. ectypa,* it is easily distinguished from *B. urania.*

The frontal area of the specimen (Pl. 8, fig. 24) is rather short and has only fine granules because it is broken and exfoliated. Identification of present specimens with *B. ectypa* is based upon examination of the holotypes of *B. urania* and of the ten species described by Resser (1942b).

OCCURRENCE: *Burnetiella ectypa* is rare in the *Elvinia* Zone at HD 80.8; HF 8.7 (pyg.); HG 36, 45.8, 47.5; GC 63; FC 86 (pyg.), 93.7; FP 88; BC 63.8; SP 106, 108.6; BM 88.1; SC 27; CF 19; BB 49.5; GR 10.7.

Genus *Dokimocephalus* Walcott, 1924

Dokimocephalus intermedius (Resser)

(Pl. 9, figs. 29, 32)

Burnetia intermedia RESSER, 1942b, p. 80, Pl. 17, figs. 10–11

Dokimocephalus intermedius (Resser). WILSON, 1951, p. 640, Pl. 90, fig. 25 (synonymy to date)

DESCRIPTION: Border long, spatulate, bluntly terminated; anterior facial sutures converging uniformly, without marked constriction of extension of border that is present in *D. curta* (Resser).

OCCURRENCE: One well-preserved cranidium of *Dokimocephalus intermedius* has been found in the *Elvinia* Zone at GR 10.7, and one free cheek at HD 80.4.

Genus *Kindbladia* Frederickson, 1948

Kindbladia cf. *K. wichitaensis* (Resser)

(Pl. 8, fig. 23)

Berkeia wichitaensis RESSER, 1942b, p. 92, Pl. 15, figs. 31–33

Kindbladia wichitaensis (Resser). FREDERICKSON, 1948, p. 802, Pl. 123, figs. 20–23; WILSON, 1951, p. 645, Pl. 92, figs. 23–24 (synonymy to date)

DESCRIPTION: Fixed cheeks narrow, dorsal and glabellar furrows deep, glabella flat and sunken. One specimen with minute granules on fixed cheeks and posterior limbs, but not on glabella. Anterior of cranidium not preserved on any specimen, so not known whether granules present on frontal area. It appears to have had an occipital spine, which contrasts it to *K. affinis* (Walcott).

OCCURRENCE: *Kindbladia* cf. *K. wichitaensis* is rare in the *Elvinia* Zone at FP 88; BL 47.7; MC 105.4.

Genus *Kyphocephalus* Miller, 1936

Kyphocephalus bridgerensis Miller

(Pl. 9, fig. 31)

Kyphocephalus bridgerensis MILLER, 1936, p. 32, Pl. 8, figs. 30–33

REMARKS: A single large cranidium of *Kyphocephalus* from Nixon Gulch is referred to *K. bridgerensis* on the basis of the low convexity of the glabella. It is somewhat larger than typical for the species and more nearly the size of *K. ponderosus* Wilson. The specimen has a wide deep dorsal furrow and very weak ocular ridges, which also are features of *K. ponderosus.* Morphologically, intermediate specimens such as this suggest that *K. bridgerensis* and *K. ponderosus* may not be distinct.

OCCURRENCE: *Kyphocephalus bridgerensis* is very rare in the *Elvinia* Zone at Nixon Gulch (NG "top of reef"). The one known specimen was collected by C. Lochman.

Kyphocephalus ? sp.

(Pl. 9, fig. 28)

DESCRIPTION: Species characterized by high bulbous glabella and steeply downsloping frontal area consisting of narrow convex brim and narrow convex border with transverse striations. Fixed cheeks about one-half width of glabella; surface of glabella covered with minute granules. Anterior facial sutures flare outwards, as is typical of species of *Kyphocephalus.*

REMARKS: Several small cranidia from the *Elvinia* Zone probably belong to a species of *Kyphocephalus.* They differ from *K. bridgerensis* Miller in having high bulbous glabellas with very faint glabellar furrows. They are close to *K. ponderosus* Wilson (1951, p. 646, Pl. 93, especially fig. 19), but differ in their higher glabellas and much smaller size.

OCCURRENCE: *Kyphocephalus* ? sp. is rare in the *Elvinia* Zone at HF 8.7 and BC 63.8.

Genus *Pinctus* Wilson, 1951

REMARKS: Two species are assigned doubtfully to *Pinctus* because of their resemblance to the type species *P. latus* Wilson (1951, p. 646, Pl. 93, figs. 1–4, 15). That species, however, is broadly constituted, with the holotype bearing little resemblance to one of the paratypes (Fig. 15). The genus seems to be an assemblage of small, *Sulcocephalus*-like trilobites whose characteristics are sufficiently different from those of *Sulcocephalus* to preclude assignment to that genus. Therefore, the two species are referred only tentatively.

Pinctus ? *artus* Grant n.sp.
(Pl. 8, fig. 19)

? *Berkeia* sp. FREDERICKSON, 1949, p. 347, Pl. 68, fig. 20

DESCRIPTION: Cranidium small (1.5–2.5 mm long), wider than long, moderately convex; glabella truncate, tapered evenly or slightly bulged at posterior glabellar furrows; two or three sets of glabellar furrows, posterior pair moderately impressed, anterior pair weak or absent; occipital furrow deeper at sides than at axis, bent slightly forward at axis making occipital ring thicker than at sides; frontal area flat and moderately downsloping at axis, more steeply downsloping anterolaterally; brim flat or very slightly concave; border very slightly raised and very slightly convex, continuing downslope of brim; no true marginal furrow, line of juncture between brim and border arcuate, either parallel to anterior margin or intersecting it at anterior corners of cranidium, producing a crescentic border; facial sutures straight or slightly divergent anterior to eyes; fixed cheeks not more than half as wide as glabella; ocular ridges present; eyes near midline of glabella; posterior limbs extended, tapering, downsloping. Free cheeks and pygidium unknown.

HOLOTYPE: USNM 142271, Plate 8, figure 19

ETYMOLOGY: *Artus,* L. narrow, referring to the fixed cheeks which are narrower than in *P. latus.*

REMARKS: *Pinctus* ? *artus* differs from *P. latus* Wilson (1951, p. 646, Pl. 93, figs. 1–4, 15) and *P.* ? *pullus* n.sp. by its tapered glabella, narrower fixed cheeks, and especially by its flat, evenly downsloping frontal area with only very slightly raised border. It differs from species of *Sulcocephalus* by its truncate glabella, shallower dorsal furrow, less arcuate anterior margin, and especially by its flat to concave brim. One specimen of *P.* ? *artus* is only slightly smaller than a specimen of *Sulcocephalus granulosus,* substantiating Wilson's (1951, p. 646) contention that *Pinctus* is not merely an immature *Sulcocephalus* (*olim Berkeia*).

OCCURRENCE: *P.* ? *artus* is rare in the *Elvinia* Zone. Ten cranidia were found at HG 36, one at HG 45.8, one at HG 47.5, and one at HH 68.9.

Pinctus ? *pullus* Grant n.sp.
(Pl. 14, figs. 18–19)

DESCRIPTION: Cranidium small (average: 1 mm), length about equal to width, convex; glabella elongate, slightly tapered, elevated, rounded-truncate anteriorly, marked by three or four pairs of very faint glabellar furrows at sides of glabella; occipital furrow well impressed; occipital ring produced posteriorly into slight node; dorsal furrow deeper at sides of glabella than at anterior; frontal area short; brim flatly convex or concave, slightly downsloping; border equal to or wider than brim, upturned, crescentic; fixed cheeks about two thirds as wide as glabella, very convex; palpebral lobes small, situated just anterior to mid-line of glabella; posterior limbs almost as wide as occipital ring; surface of carapace finely granulose.

Pygidium semicircular; axial lobe prominent, broad, with three or four segments, extended at posterior to form low ridge across border, reaching margin; border broad, gently flexed, lightly striated, striations stronger on exfoliated specimens; pleural segments short, narrow, in low relief. Free cheeks unknown.

HOLOTYPE: USNM 142300, Plate 14, figure 18

ETYMOLOGY: *Pullus,* L. young, indicating that this species occurs higher in the section than do other known species of *Pinctus.*

REMARKS: The upturned border and finely granulose surface distinguish *P.* ? *pullus* from *P.* ? *artus* and indicate possible relationship with *P. latus* Wilson. It is distinguished from *P. latus* by its much shallower glabellar furrow, less downsloping frontal area, and more elongate glabella. It is similar to *Phoreotropis* ? *marginata* Rasetti (1945, p. 471, Pl. 61, figs. 28–29) from which it is distinguished by its finely granulose surface, lack of ocular ridges, less downsloping frontal area with more sharply upturned border, straight, not anteriorly bowed, occipital furrow, and wider fixed cheeks.

OCCURRENCE: *Pinctus* ? *pullus* is moderately common in the *Idahoia serapio* Subzone at HD 140.4, 146.2, 148.2; HH 128.8; BC 126.3.

Genus *Sulcocephalus* Wilson, 1948

Sulcocephalus WILSON, 1948, p. 30; WILSON and FREDERICKSON, 1950, p. 896; LOCHMAN, 1958, p. 247; LOCHMAN, *in* HARRINGTON and OTHERS, 1959, p. 0281
Berkeia RESSER, 1937, p. 3, (*B. typica* only)

REMARKS: Lochman (1953a, p. 888) considers species of *Sulcocephalus* congeneric with species assigned to *Berkeia.* She finds (*in* Harrington and others, 1959, p. 0256, 0281) that the name *Berkeia* is an objective synonym of *Camaraspis* Ulrich, and that the previously rejected name *Sulcocephalus* must be revived.

Sulcocephalus granulosus (Wilson)
(Pl. 8, fig. 21)

Berkeia granulosa WILSON, 1951, p. 624, Pl. 89, figs. 3–6

REMARKS: This species is recognized by its granulose outer surface, deep furrows, and "slightly notched" brim (Wilson, 1951). The wide fixed cheeks distinguish it from species of *Kindbladia* Frederickson.

OCCURRENCE: *Sulcocephalus granulosus* was found in the *Elvinia* Zone at HG 36; YG 3.4a

Sulcocephalus sp. undet. 1

REMARKS: One specimen of a species of *Sulcocephalus* was found associated with *Irvingella major* and *Comanchia lippa.* It is too fragmentary to describe or illustrate, but it most resembles *S. candida* (Resser), which has been reported from the same biostratigraphic level in central Texas and the upper Mississippi Valley (Wilson and Frederickson, 1950). It is mentioned to record presence of a similar, possibly the same, species at this level.

OCCURRENCE: One cranidium of *Sulcocephalus* sp. 1 was found in the *Irvingella major* Zonule at MC 111.7.

Sulcocephalus sp. undet. 2
(Pl. 8, fig. 20)

REMARKS: Three poorly preserved specimens are referable to *Sulcocephalus.* They resemble *S. occidentalis* (Lochman, 1950a, p. 332, Pl. 48, figs. 1–10) and *Berkeia* sp. (Frederickson, 1949, p. 347, Pl. 68, fig. 21) in their small size and rather straight (for *Sulcocephalus*) anterior margins.

OCCURRENCE: Specimens of *Sulcocephalus* sp. 2 were found in the *Elvinia* Zone, one in each of localities HG 47.5; SP 108.6; and GR 10.7.

Family ELVINIIDAE Kobayashi, 1935
Genus *Drumaspis* Resser, 1942

Drumaspis RESSER, 1942b, p. 28

TYPE SPECIES: *Drumaspis walcotti* RESSER, 1942b, p. 28–29, Pl. 4, figs. 37–41

DESCRIPTION: Glabella convex, quadrate, fixed cheeks wide, downsloping; palpebral lobes large with distinct palpebral furrows; posterior limbs long and wide, sloping steeply downward; frontal area short, consisting of short brim, shallow marginal furrow, and convex ropelike border.

REMARKS: In his descriptions of species of *Drumaspis*, Resser (1942b, p. 28–35) gives few criteria by which species can be distinguished. Snowy Range specimens divide into two biostratigraphically significant groups on the basis of connection of the posterior pair of glabellar furrows across the axis of the glabella. In *D. briscoensis* the posterior pair of glabellar furrows does not connect across the axis of the glabella. This species occurs in the lower part of the range of the genus, most commonly in the *Idahoia wyomingensis* and *I. wisconsensis* subzones. *D. idahoensis* has the posterior pair of glabellar furrows connected across the axis and occupies the upper part of the range of the genus: upper *I. wisconsensis* and *I. serapio* subzones. At many localities there are one or two beds within the *I. wisconsensis* Subzone in which the two species of *Drumaspis* occur together.

If specimens of *Drumaspis* were more abundant, a "*Drumaspis* Zone" with two subzones might be established. It would correspond to the *Ptychaspis-Prosaukia* Zone of central Texas and the upper Mississippi Valley, and to the *Idahoia* Zone of Montana-Wyoming, although the division between the two subzones would not necessarily fall at the same biostratigraphic horizons. A similar succession of species of *Drumaspis* was observed in Minnesota (Grant, 1962), where they hold the same biostratigraphic positions relative to one another and to other genera of the *Ptychaspis-Prosaukia* Zone.

Bell and Ellinwood (1962, p. 391) report a similar significant morphologic change involving different species in central Texas. There, *D. deckeri* Resser, with parallel-sided glabella and connected posterior glabellar furrows, occurs high in the range of the genus, with *D. texana* Resser characterized by its tapered glabella and unconnected furrows occurring lower.

Lochman and Hu (1959, p. 416) identify only *D. walcotti* in their *Ptychaspis* faunule from Idaho and include in its synonymy three other species which this author believes are distinct. As originally constituted by Resser (1942b, Pl. 4, figs. 37–41), *D. walcotti* included specimens with tapered glabella and posterior pair of furrows not meeting (holotype, fig. 37), along with specimens with quadrate glabella and connected furrows (paratype, fig. 41). Study of Resser's specimens in the collection of the U.S. National Museum led to the conclusion that the paratype is not conspecific with the holotype. Possibly Resser collected them from the zone in the range of the genus where more than one species normally occur together. Lochman and Hu may have a similar situation involving at least two species. They mention (p. 416) that the posterior pair of glabellar furrows normally connect, implying that some do not, and they illustrate both forms. *D. idahoensis* Resser and *D. briscoensis* Resser seem to be distinct, both different from *D. walcotti*. The third species assigned to synonymy by Lochman and Hu is *D. nitida* Resser, originally described from the Arbuckle Mountains of Oklahoma. This species is different from any of the three Western species discussed above, clearly distinguished by its lower (but not less convex) glabella, somewhat longer, more concave brim, and especially by the strong vermicular ornament on the external surface. Resser (1942b, Pl. 5) shows these differences clearly.

Pygidia that Lochman and Hu (1959, Pl. 60, figs. 8–9) assigned to *D. walcotti* are remarkably different from those found associated with species of the genus in the Snowy Range. Further collecting and study are needed to determine certainly the generic form of the pygidium of *Drumaspis* and to establish specific differences.

Drumaspis briscoensis Resser
(Pl. 14, figs. 7–9)

Drumaspis briscoensis RESSER, 1942b, p. 30, Pl. 5, figs. 4–8

DESCRIPTION; Glabella almost quadrate, with only slight anterior taper, fixed cheeks about one fourth as wide as glabella, surface smooth, two or three pairs of glabellar furrows, none of which connect across axis of glabella.

REMARKS: The discontinuous posterior glabellar furrow is the most obvious difference between *D. briscoensis* and *D. idahoensis,* which occurs at a higher biostratigraphic level. *D. briscoensis* is similar to *D. texana* Resser, but the glabella of *D. briscoensis* is less strongly tapered and its fixed cheeks narrower.

This species occupies the lower part of the range of *Drumaspis* in Montana and Wyoming. It is a good indicator for the lower half of the *Idahoia* Zone.

OCCURRENCE: *Drumaspis briscoensis* is moderately common in the *Idahoia wyomingensis* Subzone at HD 131.6; HI 115.8; FC 148.8, 151; RP 89.6, 92.8, 94.3, 132.2; MC 164.4, 168, and in the *Idahoia wisconsensis* Subzone at HD 140.4; HH 124.4; GC 137.3; FP 179.5; BC 109.9, 114.2, 116.7; SP 156; BM 148.1, 150.8, 153.9; MC 170.6. Its range extends up into the *Idahoia serapio* Subzone at SP 161; BM 156.9.

Drumaspis idahoensis Resser
(Pl. 14, figs. 11–12)

Drumaspis idahoensis RESSER, 1942b, p. 29, Pl. 4, figs. 32–36; LOCHMAN and HU, 1959 (part), p. 416–417, Pl. 60, figs. 2–3 (in synonymy with *D. walcotti* Resser)

DESCRIPTION: Glabella quadrate to slightly elongate, tapered, fixed cheeks about one third as wide as glabella, two or three pairs of glabellar furrows with posterior pair connected across the axis of the glabella, and surface essentially smooth.

REMARKS: The connected posterior glabellar furrows is the most obvious distinction between this species and *D. briscoensis,* but the glabella also is more convex and less flattened dorsally than in *D. briscoensis. D. idahoensis* is distinguished from *D. texana* Resser by its typically elongate glabella, wider fixed cheeks, and smooth or only faintly textured external surface. It differs from *D. deckeri* Resser only slightly, mainly in its shorter and less concave brim and more strongly arcuate border. It occurs biostratigraphically higher than *D. briscoensis,* although the two species have been found together in a few feet of rock at a few localities.

OCCURRENCE: *Drumaspis idahoensis* is moderately common in the *Idahoia wisconsensis* Subzone at HD 140.4; HH 124.4; BP 156.8, and in the *Idahoia serapio* Subzone at HD 146.2, 148.2, 150.6; HH 128.8; HI 121.2, 124.3; SP 161, 163; BP 161.2, 173.8; BM 182.1; MC 178, 185.3.

Genus *Elvinia* Walcott, 1924

Elvinia roemeri (Shumard)
(Pl. 9, fig. 22)

Dikelocephalus roemeri SHUMARD, 1861, p. 220–221

Elvinia roemeri (Shumard). WALCOTT, 1924b, p. 56; WALCOTT, 1925, p. 88–89, Pl. 17, figs. 9–13; BRIDGE and GIRTY, 1937, p. 251, Pl. 69, figs. 1–21 (synonymy to date); WILSON, 1949, p. 38, Pl. 10, figs. 5, 9–10, 12–13; FREDERICKSON, 1949, p. 352–353, Pl. 69, figs. 19–21; LOCHMAN, 1950a, p. 333–334, Pl. 47, figs. 21–23; WILSON, 1951, p. 642, Pl. 92, figs. 18–22; NELSON, 1951, p. 775, Pl. 107, fig. 8; BELL, FENIAK, and KURTZ, 1952, p. 183, Pl. 30, figs. 1a–d; LOCHMAN and HU, 1960, p. 814, Pl. 96, figs. 38–47; PALMER, 1960, p. 70–71, Pl. 6, fig. 7 (extended synonymy)

REMARKS: Two fragmentary cranidia can be recognized as *Elvinia roemeri* by the characteristic tapering truncate glabella with single well-impressed glabellar furrow continuous across the glabella, the wide fixed cheeks, low cranidial convexity, and smooth external surface. They fell well within the fairly broad limits of variation of the species as constituted by Frederickson (1949) and Palmer (1960).

OCCURRENCE: *Elvinia roemeri* is rare in the *Elvinia* Zone at GR 15.9; SP 108.6.

Family Eurekiidae Hupé, 1953
Genus *Eurekia* Walcott, 1924
Eurekia binodosa (Hall)
(Pl. 15, figs. 15, 18)

Conocephalites ? *binodosus* Hall, 1863, p. 160, Pl. 7, fig. 47
Eurekia binodosa (Hall). Ellinwood, 1953, Ph.D. thesis, Univ. Minnesota, p. 89–90, Pl. 7, figs. 19–20 (synonymy to date)

Description: Glabella elongate, anteriorly rounded, glabellar furrows absent, frontal area large, surface smooth or granulose.

Remarks: Specimens from Montana and Wyoming have less bulbous glabellas and flatter more horizontal frontal areas than do those from Texas. Several specimens (from BC 225.5, BM 284, ME 47.6) are more bulbous than other western specimens and have the posterior pair of glabellar furrows faintly visible; they appear to be intermediate between *E. binodosa* and *E. granulosa* Walcott.

Occurrence: *Eurekia binodosa* is moderately common in Trempealeauan at BC 205.5; BM 279.1, 284; ME 31.1, 47.6, 49.1; MC 285.5, 290.5, 293.5; YO 269.3; UYO 267.6, 278.6.

Genus *Maladia* Walcott, 1924
Maladia americana Walcott
(Pl. 14, figs. 15–16, 20)

Maladia americana Walcott, 1924b, p. 59, Pl. 12, fig. 2; Walcott, 1925, p. 105, Pl. 16, figs. 23–26

Description: Cranidium quadrate, moderately convex, surface smooth; glabella quadrate, parallel-sided to slightly tapered, anteriorly rounded or truncate, moderately convex; glabellar furrows weak or absent; dorsal furrow distinct, not deep; occipital furrow shallow, wide, shallower distally than axially, terminated before reaching dorsal furrow on some specimens; occipital ring wide, widest on axial line; frontal area steeply downsloping at axial line, more steeply downsloping at anterolateral corners, length between one-third and one-fifth length of cranidium; brim flatly convex, steeply downsloping; marginal furrow shallow, straight to slightly arcuate; border slightly convex, horizontal to slightly downsloping; fixed cheeks and palpebral lobes flatly convex, horizontal to slightly downsloping; palpebral lobes near midline of glabella; palpebral furrow faint, arcuate; posterior limbs long, narrow, with shallow furrow; anterior facial sutures divergent, some less commonly parallel or slightly convergent at anterolateral corners, less commonly continuing divergent.

Pygidium wider than long; axis high, with posterior segment terminated in two gently rounded nodes; interpleural furrows shallow; each pleuron extended beyond border to form marginal spine; normally five or six pairs of marginal spines.

Remarks: *Maladia americana* is characterized by its convex quadrate cranidium and glabella, short, downsloping, and anterolaterally flexed frontal area, and binodose, spinose pygidium. The pygidium is similar to that of *Eurekia* Walcott, but the axial nodes are very low and blunt and the marginal spines terminate in sharp points.

The cranidium of *M. americana* is similar to that of *Stigmacephalus flexifrons* Feniak (*in* Bell, Feniak, and Kurtz, 1952, p. 194), and the two species occur in the upper *Idahoia* Zone. *M. americana* differs from *S. flexifrons* in its straighter marginal furrow, less convex brim, slightly more truncate glabella, and normally divergent facial sutures although some specimens of *M. americana* have the sutures bent axially at the anterolateral corners of the cranidium, and some specimens of *S. flexifrons* have continuously divergent sutures. These differences in the cranidia of the two species are slight and may indicate a close relationship between them. Unfortunately, the pygidium of *S. flexifrons* is unknown. When pygidia are assigned to that species its relationship to *Maladia* should become clear.

Occurrence: *Maladia americana* is rare in the *Idahoia wyomingensis* Subzone at RP 92.5, 94.3, 132.2; MC 164.4. It is moderately common in the *I. wisconsensis* Subzone at HD 140.4, 142; SP 156; BM 148.1, 153.9; MC 170.6, and in the *I. serapio* Subzone at HD 150.6; HI 121.2, 124.3; BC 130.5; SP 161, 163, 181.5; BP 173.8; MC 185.3; YO 159.5; FOX 118.6.

Family HOUSIIDAE Hupé, 1953
Genus *Housia* Walcott, 1916
Housia vacuna (Walcott)
(Pl. 10, figs. 2, 5)

Ptychoparia vacuna WALCOTT, 1891, p. 275, Pl. 21, figs. 8, 12
Housia vacuna (Walcott). RESSER, 1936, p. 23; WILSON, 1951, p. 643–645, Pl. 93, figs. 5–13

REMARKS: Three fragmentary cranidia and one pygidium of *Housia* are assigned to *H. vacuna* rather than to *H. varro* (Walcott) on the basis of the shape of the pygidium. Wilson (1951) says that the pygidium of *H. vacuna* has no long backward-drooping anterior segment like that of *H. varro* or *H. canadensis* (Walcott). The pygidium from Montana is comparable to those figured by Wilson (1951, Pl. 93, figs. 11–12) in that it has no enlarged anterior segment. It differs from the pygidium of *H. varro* (Bell, Feniak, and Kurtz, 1952, Pl. 30, fig. 3d) in that its axial lobe is less tapered and its border maintains its width around the axis.

This species can be distinguished from *H. ovata* Palmer (1960, p. 75, Pl. 7, figs. 1–7, 9) by differences in the cranidium as well as in the pygidium. The cranidium of *H. vacuna* is less convex, having a lower glabella, a dorsal furrow barely impressed, a shallower marginal furrow, a border shorter and less arcuate, and an absence of coarse pitting of the brim. The pygidium is much more transverse, about twice as wide as long, and like the cranidium most features are weaker, and there is no pitted ornament.

OCCURRENCE: *Housia vacuna* is rare in the *Camaraspis* Subzone of the *Elvinia* Zone at MC 105.4; SL 65.

Family IDAHOIIDAE Lochman, 1956
Genus *Comanchia* Frederickson, 1950
Comanchia lippa Grant n.sp.
(Pl. 10, figs. 7, 10, 13)

REMARKS: This species differs from *C. amplooculata* Frederickson (1948), which occurs in Oklahoma and Texas (Wilson, 1949; Bell and Ellinwood, 1962), primarily by its wider and more strongly bowed palpebral lobes. They are almost semicircular in outline, whereas those on *C. amplooculata* are much more flatly arched. Other differences are as follows: the Western species nearly always has an occipital node; the brim-border ratio is commonly nearer 2:3 than to the 1:2 that characterizes the Oklahoma-Texas species (Wilson, 1949, p. 42; Wilson and Frederickson, 1950, p. 900); the Western species appears to have wider posterior limbs although it is difficult to be certain that this feature is other than individual variation on the few specimens from which the limbs have not been broken. The population of *C. lippa* contains individuals with tapered glabellas, rather than the typically quadrate glabella of *C. amplooculata*.

Pygidia of the two species are similar except that the Oklahoma-Texas species has three axial rings plus a terminal segment and an indistinct marginal furrow (Wilson, 1949, p. 43), whereas the Montana-Wyoming form has four axial rings plus a terminal segment and distinct marginal furrow.

C. amplooculata from Oklahoma and Texas occurs with *Irvingella major* at the same biostratigraphic horizon occupied in Montana and Wyoming by *C. lippa*, but the two populations are different and easily recognizable.

HOLOTYPE: USNM 142321, Plate 10, figure 10

ETYMOLOGY: *Lippa*, L. bleary-eyed, referring to the strongly bowed palpebral lobes

OCCURRENCE: *Comanchia lippa* is locally extremely abundant. It occurs in the *Irvingella major* Zonule at the top of the *Elvinia* Zone at GC 85.8; MC 111.7; and YO 69.4.

Genus *Idahoia* Walcott, 1924

Idahoia WALCOTT, 1924b, p. 58

TYPE SPECIES: *Idahoia serapio* WALCOTT, 1924b, p. 58, Pl. 14, fig. 1

REMARKS: Walcott states (1925, p. 95) that

"The genus *Idahoia* is characterized by the unusual development of the frontal limb. The glabella occupies only about half the length of the cranidium and has no glabellar nor occipital furrow."

More precisely, the frontal area is more than half the length of the glabella, measured to the posterior of the occipital ring, and although glabellar and occipital furrows may be present, they are weak. These features distinguish the genus from *Saratogia* (*q.v.*, for contrasting diagnoses of the two genera).

Prior to this study (Grant, 1958, Ph.D. thesis, Univ. Texas) the type species, *Idahoia serapio* Walcott, had been recognized in few Franconian faunas although now it proves to be widespread. It is characterized by a brim-border ratio near 1:1, and, where correctly identified, it is the latest Franconian species in a series with a marked trend toward reduction in length of brim and proportionate increase in length of border. This trend begins in the Montana-Wyoming area at the base of the *Idahoia* Zone, beginning with *I. wyomingensis* Resser (brim-border ratio about 3:1), progresses through *I. wisconsensis* (Owen) (brim-border ratio between 3:1 and 4:3), culminating in *I. serapio* whose brim and border are nearly equal in sagittal length. *I. serapio* is common in the upper Mississippi Valley (Grant, 1962, p. 986) where it was previously not identified. It was collected and illustrated under the name *I. wisconsensis* by Bell, Feniak, and Kurtz (1952, Pl. 37, figs. 3a, d) and Berg (1953, Pl. 61, fig. 11). There, it occupies the same position high in the range of *Idahoia* in the upper part of the *Ptychaspis* Subzone of the *Ptychaspis-Prosaukia* Zone. Lochman and Hu (1959) identified it subsequently in the same relative biostratigraphic position in the Bear River Range of Idaho.

Lochman and Hu (1959) treated *Meeria* Frederickson (1949) as a subgenus of *Idahoia*. However, that genus exhibits some generic characteristics of *Saratogia* Walcott (*q.v.*, for discussion of these relationships).

Idahoia serapio Walcott
(Pl. 14, fig. 17)

Idahoia serapio Walcott, 1924b, p. 58, Pl. 14, fig. 1; Walcott, 1925, p. 96, Pl. 19, figs. 1–12; Kobayashi, 1935b, p. 235; Lochman and Hu, 1959, p. 417, Pl. 60, figs. 28–36; Lochman *in* Harrington and others, 1959, p. O252, fig. 189, no. 2a–c; Grant, 1962, p. 986, Pl. 139, fig. 5b

Idahoia wisconsensis (Owen). Bell, Feniak, and Kurtz, 1952 (part), p. 189, Pl. 37, figs. 3a, d; Berg, 1953, p. 566, Pl. 61, fig. 11

Description: Cranidium large, facial sutures anteriorly divergent, producing wide and proportionately long frontal area, glabella quadrate but anteriorly tapering, marginal furrow normally with single row of pustules, brim-border ratio near 1:1.

Remarks: *I. serapio* is the culmination of an evolutionary trend toward lengthening of the border, and this is its chief difference from *I. wisconsensis* (Owen), whose border normally is significantly shorter. There are, however, intermediate specimens as would be expected in a direct evolutionary line where all stages have been sampled. *I. serapio* differs from *I. wyomingensis* Resser in its normally larger size, much longer border, proportionately longer frontal area, less convex brim, and less downsloping border. Glabellar outline and furrows are similar in all three species.

This species was described by Walcott (1924b) from a locality near Malad, Idaho, about 200 miles from Snowy Range outcrops. Lochman and Hu (1959, p. 417) report it from the Bear River Range in Idaho, a few miles from Malad. Their specimens are similar in all essential features, and there is no doubt of their identity or of their conspecificity with Walcott's specimens (examined in the U.S. National Museum).

Occurrence: Except for one anomalous occurrence in the *Idahoia wisconsensis* Subzone at BM 148.1, *Idahoia serapio* is confined to the *I. serapio* Subzone. It is common at HD 146.2, 150.6; HH 127.1, 128.8, 132.8; HI 121.2, 124.3; BC 120.6, 126.3; SP 161, 163, 181.5; BP 161.2, 173.8; BM 156, 161.2, 163.8, 180.2; MC 178, 185.3; YO 149.4; FOX 118.6.

Idahoia wisconsensis (Owen)
(Pl. 14, fig. 13)

Crepicephalus ? wisconsensis OWEN, 1852, Fig. 13, Table 1
Idahoia wisconsensis (Hall). RESSER, 1935, p. 35
Idahoia wisconsensis (Owen). BELL, FENIAK, and KURTZ, 1952 (part), p. 189–190 (synonymy to date), Pl. 37, figs. 3b–c, 3e–f (not figs. 3a, d: *I. serapio* WALCOTT); BERG and ROSS, 1959, p. 111, Pl. 22, fig. 10; LOCHMAN and HU, 1959 (part), p. 417, Pl. 59, figs. 12–21, 25–32 (not figs. 22–24: *Saratogia fria* LOCHMAN and HU); BELL and ELLINWOOD, 1962, p. 393, Pl. 52, figs. 19–21; GRANT, 1962, p. 986, Pl. 139, fig. 5a
Idahoia latifrons (Shumard). BERG, 1953, p. 566, Pl. 60, fig. 11
Not *Idahoia wisconsensis* (Owen). BERG, 1953, p. 566, Pl. 61, fig. 11 (*I. serapio* Walcott)

REMARKS: *Idahoia wisconsensis* is characterized by its frontal area that is more than half as long as the glabella, consisting of a wide brim and somewhat narrower border, in the ratio of about 2:1. Specimens that occur low in the range of the species have brim-border ratios near 3:1, approaching that of *I. wyomingensis* Resser. Those near the top of the range of the species may have ratios of 4:3, approaching the 1:1 ratio of *I. serapio* Walcott. The brim is gently convex and slightly downsloping. The border may be horizontal or may continue the downslope of the brim. It turns upward only in crushed or otherwise deformed specimens.

I. latifrons (Shumard), as illustrated and described by Berg (1953, p. 566, Pl. 60, fig. 11), has been included in the synonymy of *I. wisconsensis* for three reasons: (1) It is morphologically indistinguishable from *I. wisconsensis;* (2) The type specimen of *I. latifrons* was lost years ago, so only Hall's (1863, Pl. 7, fig. 40) illustration, cited by Resser (1935, p. 35) is available as a basis for comparison with other species. (Incidentally, Hall identified figure 40 as *I. wisconsensis*.); (3) Berg's one specimen was found in the *Ptychaspis granulosa* Subzone at Minnieska, Minnesota, only a few miles southeast of the area where detailed collecting produced only abundant *I. wisconsensis sensu stricto* (Grant, 1962).

OCCURRENCE: *Idahoia wisconsensis* is common in the *I. wisconsensis* Subzone of the *Idahoia* Zone at HD 140.4, 142; HH 124.4; GC 137.3, 138.8; FC 148.8; FP 179.3; BC 109.9, 116.7; SP 156; RP 144.6, 146.1; BP 158.8; BM 148.1, 150.8, 153.9; MC 164.4, 170.6; YO 135.7, 147.5. It is rare in the top part of the *I. wyomingensis* Subzone at RP 91.1, and in the base of the *I. serapio* Subzone at HD 146.2; HH 127.1; SP 161.

Idahoia wyomingensis Resser
(Pl. 13, figs. 22–25)

Ptychoparia (*Lonchocephalus*) *wisconsensis* WALCOTT (not OWEN), 1899 (part), p. 461, Pl. 64, figs. 1, 1a (not fig. 1b: *Saratogia* sp.; 1c: *Wilbernia* sp.)
Saratogia wisconsensis (Walcott). WALCOTT, 1916a, p. 198–199, Pl. 34, figs. 5, 5a–c
Idahoia wyomingensis RESSER, 1937, p. 14

DESCRIPTION: Cranidium convex, slightly elongate, surface smooth; glabella slightly convex longitudinally, moderately convex transversely, may be faintly keeled, width at posterior normally equal to length, sides slightly tapered, anterior truncate with abruptly rounded anterolateral corners; dorsal furrow deep; glabellar furrows faint or absent; occipital furrow distinct, shallow across axis; occipital ring with long median spine; frontal area more than half glabellar length, commonly about two thirds glabellar length; brim convex, moderately downsloping; border slightly convex, about one third width of brim, continuing downslope of brim; marginal furrow shallow but distinct, may have row of pustules running transversely; palpebral lobes wide, flat to slightly upsloping; palpebral furrows distinct, arcuate; some specimens with faint ocular ridges; fixed cheeks one fourth to half width of glabella; posterior limbs long and narrow, with well-marked furrow.

Pygidium wide, diamond shaped (similar to that of *Psalaspis patersoni* [Hall]); axis bluntly rounded, reaching only to marginal furrow, consisting of three or four axial segments; pleural lobe with distinct pleura and interpleural furrows, pleural furrows very shallow or absent; marginal furrow shallow; border convex; posterior margin smooth, without spines.

REMARKS: *Idahoia wyomingensis* resembles *Saratogia hera* Walcott of the upper Mississippi Valley; its cranidium is characterized by considerable convexity and a brim-border ratio of about 3:1. It can be distinguished from *Psalaspis patersoni* (Hall) by its deeper dorsal furrow, more convex glabella, and more distinct marginal furrow; from *S. hera* by its downsloping border, by the row of pustules commonly present in the marginal furrow, and by its proportionately longer frontal area.

Near the top of its range *I. wyomingensis* occurs with *I. wisconsensis,* but it can be distinguished from that species by its greater convexity, less divergent anterior facial sutures, much more steeply downsloping frontal area, more convex brim, downsloping instead of horizontal border, and especially by its brim-border ratio of about 3:1, in contrast to the ratio of near 2:1 in *I. wisconsensis.*

The above description of the cranidium and pygidium is the first for *I. wyomingensis.* In his designation of the species, Resser (1937, p. 14) remarked only that it is shorter and smaller than *I. wisconsensis,* which is not consistently true.

OCCURRENCE: *Idahoia wyomingensis* is abundant in the *Idahoia wyomingensis* Subzone at HD 117.9, 125.1, 131.6; HG 77.3, 79.3, 81.3; HH 103.4, 104.9; HI 106.5, 115.8; HK 109.1; GC 126.2, 129.6, 132.2, 133, 135.4; FC 142.7, 143.2, 143.7, 144.6, 146.2, 148, 148.8, 151; FP 167.7; JC 103.6, 106.6; BC 103.6, 106.4; SP 146.6, 150.6, 153.4; RP 84.9, 91.1, 94.3, 121.7, 132.2, 134.7, 136.7, 140.1; BM 137.9, 140.9, 144.4; MC 155, 164.1; YO 122.3, 125.9. Its range extends into the *I. wisconsensis* Subzone at HD 140.4; SP 156.

Genus *Saratogia* Walcott, 1916

Saratogia WALCOTT, 1916a, p. 195–196; LOCHMAN and HU, 1959, p. 420–421; LOCHMAN, *in* HARRINGTON AND OTHERS, 1959, p. 0252

TYPE SPECIES: *Conocephalites calciferous* WALCOTT, 1879, p. 129–130 (first adequately illustrated by WALCOTT, 1912a, Pl. 43, figs. 7–10a)

REMARKS: Since establishment of the genus *Idahoia* (Walcott, 1925, p. 95–96) until its recognition by Lochman and Hu (1959), the genus *Saratogia* was divested of species and no new species added to it. This practice apparently stemmed from a belief that *Saratogia* is confined to the upper Trempealeauan (Wilson, 1951, p. 648; Lochman, 1956, p. 460), despite the fact that Walcott assigned Dresbachian and Franconian species to it in addition to the supposedly Trempealeauan type species (Walcott, 1916a, p. 196). This restriction of *Saratogia* to the Trempealeauan removed a significant genus from consideration among Franconian faunas and left a peculiar gap in Lochman's (1956, p. 460, Fig. 7) diagram of evolution of the Idahoiidae.

Recent literature concerning Trempealeauan faunas contains no mention of the genus *Saratogia* except listings of Walcott's original citation of *S. calcifera* from the Hoyt Formation of New York (Clark, 1924; Kobayashi, 1935a; 1935b; 1937; 1938; Rasetti, 1944; 1945; Raymond, 1937; Shaw, 1951; 1953; 1954; Shaw and DeLand, 1955; Wilson, 1954). This indicates that if *Saratogia* occurs in the Trempealeauan at all, it is a rare and local constituent.

Many cranidia from the *Idahoia* Zone of Montana and Wyoming fit the definition of *Saratogia* in all respects and differ consistently from species of *Idahoia.* Confusion of *Saratogia* with *Idahoia* led to the conclusion by Lochman (1956, p. 460, Fig. 7) that *Idahoia* is polyphyletic. Differences between the two genera are stated clearly in Walcott's original descriptions of *Saratogia* (1916a, p. 195–199) and *Idahoia* (1924b, p. 58; 1925 p. 25–96) and are implicit in later discussions and illustrations of *Idahoia* by other authors (Nelson, 1951, p. 778, Pl. 109; Bell, Feniak, and Kurtz, 1952, p. 189–191, Pls. 32–33, 36–37; Berg, 1953, p. 566, Pls. 60–61). These descriptions, discussions and illustrations, plus study and measurement of specimens of *Idahoia* and *Saratogia* from Montana and Wyoming and examination of the type-species collections in the U.S. National Museum are the basis for the following criteria by which the two genera can be differentiated:

Saratogia: (1) Glabellar furrows normally visible
(2) Occipital furrow well impressed, visible across axis
(3) Fixed cheeks narrow anterior to palpebral lobes
(4) Outer surface granular or smooth, brim on many striated longitudinally
(5) Anterior facial sutures of early species narrowly divergent; of later species more widely divergent
(6) Palpebral lobes large, flat, nearly semicircular
(7) Brim downsloping, border upturned (a few horizontal), convex, narrow
(8) Most important: frontal area less than one half glabellar length (measured to posterior of occipital ring)

Idahoia: (1) Glabellar furrows normally absent, faint where present
(2) Occipital furrow shallow, faint across axis
(3) Fixed cheeks moderately wide anterior to palpebral lobes
(4) Outer surface smooth
(5) Anterior facial sutures widely divergent
(6) Palpebral lobes longer, narrower than in *Saratogia*
(7) Brim gently convex, downsloping, border flat to slightly convex, normally continuing downslope of brim
(8) Most important: frontal area longer than one half glabellar length (measured to posterior of occipital ring)

Lochman and Hu (1959, p. 421) presented comparative diagnoses of *Saratogia* and *Idahoia* based primarily on characters of the pygidia. Their cranidial diagnoses are identical, except that the palpebral lobes are said to be slightly farther posterior and the frontal area slightly narrower in *Saratogia.* As no pygidia have been found which can be associated with certainty with any species of *Saratogia* from the West, their generic characters must be regarded as undetermined.

The most obvious feature in the evolution of *Saratogia* is its trend toward lengthening of the frontal area and increase in the divergence of the anterior facial sutures. *S. carita* n.sp. has the facial sutures subparallel, although somewhat bowed laterally, and the frontal area slightly less than one fifth the length of the glabella (measured to the posterior of the occipital ring). *S. fracida* n.sp. has the frontal area slightly greater than one fifth the glabellar length, and the facial sutures moderately divergent. In *S. fria* Lochman and Hu the frontal area is about one third as long as the glabella, and the anterior facial sutures are strongly divergent. In *Saratogia* (*Meeria*) Frederickson (1949) on the other hand, there is no apparent change in divergence of the anterior facial sutures, but the frontal area appears to shorten proportionately between *M. lirae* Fredrickson low in the range, and *M. modesta* Lochman and Hu which is biostratigraphically higher.

Saratogia carita Grant n.sp.
(Pl. 13, figs. 16–17)

Description: Cranidium subrectangular, moderately convex; glabella moderately convex both longitudinally and transversely, slightly tapered, rounded-truncate anteriorly, with three pairs of glabellar furrows; occipital furrow well impressed throughout its length, but slightly shallower across axis; occipital ring with median spine; dorsal furrow moderately impressed, of even depth around glabella; frontal area less than half glabellar length; brim convex, downsloping, with faint longitudinal anastomosing lines; marginal furrow a broad moderately deep trough, slightly arcuate; border about one third as wide as brim, upturned or horizontal, convex; palpebral lobes wide, semicircular, with strong palpebral furrow, located on midline of glabella; anterior facial sutures divergent just anterior to palpebral lobes, nearly parallel lateral to frontal area. Posterior limbs, free cheeks, and pygidium unknown.

Holotype: USNM 142413, Plate 13, figure 17

Etymology: *Carita,* L., devoid of, lacking; referring to absence of granules on surface, main distinction between this species and the type species *S. calcifera* Walcott.

Remarks: *Saratogia carita* differs from species of *Idahoia* by its shorter frontal area, more semicircular palpebral lobes, and convex, slightly upturned border. It differs from *S. fracida* n.sp. by its less convex glabella, weaker glabellar furrows, less convex and downsloping frontal area, less divergent anterior facial sutures and lack of anterolateral pits in the dorsal furrow. It differs from *S. fria* Lochman and Hu by its much less divergent anterior facial sutures, broader marginal furrow, and less upturned border. It most closely resembles *S. calcifera,* the type species of the genus, but differs by its lack of granular ornamentation.

Occurrence: *Saratogia carita* occurs with and below *S. fracida* in the lower part of the *Idahoia wyomingensis* Subzone of the *Idahoia* Zone. It is rare at HD 117.9; HG 77.3, 81.3; HH 103.4; GC 126.2; FC 143.2; BC 103.6; SP 146.6; RP 84.9, 89.6.

Saratogia fracida Grant n.sp.
(Pl. 13, figs. 18–20)

Description: Cranidium rather strongly convex, length about one third greater than width across palpebral lobes; glabella moderately high, strongly convex longitudinally and transversely, slightly longer than wide, somewhat tapered anteriorly, sides slightly bowed laterally, anteriorly rounded, with shallow pits at anterolateral corners; three pairs of glabellar furrows, becoming more strongly impressed toward posterior; occipital furrow deep, normally maintaining depth across axis; dorsal furrow fairly deep, shallowest on axial line at anterior; frontal area relatively short; brim strongly convex, strongly downsloping; border narrow, convex, upturned relative to brim; marginal furrow broad, deep, troughlike, somewhat arcuate in some specimens; palpebral lobes large, outline semicircular, located slightly anterior to midlength of glabella; anterior course of facial sutures moderately divergent; anterior margin with variable curvature; posterior limbs short (sag.), rather wide, with deep furrow; occipital spine on some specimens; surface of carapace smooth except for faint transverse liration of occipital ring. Free cheeks and pygidium not observed.

Holotype: USNM 142415, Plate 13, figure 19

Etymology: *Fracidus,* L., ripe, mellow; referring to the bulbous convexity of the cranidium of this species.

Remarks: *Saratogia fracida* is characterized by its relatively convex tapered glabella with visible glabellar furrows, short frontal area consisting of a strongly convex downsloping brim and narrow upturned border, pair of shallow pits in the anterolateral corners of the dosal furrow, and its moderately divergent anterior glabella furrows.

It differs from *S. calcifera* Walcott, the type species, by its smooth external surface, shorter frontal area with less widely divergent anterior facial sutures, and its more convex glabella and brim. The smooth surface is similar to that of *S. carita* n.sp.; otherwise the same features distinguish these two species. The anterior facial sutures are less widely divergent than in *S. fria* Lochman and Hu, the glabella and brim less convex, the glabellar furrows stronger, and the brim lacking in ornamentation. It is distinguished from *S.* (*Meeria*) *modesta* Lochman and Hu by its larger size, more tapered and convex glabella, longer frontal area, stronger glabellar furrows, and more strongly upturned border.

Occurrence: *Saratogia fracida* is common in the *Idahoia wyomingensis* Subzone of the *Idahoia* Zone at HD 117.9; HI 115.8; GC 126.2, 127.5; FC 143.2, 144.6; JC 101.6; BC 103.6, 106.4; SP 146.6, 150.6, 153.4; RP 84.9, 89.6, 136.7; BM 137.9; MC 164.4. It is a rare constituent of the *I. wisconsensis* Subzone at MC 170.6.

Saratogia fria Lochman and Hu
(Pl. 13, fig. 21)

Saratogia fria Lochman and Hu, 1959, p. 422, Pl. 59, figs. 1–11; Bell and Ellinwood, 1962, p. 394, Pl. 53, figs. 13–21

Description: Anterior facial sutures strongly divergent, border narrow, upturned, brim gently convex, slightly downsloping with light longitudinal liration, marginal furrow broad, glabellar furrows weak or absent, palpebral lobes long.

Remarks: This species is distinguished from other species of *Saratogia* by its less downsloping brim, more divergent anterior facial sutures, proportionately longer frontal area, and longer palpebral lobes.

The facial sutures of *S. fria* are more strongly divergent than are those of other species of *Saratogia;* the species resembles *Idahoia* in this respect. However, the frontal area that is less than half the length of the glabella, lightly ornamented brim, and the upturned border distinguish it from all species of *Idahoia.*

This species continues the evolutionary trend in *Saratogia* toward increasing divergence of the anterior facial sutures. It occurs biostratigraphically higher than *S. fracida* and *S. carita* and probably descended from them.

OCCURRENCE: *Saratogia fria* is moderately common in the *Idahoia wyomingensis* Subzone of the *Idahoia* Zone at HD 131.6; HG 81.3; HI 115.8; GC 127.5; FC 146.2, 147.3, 148.8; JC 101.6, 103.6; BC 106.4; SP 153.4; RP 139.7, 140.1; MC 164.1, 164.4, 168. It is rare in the *I. wisconsensis* Subzone at MC 170.6 and rare in the *I. serapio* Subzone at SP 161.

Genus *Wilbernia* Walcott, 1924
Wilbernia diademata (Hall)
(Pl. 13, fig. 27)

Conocephalites diadematus HALL, 1863 (part), p. 167, Pl. 7, fig. 36, Pl. 8, fig. 21 (not Pl. 7, figs. 37–38: *W. halli* RESSER, not Pl. 8, fig. 18: *W. pero* [Walcott])
Wilbernia diademata (Hall). RESSER, 1937, p. 28; NELSON, 1951, p. 782, Pl. 109, figs. 8, 11–12 (synonymy to date); BELL and ELLINWOOD, 1962, p. 395, Pl. 54, figs. 9–10

REMARKS: *Wilbernia diademata* is characterized by a brim-border ratio of approximately 1:2 and a parallel-sided or slightly tapered glabella. *W. halli* Resser has the same brim-border ratio, but a conspicuously tapered glabella. *W. expansa* Frederickson and *W. pero* (Walcott) have brim-border ratios between 1:4 and 1:7 and *W. explanata* (Whitfield) has a ratio of 1:1.

OCCURRENCE: *Wilbernia diademata* is rare in the *Idahoia wyomingensis* Subzone at HG 77.3, 81.3; HI 106.5; GC 126.2; FC 143.7; BC 103.6; MC 168; YO 122.3, and in the *I. wisconsensis* Subzone at SP 156.

Wilbernia expansa Frederickson
(Pl. 14, fig. 5)

Wilbernia expansa FREDERICKSON, 1949, p. 362, Pl. 72, figs. 13–16; BELL, FENIAK, and KURTZ, 1952, p. 187, Pl. 32, figs. 3a–c; BELL and ELLINWOOD, 1962, p. 395, Pl. 54, figs. 11–12

REMARKS: *Wilbernia expansa* is distinguished from other species of *Wilbernia* by its brim-border ratio between 1:4 and 1:6 and its concave border. *W. pero* (Walcott) has a similarly proportioned frontal area, but a raised convex border.

OCCURRENCE: *Wilbernia expansa* is sporadically present, but rare in all three subzones of the *Idahoia* Zone. It has been found in the *Idahoia wyomingensis* Subzone at HD 121.1; HH 103.4; HI 106.5; FP 159.9; JC 103.6; SP 150.6, in the *I. wisconsensis* Subzone at HH 124.4, and in the *I. serapio* Subzone at HD 146.2; SP 181.5.

Wilbernia explanata (Whitfield)
(Pl. 14, fig. 4)

Conocephalites (Ptychaspis?) explanatus WHITFIELD, 1880, p. 48; 1882, p. 181, Pl. 1, figs. 27–28
Wilbernia explanata (Whitfield). TWENHOFEL, RAASCH, and THWAITES, 1935, p. 1742; NELSON, 1951, p. 782, Pl. 109, fig. 10 (synonymy to date); BELL, FENIAK, and KURTZ, 1952, p. 195, Pl. 34, figs. 4a–e

REMARKS: *Wilbernia explanata* is characterized by a brim-border ratio of 1:1 and a parallel-sided glabella. Some individuals of *W. halli* may have a similar brim-border ratio, but a tapered glabella.

OCCURRENCE: *W. explanata* is rare in the *Idahoia wyomingensis* Subzone. A few fragmentary cranidia have been found at FC 143.2.

Wilbernia halli Resser
(Pl. 12, fig. 23)

Conocephalites diadematus HALL, 1863 (part), Pl. 7, figs. 37–38
Wilbernia halli RESSER, 1937, p. 28; NELSON, 1951, p. 777, Pl. 107, figs. 17, 19; BELL, FENIAK, and KURTZ, 1952, p. 188, Pl. 32, figs. 5a–b; BERG, 1953, p. 556–559; BELL and ELLINWOOD, 1962, p. 395, Pl. 54, figs. 13–18

REMARKS: *Wilbernia halli* is distinguished from other species of *Wilbernia* by its tapering glabella, brim-border ratio between 1:1 and 1:2, convex, slightly downsloping brim, and flat border. It is distinguished from species of *Orygmaspis* with which it occurs by its convex downsloping brim, flat border, much larger and more posterior palpebral lobes, deeper palpebral furrows, and smaller posterior limbs.

OCCURRENCE: *W. halli* is rare in the *Taenicephalus* Zone at HC 14.6; HG 51; GC 92.6; FC 131; JC 69.6; SP 111.9, 117.4; BP 102.4; MC 116.4, 117.1; CF 51.8; YO 75.7.

Wilbernia halli Resser, var. A. Ellinwood
(Pl. 12, fig. 8)

Wilbernia halli RESSER, var. A. ELLINWOOD, *in* BELL and ELLINWOOD, 1962, p. 395, Pl. 54, figs. 16–18

REMARKS: A few cranidia in the present collection correspond to *W. halli,* var. A. of Ellinwood in that their brims are much wider than is typical of *W. halli.* The brim-border ratio of these variants is about 2:1. Other features link them closely to *W. halli.*

OCCURRENCE: *W. halli* var. A occurs in the *Taenicephalus* Zone at SP 111.9, 117.4.

Wilbernia pero (Walcott)
(Pl. 14, fig. 6)

Conocephalites diadematus HALL, 1863 (part), Pl. 8, fig. 18
Ptychoparia pero WALCOTT, 1890, p. 274, Pl. 21, fig. 6
Wilbernia pero (Walcott). WALCOTT, 1924b, p. 60, Pl. 13, fig. 4; NELSON, 1951, p. 782, Pl. 109, fig. 13 (synonymy to date); LOCHMAN and HU, 1959, p. 422, Pl. 60, figs. 15–18; BELL and ELLINWOOD, 1962, p. 396, Pl. 54, figs. 19–21; GRANT, 1962, p. 989, Pl. 139, figs. 8a–c
Wilbernia cf. *W. pero* (Walcott). BELL, FENIAK, and KURTZ, 1952, Pl. 34, figs. 5a–c

DESCRIPTION: Glabella parallel-sided, flatly convex, brim-border ratio from about 1:7 to 1:3. Its raised convex border distinguishes it from *W. expansa* which has a concave border.

REMARKS: This species probably descended from *W. diademata* which also has a convex border. Specimens from Minnesota low in the range of the species have wider brims than do those higher up. That is, those that are biostratigraphically closest to *W. diademata* are also morphologically close (Grant, 1962). Too few specimens are present in the Montana-Wyoming collections to determine whether the pattern holds consistently in this area.

OCCURRENCE: *Wilbernia pero* is rare in the *Idahoia wyomingensis* Subzone at HD 129.4; MC 164.4, 168, in the *I. wisconsensis* Subzone at BC 116.7; MC 170.6, and in the *I. serapio* Subzone at MC 178, 185.3.

Family ILLAENURIDAE Vogdes, 1890
Genus *Illaenurus* Hall, 1863

Illaenurus HALL, 1863, p. 176
TYPE SPECIES: *Illaenurus quadratus* HALL, 1863, p. 176–177, Pl. 7, figs. 52–57

REMARKS: Cranidia of *Illaenurus* from Montana and Wyoming show a consistent evolutionary pattern of enlargement of the portion anterior to the eyes. In the lower part of the range of the genus cranidia are wider than long, and have eyes anterior to the midline of the cranidium. Specimens higher in the range are more quadrate, with eyes nearly on the midline. Near the top of the range the anterior portion of the cranidium is longer, and the anterior facial sutures more divergent, resulting in a relatively larger cranidium.

There is a similar ontogenetic trend at each biostratigraphic level. Normally the smaller cranidia (earlier molts) at one horizon have the shape and development of the anterior resembling the larger cranidia of the subjacent horizon. Therefore, species of *Illaenurus* must be distinguished by consideration of their development as well as of the shape of adult cranidia. Subdivision of the genus may seem somewhat arbitrary where several species are found in one region; however, the species were described originally from widely separated areas. Although four occur in Montana and Wyoming, they are readily distinguishable and biostratigraphically significant. Their ranges overlap slightly at some localities, but this is to be expected in a consistently evolving group in which species are subdivisions of a continuum.

Illaenurus montanensis Kobayashi
(Pl. 15, fig. 24)

Illaenurus montanensis Kobayashi, 1935a, p. 48, Pl. 10, figs. 1–3
Illaenurus albertensis Resser, 1942b, p. 38–39, Pl. 6, figs. 8–12, Pl. 14, fig. 18

Description: Cranidium longer than wide, eyes posterior to midline, anterior facial sutures divergent.

Remarks: *Illaenurus "albertensis"* Resser is similar in every respect to *I. montanensis.* The diagnostic feature of both is the divergence of the anterior facial sutures.

Occurrence: *Illaenurus montanensis* is rare in the Trempealeauan at MC 293.5

Illaenurus quadratus Hall
(Pl. 15, fig. 23)

Illaenurus quadratus Hall, 1863, p. 176–177; Nelson, 1951, p. 783, Pl. 110, fig. 11 (synonymy to date); Bell and Ellinwood, 1962, p. 396, Pl. 55, figs. 1–3

Description: Cranidium longer than wide (exclusive of the palpebral lobes), anterior facial sutures parallel, eyes posterior to midline of cranidium.

Occurrence: *I. quadratus* is rare in the Trempealeauan at BC 192.6; BM 284; ME 31.1, 33, 46, 51.1; FOX 240.1.

Illaenurus sinclairensis Resser
(Pl. 15, figs. 20–21)

Illaenurus (?) *sinclairensis* Resser, 1942b, p. 39, Pl. 6, figs. 13–15

Description: Cranidium wider than long, eyes anterior to midline; species occurs in lower part of range of *Illaenurus.*

Occurrence: *I. sinclairensis* is rare in the Trempealeauan at BC 191.1, 192.6; BM 279.1; ME 47.6; MC 285.5; YO 240.7; UFOX 55.

Illaenurus truncatus Feniak
(Pl. 15, fig. 22)

Illaenurus truncatus Feniak, *in* Bell, Feniak, and Kurtz, 1952, p. 196, Pl. 38, figs. 3a–b

Remarks: Cranidium nearly quadrate, eyes on midline. The species occurs low in the range of *I. quadratus* with *I. sinclairensis,* but normally is larger. It ranges biostratigraphically higher than *I. sinclairensis.*

Occurrence: *I. truncatus* is rare in the Trempealeauan at BC 191.1, 192.6, 205.5; UFOX 55.

Family Kingstoniidae Kobayashi, 1933
Genus *Bynumiella* Resser, 1942
Bynumiella typicalis Resser
(Pl. 15, figs. 16, 19 [?])

Bynumiella typicalis Resser, 1942b, p. 57, Pl. 10, figs. 1–2

Remarks: *Bynumiella typicalis* is characterized by its arrowhead-shaped cranidium and small size. Resser (1942, p. 57) refers to a "swollen neck ring." This feature is exaggerated in the two specimens from Montana and is produced into a short, stout occipital spine. In other respects the specimens are identical to Resser's illustrations of *B. typicalis.*

A small pygidium (Pl. 15, fig. 19) is tentatively assigned to this species on the basis of its association with a cranidium. It has posteriorly directed pleural segments, and the margin has small cuspate projections at the postero-lateral corners.

OCCURRENCE: *Bynumiella typicalis* is rare in the Trempealeauan. One cranidium and pygidium were found at BC 205.5; one cranidium at MC 293.5; one at YO 240.7.

Genus *Bynumina* Resser, 1942
Bynumina terrenda Wilson
(Pl. 8, fig. 11)

Bynumina terrenda WILSON, 1951, p. 628, Pl. 89, figs. 7–11

REMARKS: This species from the *Elvinia* Zone differs from the type species *B. caelata* Resser (1942) in its shallow furrows, untapered posterior limbs, and nonconvergent facial sutures just anterior to the eyes. It resembles *B. globosa* (Walcott) which Palmer (1960) reported from the *Elvinia* Zone of the Dunderberg Shale of Nevada, differing in its more nearly circular glabellar outline, shorter, less convex, and raised frontal area, and wider fixed cheeks.

OCCURRENCE: *Bynumina terrenda* is rare in the *Elvinia* Zone. One cranidium was found at FP 88 and one at CF 19.

Bynumina sp. undet.
(Pl. 15, fig. 17)

REMARKS: This undetermined species is represented by three cranidia which resemble Resser's (1942b, Pl. 10) illustrated specimens of *Bynumina caelata* and *B. missouriensis,* but differ in their greater proportionate width, shorter glabellas with weaker furrows, and greater convexity, especially of the glabellas. Palmer (1960, p. 94) says that Resser's illustrated specimens are exfoliated, and that nonexfoliated specimens more nearly resemble *B. terrenda.* Therefore the resemblance of these few specimens from Montana and Wyoming to Resser's probably is not significant. Furthermore, Resser's species are from the *Elvinia* Zone, whereas these occur in the Trempealeauan.

OCCURRENCE: *Bynumina* sp. is rare in the Trempealeauan; one cranidium was found at ME 46, two at UFOX 55.

Family KOMASPIDIDAE Kobayashi, 1935
Genus *Irvingella* Ulrich and Resser *in* Walcott, 1924
Irvingella major Ulrich and Resser
(Pl. 10, figs. 8–9, 11)

Irvingella major Ulrich and Resser. WALCOTT, 1924b, p. 58, Pl. 10, fig. 3; WALCOTT, 1925, p. 98, Pl. 15, figs. 26–29; FREDERICKSON, 1949, p. 353–355, Pl. 69, figs. 5–7 (partial synonymy to date); GAINES, 1951, p. 609–615, Pl. 1, figs. 1–32 (synonymy to date); BELL and ELLINWOOD, 1962, p. 397, Pl. 55, figs. 4–5

REMARKS: Resser (1942b, p. 13–25, Pl. 2, figs. 22–49, Pl. 3, figs. 1–54, Pl. 4, figs. 1–14) described 22 species of *Irvingella.* All but six have been placed in synonymy with *I. major* by Frederickson (1949), Gaines (1951), and Bell and Ellinwood (1962). Resser did not describe species of *Irvingella* from Montana, Wyoming, or vicinity. Collections from the Snowy Range show great variation, but all occur in the same biostratigraphic position, and fall well within the concept of *I. major* as constituted by the above authors.

The population of *I. major* that occurs in the Snowy Range Formation contains cranidia that range in length from 2 mm to 12 mm. The ratio of width of fixed cheek to glabella ranges from 1:2 to 1:3. The frontal area may be from one fifth to one twelfth of the cranidial length. Glabellas retain a length-width ratio of approximately 4:3 throughout the otherwise quite variable population.

OCCURRENCE: *Irvingella major* is common in the *Irvingella major* Zonule at the top of the *Elvinia* Zone at HD 80.4; GC 85.8; YO 69.4, 70.6 and in the lowermost beds of the *Taenicephalus* Zone at HG 47.7; MC 111.7; BB 55.

Subgenus *Parairvingella* Kobayashi, 1938

Irvingella (Parairvingella) KOBAYASHI, 1938, p. 175

TYPE SPECIES: *Chariocephalus ? tumifrons* WALCOTT, 1884, p. 61, Pl. 10, fig. 16 (not *C. tumifrons* HALL and WHITFIELD, 1877)

REMARKS: Lochman (1953a, p. 887) considers *Parairvingella* Kobayashi to be a subjective junior synonym of *Irvingella* Ulrich and Resser. She says,

"I agree with Westergård (1947) that among known species of *Irvingella* there is continuous gradation in the width of the pre-glabellar area and the degree of obsolescence of the anterior border furrow, and that consequently these features are not of generic value."

Specimens from low in the *Elvinia* Zone at Nixon Gulch, 11 feet below the first occurrence of *Irvingella major,* have the long frontal area that characterizes species of *I.* (*Parairvingella*). Palmer (1960, p. 73) agrees that these characters are sufficiently different from *Irvingella* to deserve a separate category. This usage also agrees with statements by Lochman, Westergård, and Kobayashi that *I.* (*Parairvingella*) does not deserve full generic rank. Elevation from subgenus to genus was by Resser (1942b, p. 25) who considered *Parairvingella* transitional between *Drumaspis* and *Elvinia.*

Irvingella (*Parairvingella*) *eurekensis* Resser
(Pl. 8, fig. 8)

Parairvingella eurekensis RESSER, 1942b, p. 26–27, Pl. 4, figs. 15–17

REMARKS: This species has the tumid glabella, wide fixed cheeks, and large palpebral lobes that typify species of *Irvingella.* It differs from species of *Irvingella* (*Irvingella*) in its longer, narrower glabella, longer frontal area divided into distinct brim and border, and in its somewhat lower, total cranidial convexity. The frontal area is slightly longer than one third the glabellar length, consisting of a downsloping brim and border, with brim-border ratio of about 3:2.

I. (*P.*) *eurekensis* differs from *Elvinia hamburgensis* (Resser) in having a downsloping rather than sharply upturned border, more gibbous glabella, and smaller frontal area. It differs from *I.* (*P.*) *angustilimbata* Kobayashi and *I.* (*P.*) *intermedia* Resser in its longer, more tapered glabella, longer frontal area, and narrower fixed cheeks. *I.* (*P.*) *eurekensis* more closely resembles *Elvinia* than do these two species, which are closer to *Irvingella* (*Irvingella*).

This species occurs low in the *Elvinia* Zone, probably representing an early stage in the evolution of *Irvingella.*

OCCURRENCE: *Irvingella* (*Parairvingella*) *eurekensis* is rare in the *Elvinia* Zone at HG 36.

Family LECANOPYGIDAE Lochman, 1953
Genus *Rasettia* Lochman, 1953
Rasettia snowyensis Grant n.sp.
(Pl. 15, figs. 8, 11)

DESCRIPTION: Cranidium subquadrate, strongly convex; glabella slightly tapered anteriorly, dorsal furrow rather shallow, deepest at posterior, becoming shallower anteriorly, absent around anterior of glabella; occipital furrow shallow, glabellar furrows weak or absent; anterior rim narrow, slightly raised, weakly striated transversely, anterior margin weakly convex anteriorly; fixed cheeks relatively wide, palpebral lobes short, semielliptical, posterior limbs elongate, downsloping, with distinct furrow; occipital ring short, convex.

Pygidium subelliptical in outline; axial lobe high, convex, rather strongly tapering posteriorly, not clearly outlined at posterior median line, only two or three anterior segments clearly marked; pleural lobes wide, flatly convex, pleural segments visible only at anterior, furrows fading toward margins; pleural platform smooth, broad.

HOLOTYPE: USNM 142401, Plate 15, figure 11

ETYMOLOGY: *Snowyensis,* named for occurrence in the Snowy Range Formation

REMARKS: This species is characterized by its convex cranidium with relatively wide fixed cheeks, narrow brim, flatly convex anterior margin, and rather convex occipital furrow; its relatively narrow pygidium with distinct axial and pleural furrows, and high tapered axial lobe which slopes posteriorly to fade into the pleural platform. It differs from the type species *R. capax* (Billings) in its somewhat wider fixed cheeks, longer and flatter occipital ring, flatter pleural lobes with two instead of only one pleural furrow on each side, and especially in its narrower pygidium with proportionately longer axial lobe which is more strongly tapered and not outlined clearly at the posterior axis. It differs from *R. dubia* (Billings), *R. marcoui* (Clark), and *R. depressa* (Rasetti) in size and convexity of the cranidium, but primarily in its lack of a preglabellar area behind the rim (*see* Rasetti, 1944, p. 250, Pl. 39).

The cranidium differs from that of *R. quinnensis* (Resser) or *R. wichitaensis* (Resser, 1942b, Pl. 6) in its much narrower rim and less strongly convex anterior margin. The pygidium is narrower and has a higher axial lobe than in *R. sinclairensis* (Resser) and *R. oklahomensis* (Resser); it has a higher, longer, and more distinct axial lobe, and more distinct segmentation than *R. witchitaensis* (Resser) and *R. highlandensis* (Resser).

The cranidium most nearly resembles *R. capax,* differing as remarked above, but its pygidium is greatly different. The pygidium is similar to some assigned by Resser (1942b) to *R. wichitaensis,* but the cranidium lacks the large and gently sloping rim that is present on all of Resser's species. Therefore, this combination of pygidium and cranidium appears to be unique and to constitute a new species.

OCCURRENCE: *Rasettia snowyensis* is rare in the Trempealeauan at HJ 246.2; BC 205.5; BM 249.2; MC 290.5; YO 269.3; UYO 268.6.

Family MARJUMIIDAE Kobayashi, 1935
Genus *Deadwoodia* Resser, 1938
Deadwoodia duris (Walcott)
(Pl. 8, fig. 17)

Asaphiscus ? duris WALCOTT, 1916b, p. 392, Pl. 63, figs. 8, 8a

Deadwoodia duris (Walcott). WILSON, 1948, p. 33, Pl. 8, figs. 9–17; 1951, p. 633, Pl. 92, figs. 1–5; BELL, FENIAK, and KURTZ, 1952, p. 183, Pl. 29, figs. 3a–b; DELAND and SHAW, 1956, p. 551, Pl. 65, figs. 7–10

DESCRIPTION: Glabella high, convex, quadrate; frontal area relatively short, strongly downsloping, brim slightly concave with distinct preglabellar platform; border nearly horizontal.

REMARKS: *D. duris* differs from the type species *D. panope* (Walcott) primarily by its shorter, more steeply downsloping brim with distinct preglabellar platform.

It resembles species of the genus *Dellea,* especially *D. suada* (Walcott), differing in its more quadrate glabella and concave brim with preglabellar platform. Undoubtedly there is close relationship between species of *Deadwoodia* and *Dellea;* their morphologic affinities are discussed below under *Dellea.*

OCCURRENCE: *Deadwoodia duris* is rare in the *Elvinia* Zone at HG 36, 40; NG "top-of-reef"; HH 51.6; MC 105.4; BB 49.5.

Genus *Dellea* Wilson, 1949

Dellea WILSON, 1949, p. 34

Eshelmania WILSON, 1951, p. 641

TYPE SPECIES: *Ptychoparia suada* WALCOTT, 1890, p. 274, Pl. 21, fig. 9 = *Dellea wilbernsensis* WILSON, 1949, p. 35, Pl. 11, figs. 1–2, 4–7, 12

REMARKS: Wilson says in his discussion of the genus *Eshelmania* (1951, p. 642),

"This genus is comparable to *Dellea* in its similar proportions and depth of furrows. It differs fundamentally from *Dellea* in its long quadrate glabella with three pairs of furrows and in the recurvature of the posterior limbs."

Measurement of all of Wilson's photographs of *Dellea* and *Eshelmania* (Wilson, 1949; 1951), of seven topotype specimens of *Eshelmania* in his collection no. 47–1w7, and of two specimens of *Eshelmania* and several of *Dellea* in the Snowy Range collection shows only slight difference in the mean glabellar length-width ratios of the two groups. Except for one very aberrant *Eshelmania* (*E. convexa* Wilson, 1951, p. 642, Pl. 92, figs. 7–8), the glabellar length-width ratios of *Dellea* and *Eshelmania* are similar.

Wilson (1951, p. 639) states concerning *Dellea butlerensis* Frederickson that, "The posterior limbs are directed slightly backward, more so in this species than any other in the genus." Therefore, recurvature of the posterior limbs cannot be considered a valid criterion for distinguishing between *Dellea* and *Eshelmania*. *Dellea saratogensis* (Resser) has well-impressed glabellar furrows, so this feature does not distinguish the *Eshelmania* group from *Dellea*.

As Wilson's criteria for distinguishing *Eshelmania* from *Dellea* appear not to be generically significant, *Eshelmania* is included with *Dellea*. The slightly elongate glabella, well-marked glabellar furrows, and recurved posterior limbs characterize *Dellea snoburgensis* (Wilson).

Five species of *Dellea* are recognized currently in the literature: *D. butlerensis* Frederickson, *D. juvenalis* Frederickson, *D. saginata* DeLand, *D. saratogensis* (Resser), and *D. suada* (Walcott). These five, plus *D. snoburgensis* (Wilson), form a morphological continuum that approaches *Sulcocephalus* on the one hand and *Deadwoodia* on the other. *Dellea saratogensis* resembles *Sulcocephalus typicus* in its sunken tapering glabella, distinct glabellar furrows, wide dorsal furrow, upsloping fixed cheeks (exclusive of posterior limbs), brim-border ratio from "1.5 to 2.4" (Wilson, 1951, p. 638). *Dellea suada* approaches the form of *Deadwoodia duris* with its quadrate glabella, "horizontal or gently convex cheeks" (Wilson, 1951, p. 636), well-defined preglabellar platform, and "brim non-convex, but steeply deflexed" (Wilson, 1951, p. 637). Other species of *Dellea* fall between these extremes and differ from each other by slight and intergrading variations.

Dellea butlerensis Frederickson
(Pl. 8, fig. 18)

Dellea butlerensis FREDERICKSON, 1949, p. 351, Pl. 69, figs. 16–18; WILSON, 1951, p. 639, Pl. 91, figs. 1–3, 11

DESCRIPTION: Relatively narrow brim and wide flat border which results in a brim: border ratio near 1+:1; arcuate marginal furrow (radius of curvature of the marginal furrow approaching that of some specimens of *Sulcocephalus*); high, convex glabella; slightly recurved posterior limbs.

OCCURRENCE: *D. butlerensis* is rare in the *Elvinia* Zone at HG 36, 40, 47.5; NG "top-of-reef"; HH 51.6; BB 49.5; SL 65.

Dellea juvenalis Frederickson
(Pl. 8, fig. 13)

Dellea juvenalis FREDERICKSON, 1949, p. 351, Pl. 69, figs. 8–15

REMARKS: *Dellea juvenalis* is distinguished by its upturned border and steeply downsloping lateral areas of the brim, which results in apparent strong divergence of the anterior facial sutures. *D. saginata* (DeLand and Shaw, 1956, p. 552–553, Pl. 66, figs. 4–7) is close to *D. juvenalis,* differing primarily in its higher glabella and less steeply upturned border.

OCCURRENCE: *Dellea juvenalis* is rare in the *Elvinia* Zone at NG "top-of-reef"; FC 86; BC 63.8; YG 3.4a (= YG 20).

Dellea snoburgensis (Wilson)
(Pl. 8, figs. 15–16)

Eshelmania snoburgensis WILSON, 1951, p. 642, Pl. 92, figs. 9–15

DESCRIPTION: Species characterized by elongate, moderately elevated glabella (elevation intermediate between *D. suada* and *D. saratogensis*), and strongly recurved posterior limbs.

OCCURRENCE: *Dellea snoburgensis* is rare in the *Elvinia* Zone. One cranidium was found at HG 36, and one at HH 65.9.

Dellea saratogensis (Resser)
(Pl. 8, fig. 9)

Berkeia saratogensis RESSER, 1942b, p. 91, Pl. 15, figs. 22–25
Berkeia glabellamersa WILSON, 1949, p. 36, Pl. 11, figs. 13–15
Dellea saratogoensis (Resser). WILSON, 1951, p. 638, Pl. 91, figs. 12–17 (species name misspelled)

DESCRIPTION: Glabella furrows weak to well impressed; dorsal furrow deep; glabella non-elevated to sunken, tapering; fixed cheeks high; brim and border convex; occipital ring with node; border may be transversely striated, and distinct ocular ridge may be present. Wilson (1951, p. 638) says that the posterior limbs do not recurve, but extend straight out. Many specimens which correspond to *D. saratogensis* in every other respect have slightly recurved posterior limbs.

REMARKS: *Dellea saratogensis* is one of the extremes in variation of the genus *Dellea*. It approaches the form of *Sulcocephalus* in the features mentioned above (discussion of genus *Dellea*).

OCCURRENCE: *Dellea saratogensis* is common in the *Elvinia* Zone at HC 6.5; HD 80.4, 80.8; HG 36, 47.5; NG "top-of-reef"; FC 90; BC 63; SP 108.6; CF 29.2; FOX 51.1.

Dellea suada (Walcott)
(Pl. 8, figs. 10, 14)

Ptychoparia suada WALCOTT, 1890, p. 274, Pl. 21, fig. 9
Dellea suada (Walcott). WILSON, 1951, p. 636, Pl. 91, figs. 4–10, 18, 20–23, 25–26 (synonymy to date); DELAND and SHAW, 1956, p. 554, Pl. 66, figs. 8–9; LOCHMAN and HU, 1960, p. 813, Pl. 96, figs. 22–27

DESCRIPTION: Glabella moderately elevated; fixed cheeks horizontal or gently convex; posterior limbs slightly recurved; brim "non-convex but steeply deflexed" (Wilson, 1951, p. 637).

REMARKS: This last feature, combined with the somewhat quadrate glabella shown by some specimens, indicates relationship to *Deadwoodia duris* (Walcott). A few cranidia (*from* HG 36) are covered with minute granules. According to Wilson (1949, p. 35), granulation may be present on *D. suada,* but is not a diagnostic feature.

Some specimens have ocular ridges and occipital nodes like *D. saratogensis*. These differ from *D. saratogensis* by the higher glabella, faint glabellar furrows, and "non-convex" brim. *D. suada* is at the opposite extreme of the variation of the genus from *D. saratogensis*. Features in common emphasize the close relationship between these two end members of the genus.

OCCURRENCE: *Dellea suada* is common to rare in the *Elvinia* Zone at HD 80.4; HG 36, 45.8; NG 48; HH 65.9; GC 71.2; FC 93.7; FP 88; BC 63.8; SP 108.6; CF 21.2; SL 65.

Family PAGODIIDAE Kobayashi, 1935
Genus *Kiowaia* Frederickson, 1949
Kiowaia cf. *K. timberensis* Frederickson
(Pl. 10, fig. 12)

Kiowaia timberensis FREDERICKSON, 1949, p. 356–357, Pl. 10, figs. 18–22

REMARKS: An abraded cranidium found with *Irvingella major* is identified tentatively with *Kiowaia timberensis* on the basis of its small eyes, moderately wide posterior limbs, and especially by the narrow brim, marginal furrow that is tangential to the anterior of the glabella, and the convex border. It can be distinguished from an abraded cranidium of *Irvingella* by the narrow fixed cheeks, longer frontal area, and weak or absent glabellar furrows. This specimen is mentioned and figured to show similarity of the *Irvingella major* faunule of the Snowy Range Formation to that of the Honey Creek Formation of Oklahoma.

OCCURRENCE: *Kiowaia* cf. *K. timberensis* is very rare in the *Irvingella major* Zonule at the top of the *Elvinia* Zone at YO 69.4.

Family PARABOLINOIDIDAE Lochman, 1956

Genus *Croixana* Nelson, 1951

Croixana bipunctata (Shumard)

(Pl. 13, fig. 15)

Arionellus bipunctatus SHUMARD, 1862, p. 101; HALL, 1863, p. 169, Pl. 7, figs. 50–51
Croixana bipunctata (Shumard). NELSON, 1951, p. 775–776, Pl. 107, figs. 10, 12; BELL, FENIAK, and KURTZ, 1952, p. 185–186, Pl. 32, figs. 1a–b (synonymy to date); BERG, 1953, p. 556–559

REMARKS: Cranidia of *Croixana bipunctata* from the area of study, where they are preserved in limestone, have shallower anterolateral pits in the dorsal furrow than do those from Minnesota and Wisconsin, and each has a tiny occipital node. The sandstone specimen illustrated by Nelson (1951, Pl. 107, fig. 12) does not show the node clearly, and no mention of it is made, but a sandstone cranidium figured by Bell, Feniak, and Kurtz (1952, Pl. 32, fig. 1a) has the occipital node. One specimen from the Snowy Range has a flexure of the anterior part of the steeply downsloping frontal area that results in a narrow pseudo-border. In other respects, it conforms to the diagnosis of *C. bipunctata* by Bell, Feniak, and Kurtz (1952, p. 186).

OCCURRENCE: *Croixana bipunctata* is rare at the top of the *Taenicephalus* Zone at HD 106.1, in the *Idahoia wyomingensis* Subzone at HG 77.3; FC 143.2; BC 100, 106.4.

Genus *Kendallina* Berg, 1959 (*in* Harrington and others)

Kendallina biforota (Berg)

(Pl. 10, fig. 15)

Kendallia biforota BERG, 1953, p. 562, Pl. 59, figs. 7, 10

DESCRIPTION: Frontal area smooth; anterior margin nasute; anterolateral corners of marginal furrow pitted.

REMARKS: The species is common in Minnesota and Wisconsin; there it occurs biostratigraphically segregated from *K. eryon* (Berg, 1953, p. 562). It has not been found associated with *K. eryon* in Montana, but specimens are so few that its segregation is not certainly demonstrated.

OCCURRENCE: One cranidium of *Kendallina biforota* was found with ***Taenicephalus gallupensis*** in the *Parabolinoides* Subzone at FC 109.8, and a doubtfully identified cranidium in the same subzone at FD 15.3. Lochman collected a specimen at Dry Creek 6.9 W. and one in float at NG.

Kendallina eryon (Hall)

(Pl. 12, figs. 15–18)

Conocephalites eryon HALL, 1863, p. 157, Pl. 7, figs. 10–16, Pl. 8, figs. 16, 31
Kendallia eryon (Hall). RAASCH, 1939, p. 94; BERG, 1953, p. 562–563, Pl. 59, fig. 9, Pl. 60, fig. 1 (synonymy to date)
Kendallina eryon (Hall). BERG, *in* HARRINGTON AND OTHERS, 1959, p. O272; LOCHMAN and HU, 1960, p. 811, Pl. 95, figs. 24–30

DESCRIPTION: Frontal area smooth, downsloping; palpebral lobes small, forwardly placed; posterior limbs moderately wide, morphologically intermediate between those of *Taenicephalus* and *Parabolinoides.*

REMARKS: Some specimens from Montana and Wyoming have a slightly raised ridge or row of pustules in place of a marginal furrow, or the border may be slightly raised above the level of the brim, giving the appearance of a ridge separating them.

The glabella of *K. eryon* is very low, glabellar furrows are shallow or absent, and the dorsal furrow is shallow. This smooth form is close to that of some specimens of *Orygmaspis llanoensis* (Walcott), and it is not surprising that Resser (1937, p. 22) at one time assigned *K. eryon* to *Orygmaspis*. This species can be distinguished from species of *Orygmaspis* by its wider posterior limbs and much smaller and more anteriorly placed palpebral lobes.

Identifications were made by comparison of cranidia with Berg's (1953) stereo-illustrations of Hall's holotype, and with plaster casts of the holotype in the collections of the University of Texas.

The pygidium illustrated on Plate 12 (fig. 17) differs from that assigned to the species by Hall (1863, Pl. 7, fig. 16) and by Lochman (*in* Harrington and others, 1959, Fig. 202) in its more nearly semicircular outline, stronger pleural segments, well-defined narrow border, and lack of axial indentation of the margin. Reasons for assigning this pygidium, aside from its association, involve its more "taenicephaloid" shape: it seems to have the outline and configuration of the pygidia of other of the Parabolinoididae, in contrast to the transverse pygidium of the "drumaspid" type of Hall and the Treatise.

OCCURRENCE: *Kendallina eryon* is common in the *Taenicephalus* Zone at HD 86.6, 90.1; HG 56, 63.5; HI 67.7; HK 77.9, 92.4; GC 92.6; BC 74.3; SP 117.4; FD 15.3; SC 42.7; MC 117.1; YO 75.7, 79.7; GR 98.9f; SL 80.6, 81.1, 81.5.

Genus *Maustonia* Raasch, 1939

Maustonia nasuta (Hall)

(Pl. 12, figs. 9–14)

Conocephalites nasutus HALL, 1863, p. 155, Pl. 7, figs. 3–9

Maustonia nasuta (Hall). RAASCH, 1939, p. 94; BERG, 1953, p. 563–564, Pl. 60, figs. 2–4 (synonymy to date)

REMARKS: *Maustonia nasuta* is characterized by its gently convex brim, flat border, and weak marginal furrow. The marginal furrow is not consistently straight, as stated by Berg (1953, p. 564), but may bend forward laterally as shown in Hall's illustrations and in Berg's photographs of Hall's specimens (Pl. 60, fig. 4). Many Snowy Range cranidia have the marginal furrow bent. The anterior margin normally is somewhat nasute, but may be gently rounded.

M. nasuta appears to be a relative of *Taenicephalus*. The glabella has a similar taper and similar pattern of glabellar furrows: the posterior limbs are very similar. Differences are mainly in the palpebral lobes, smaller in *M. nasuta,* and the frontal area, much less convex in *M. nasuta.* This resemblance to species of *Taenicephalus* is useful in distinguishing *M. nasuta* from species of *Kendallina* that more closely resemble *Parabolinoides* in the shape of the posterior limbs.

OCCURRENCE: The range of *Maustonia nasuta* bridges the *Parabolinoides* and *Taenicephalus* zones. *M. nasuta* occurs locally with both *Parabolinoides* and *Taenicephalus.* It is rare at HD 90.1; HE 89.3; HG 56; HI 67.7; GC 93.5; BC 74.3, 87.1; SP 117.4; RP 57.5; SC 42.7, 81.5; CF 62.3, 64.2, 65.6; YO 78.1, 79.7; SL 80.6, 81.1, 81.5.

Genus *Orygmaspis* Resser, 1937

Orygmaspis RESSER, 1937, p. 21–22

TYPE SPECIES: *Ptychoparia llanoensis* WALCOTT, 1890, p. 272, Pl. 21, figs. 3–5

REMARKS: The two species of *Orygmaspis* present in Montana and Wyoming grade into one another, but the end members are very different. Certainly they would be treated as separate species if intermediate forms were unknown. They are treated separately here so that the distinct end members might be identified. Intermediate forms were assigned arbitrarily.

Orygmaspis firma Frederickson

(Pl. 12, figs. 3, 5–6)

Orygmaspis firma FREDERICKSON, 1949, p. 359–360, Pl. 71, figs. 15–18; BELL and ELLINWOOD, 1962, p. 398, Pl. 55, fig. 16, Pl. 56, fig. 1

REMARKS: Frederickson says that *O. firma* can be distinguished from *O. llanoensis* by its convex border, impressed marginal furrow, and more blunt glabella. *O. firma* here also includes specimens in which the brim is downsloping at the normal angle (Frederickson, 1949, Pl. 21, fig. 16), but the border is either flat or convex, and either horizontal or slightly upsloping. This is further development of a trend that seems to be incipient in Frederickson's illustrated specimens.

Specimens of *O. firma* in which the brim and border meet at a fairly sharp angle have the dorsal furrow much reduced anterior to the glabella. This may have been what Frederickson meant by referring to the blunt glabella of *O. firma,* but it is not a criterion for distinguishing between *O. firma* and *O. llanoensis.* Walcott's holotype of *O. llanoensis* (USNM no. 23857) displays a blunt, nearly truncate glabella (Walcott, 1890, Pl. 21, fig. 3; 1899, Pl. 64, fig. 4).

OCCURRENCE: *Orygmaspis firma* is moderately common in the lower part of the *Taenicephalus* Zone at HB 77.8; HD 85.1, 85–88; HF 14.8; HG 47.7; NG 3d; HH 72.3, 74.3; HI 67.7; HK 77.9; GC 92.6, 93.5; JC 68.1; SP 116.4; BP 98.7; SC 40.1, 43.8; CF 51.8, 62.3; FOX 73.5; BB 56; SL 80.6, 81.5.

Orygmaspis llanoensis (Walcott)
(Pl. 12, figs. 4, 7)

Ptychoparia llanoensis WALCOTT, 1890, p. 272, Pl. 21, figs. 3–5; 1899, p. 458, Pl. 64, fig. 4
Orygmaspis llanoensis (Walcott). RESSER, 1937, p. 21–22; FREDERICKSON, 1949, p. 359, Pl. 71, figs. 19–22 (synonymy to date); LOCHMAN, *in* HARRINGTON AND OTHERS, 1959, fig. 202, no. 12a, b; BELL and ELLINWOOD, 1962, p. 398, Pl. 55, figs. 11–15

REMARKS: *Orygmaspis llanoensis* is characterized by its relatively smooth frontal area and shallow marginal furrow. Walcott's holotype cranidium shows that when the frontal area is exfoliated, it may have a slightly convex brim and distinct marginal furrow. Specimens from the Snowy Range display all stages of thickening of the border and deepening of the marginal furrow, almost to the stage represented by some of Frederickson's specimens of *Orygmaspis firma* (1949, p. 359–360, Pl. 71, figs. 17–18).

OCCURRENCE: *Orygmaspis llanoensis* is common in the lower part of the *Taenicephalus* Zone. It occurs at HC 14.6; HE 90.8; HF 14.8, 15.5, 15.6; HG 47.7; HI 67.7; HK 77.2, 77.9; GC 92.6, 93.5; BC 69.3; BP 102.4; CF 51.8, 65.6; YO 78.1, 81.1; FOX 65.4; SL 81.1.

Genus *Parabolinoides* Frederickson, 1949

Parabolinoides FREDERICKSON, 1949, p. 360
Bernia FREDERICKSON, 1949, p. 357
TYPE SPECIES: *Parabolinoides contractus* FREDERICKSON, 1949, p. 361

REMARKS: Descriptions of *Parabolinoides* and *Bernia* (Frederickson, 1949) indicate only two distinguishing differences: *Bernia* has a short glabella whereas that of *Parabolinoides* is elongated; the brim of *Bernia* is "flatly concave in front of glabella," whereas *Parabolinoides* has the "brim flatly convex."

Measurement of Frederickson's holotypes of *Bernia obtusa* and *Parabolinoides hebe* and of the photographs of his paratypes demonstrates that the cranidium of *B. obtusa* is proportionately wider across the palpebral lobes than is that of *P. hebe.* Additional data from 25 complete cranidia of *P. hebe* from Montana and Wyoming show a population with no clear-cut break in the cranidial length-width ratios. Instead, these ratios spread along a continuum, with specimens that might be called *Bernia* occupying one end and merging gradually into those which fit Frederickson's definition of *P. hebe.*

Measurements from Frederickson's holotypes and photographs demonstrate that the glabellar length-width ratios of *B. obtusa* and *P. hebe* are almost identical. Only the holotype of *B. obtusa* has a slightly higher ratio of width to length than that of the paratypes of *B. obtusa* or of any of the illustrations or the holotype specimen of *P. hebe.* Examination of the holotype of *B. obtusa* shows that this short and broad condition results from slight distortion; the specimen is deformed. Therefore this parameter is of no value in separating species and certainly valueless as a generic distinction.

In his reference to the short glabella of *B. obtusa* versus the elongate glabella of species of *Parabolinoides,* Frederickson probably meant the proportion of the cranidial length occupied by the glabella, rather than the ratio of the glabellar length to the glabellar width. This is stated in his description of *P. hebe* (1949, p. 361). Measurement of his holotypes and of illustrations of his paratypes manifests just the reverse. In the holotypes the glabella of *B. obtusa* occupies a greater proportion of the cranidial length than does the glabella of *P. hebe,* but again comparison is based on the deformed holotype of *B. obtusa.* The paratypes represent a variable population whose measurements of this feature fall along a continuum without obvious breaks. Addition of data from the Montana and Wyoming specimens of *P. hebe* fills out the curve, but does not change the conclusion.

With reference to the second difference between *Bernia* and *Parabolinoides,* "flatly concave" brims merge by way of flat brims into "flatly convex" brims; the difference is barely recognizable. Like other such sibling genera, (*e.g., Camaraspis– "Camaraspoides," Taenicephalus– "Bemaspis"*), *Parabolinoides* and *Bernia* occupy identical biostratigraphic positions (Frederickson, 1949, p. 343, Table 1).

Bernia and *Parabolinoides* are considered synonyms, but *Bernia* is suppressed rather than *Parabolinoides* despite its page priority (Frederickson, 1949). *Parabolinoides* has been recognized widely, now contains several well-known species, and gives its name to biostratigraphic subdivisions in the upper Mississippi Valley and in Texas (*e.g.,* Berg, 1953, p. 556, Table 1). *Bernia* contains but one species (Frederickson, 1949, p. 343, Table 1; p. 358), and the holotype of its type species is imperfectly preserved.

In a chart of the evolution of the Parabolinoididae, Lochman (1956, p. 454–455, Fig. 4) interprets *Bernia* as a dead-end offshoot of *Parabolinoides,* and in her discussion says, "*Parabolinoides* dominated the *Eoorthis* Subzone, and during this time gave rise only to the very similar, short-lived *Bernia.*" Recognition of *Bernia* as a synonym of *Parabolinoides* removes this anomaly.

Parabolinoides is variable, united by a few diagnostic characters. The eyes are small and situated on or forward of the anterior one third line of the glabella; the posterior limbs are long and broadly triangular. The group of species now included in *Parabolinoides* is incompletely known and in need of thorough study; therefore no species is suppressed here.

Parabolinoides contractus Frederickson
(Pl. 10, figs. 20, 23–27)

Parabolinoides contractus FREDERICKSON, 1949, p. 361, Pl. 71, figs. 4–10; BERG, 1953, p. 564, Pl. 59, fig. 3; LOCHMAN, *in* HARRINGTON AND OTHERS, 1959, p. 0272, Fig. 202, no. 8; BELL and ELLINWOOD, 1962, p. 399, Pl. 56, fig. 12

REMARKS: *Parabolinoides contractus* differs from *P. hebe* in its divergent anterior facial sutures. It differs from *P. expansus* Nelson in its horizontal to slightly downsloping brim and raised border and from *P. cordillerensis* (Lochman) in its arcuate marginal furrow without pustules.

OCCURRENCE: *Parabolinoides contractus* is rare to moderately common in the lower part of the *Taenicephalus* Zone (*Parabolinoides* Subzone). Its range extends higher in the zone than does that of *P. hebe.* It has been found at HD 85.1; HE 89.3; HG 47.7; HI 67.7; GC 93.5; BC 69.3; SC 40.1, 42.7; MC 117.1; YO 75.7; FOX 65.4; SL 81.1, 81.5.

Parabolinoides cordillerensis (Lochman)
(Pl. 11, figs. 1–5)

Maustonia cordillerensis LOCHMAN, 1950a, p. 331–332, Pl. 47, figs. 6–13
Parabolinoides cordillerensis (Lochman). BERG, 1953, p. 563 (mentioned in discussion of *Maustonia*)

REMARKS: Lochman originally assigned this species to *Maustonia,* but Berg (1953) pointed out that it was more likely a species of *Parabolinoides. Parabolinoides cordillerensis* differs from *P. hebe* in its strongly divergent anterior facial sutures, from *P. expansus* in its convex raised border, and from *P. contractus,* its closest relative, in its straight pustulose marginal furrow. Possibly *P. cordillerensis* and *P. contractus* are subspecies of a single species.

OCCURRENCE: *Parabolinoides cordillerensis* is common in the lower part of the *Taenicephalus* Zone (*Parabolinoides* Subzone). It has been collected from HB 77.8; HD 85.1; HF 15.6; HG 51; HI 67.7; HK 77.2; GC 92.6, 93.5; FC 108.6; JC 68.1; BC 69.3; SC 42.7, 52.3; CF 40; MC 117.1; YO 73.9, 75.7, 79.7; FOX 65.4; BB 56; SL 80.6.

Parabolinoides expansus Nelson
(Pl. 10, figs. 18, 21–22)

Parabolinoides expansa NELSON, 1951, p. 776, Pl. 107, figs. 1, 3; BERG, 1953, p. 564 (in synonymy of *P. contractus* FREDERICKSON); LOCHMAN and HU, 1960, p. 811, Pl. 95, figs. 32–35

REMARKS: *Parabolinoides expansus* is characterized by divergent anterior facial sutures, strongly downsloping brim, and flat or convex, horizontal or downsloping border. This configuration of the frontal area may be identical in some individuals to that of *Maustonia hedra* (Kurtz). *P. expansa* has the wide triangular posterior limbs typical of *Parabolinoides,* which differentiate it from species of *Maustonia.*

Berg (1953, p. 564) placed *P. expansus* into synonymy with *P. contractus* Frederickson, at the same time establishing *P. palatus* Berg (1953, p. 565) on grounds similar to those upon which Nelson established *P. expansus.* According to Berg, *P. expansus* differs from *P. contractus* only by its downsloping brim and flat border. *P. palatus* is distinguished by its long frontal area, wide brim, and flat or gently convex, downsloping or horizontal border. The frontal area of *P. contractus* is just as large as that of *P. palatus,* so *P. palatus* differs only in its downsloping brim, the same feature that distinguishes *P. expansus* from *P. contractus.*

The inconsistency of Berg's argument is pointed out only to justify use of *P. expansus* as a valid species in Montana and Wyoming. It would be inadvisable to suppress *P. palatus* without first examining the entire collection, especially because it has biostratigraphic significance in the upper Mississippi Valley.

OCCURRENCE: *Parabolinoides expansus* is rare in the *Taenicephalus* Zone at HC 11.9; HD 86.6; HE 89.3; HG 51; FP 112.5; BC 69.3; FD 15.3; CF 59.7 (float); YO 74.1, 75.7; SL 80.6.

Parabolinoides hebe Frederickson
(Pl. 10, fig. 19)

Parabolinoides hebe FREDERICKSON, 1949, p. 361, Pl. 70, figs. 7–8, Pl. 71, figs. 1–3; BERG, 1953, p. 564, Pl. 59, figs. 2, 4; BELL and ELLINWOOD, 1962, p. 400, Pl. 56, figs. 6–11
Bernia obtusa FREDERICKSON, 1949, p. 358, Pl. 70, figs. 1–6

REMARKS: *Parabolinoides hebe* is distinguished from other species of *Parabolinoides* by its parallel or slightly divergent anterior facial sutures, parallel-sided or slightly tapered glabella, and slightly downsloping frontal area with flat brim (ranging from flatly convex to flatly concave) and raised but not upsloping convex border. The brim and border normally are subequal, but some specimens have relatively narrower borders. No specimens with the border wider than the brim have been observed. Reasons for synonymy of *Bernia obtusa* are presented under discussion of *Parabolinoides.*

OCCURRENCE: *Parabolinoides hebe* is common in the lower part of the *Taenicephalus* Zone (*Parabolinoides* Subzone) at HB 77.8; HC 11.9, 14.6; HD 85.1; HE 89.3; HF 15.5; HG 47.7, 49, 51; HH 72.3; HK 77.2, 77.9; JC 69.6; SP 109.9, 116.4; BP 98.7; BM 92.7; SC 40.1; CF 40; MC 111.7; YO 73.9, 78.1; FOX 65.4; SL 81.1, 81.5. It is most abundant in the lower part of the zone, becoming rarer upward in the section.

Genus *Stigmacephaloides* Ellinwood, 1962
Stigmacephaloides curvabilis Ellinwood
(Pl. 14, fig. 21)

Stigmacephaloides curvabilis ELLINWOOD, *in* BELL and ELLINWOOD, 1962, p. 401, Pl. 56, figs. 2–5

REMARKS: This species is characterized by its smooth glabella and steeply downsloping frontal area which consists of subequal brim and border.

OCCURRENCE: One well-preserved cranidium was found high in the Franconian, associated with *Drumaspis idahoensis* in the *Idahoia serapio* Subzone at BM 182.1.

Genus *Taenicephalus* Ulrich and Resser *in* Walcott, 1924

Taenicephalus Ulrich and Resser. WALCOTT, 1924b, p. 59; WALCOTT, 1925, p. 116
Bemaspis FREDERICKSON, 1949, p. 357

TYPE SPECIES: *Conocephalites shumardi* HALL, 1863, p. 154

REMARKS: Frederickson (1949, p. 357) distinguished *Bemaspis* by its "short broad cranidium, large palpebral lobes and keeled glabella." Ellinwood (1953, Ph.D. thesis, Univ. Minnesota, p. 37) commented on the similarity between *Bemaspis gouldi* (the type species) and *Taenicephalus shumardi* and referred to specimens in his collections from Texas that appear to be intermediate between the two species. The Treatise on Invertebrate Paleontology (Harrington and others, 1959, p. 0306), on the other hand, not only recognizes *Bemaspis* and *Taenicephalus* as distinct genera, but assigns them to separate families.

Bemaspis is here considered a synonym of *Taenicephalus* for the following reasons: Study of Frederickson's holotype of *B. gouldi* and of his descriptions and illustrations of this and other specimens indicates that *Bemaspis* differs from *Taenicephalus* only in possession of a broader cranidium. The keeled glabella is no distinction; many specimens of *Taenicephalus* are keeled (*see* Resser, 1942b, Pls. 19–21). Breadth of the cranidium of *Bemaspis gouldi* depends upon size of the palpebral lobes; cranidia with slightly larger palpebral lobes are broader, when measured across the lobes. Possession of slightly larger palpebral lobes is insufficient ground for maintenance of *Bemaspis* as a genus separate from *Taenicephalus.* Larger palpebral lobes probably are of specific value, and cranidia that have them are recognized as *Taenicephalus gouldi* (Frederickson).

Taenicephalus gallupensis Grant n.sp.
(Pl. 12, figs. 19–20)

Taenicephalus peali RESSER, 1942b (part), Pl. 19, figs. 15–16 (not figs. 17–23: *T. shumardi*)

DESCRIPTION: Cranidium convex, elongate; glabella slightly arched longitudinally, strongly arched transversely, swelling high above palpebral lobes; length of glabella exclusive of occipital ring greater than width just anterior to occipital furrow; glabellar furrows faint or absent, up to three in number; dorsal furrow deep, with deep pits at anterolateral corners of glabella; occipital ring normally with median node; frontal area about one third length of cranidium, downsloping; brim convex, downsloping, wider than border; border convex or flat, commonly downsloping, some horizontal; palpebral lobes upsloping, horizontal or downsloping; posterior limbs wide, triangular, typical for genus.

Free cheeks unknown; pygidium same as *T. shumardi* (Hall).

HOLOTYPE: USNM 142388, Plate 12, figure 19

ETYMOLOGY: *Gallupensis,* named for occurrence on Gallup Creek, west flank of Bridger Mountains, Gallatin County, Montana

REMARKS: *Taenicephalus gallupensis* is characterized by its high glabella, deep dorsal furrow with anterolateral pits, wider brim than border, and normally by its occipital node. Features that vary are the depth of impression of the glabellar furrows, which normally are shallow, and consistently shallower than in *T. shumardi* (Hall); the border, which may be convex as in *T. altus* Nelson, flat and horizontal (approaching the form of *Maustonia hedra* [Kurtz]), or convex and downsloping, which is a condition unique to *T. gallupensis.* The attitude of the palpebral lobes varies considerably, as in most species of *Taenicephalus.*

Taenicephalus gallupensis is easily distinguished from other species of *Taenicephalus.* The glabella of *T. shumardi* is at least as wide (just anterior to the occipital furrow) as it is long; the glabella of *T. gallupensis* is longer than wide. Both *T. altus* and *T. gallupensis* have deep anterolateral pits and great cranidial relief, but *T. gallupensis* has a high glabella and occipital node that contrast with the elevated palpebral lobes and less elevated glabella of *T. altus*.

OCCURRENCE: *Taenicephalus gallupensis* is abundant in the *Taenicephalus* Zone at HB 73.8, 77.8; HE 90.8; HF 15.6; HG 51; HH 74.3; HI 69.5; HK 78.7; GC 93.5, 94.2; FC 109.8; FP 123; JC 69.6; BC 69.3, 73.3; SP 111.9, 117.4, 118.4; BM 92.7; CF 62.3, 64.2.

Taenicephalus gouldi (Frederickson)
(Pl. 12, figs. 1–2)

Bemaspis gouldi FREDERICKSON, 1949, p. 357, Pl. 71, figs. 11–14; LOCHMAN, *in* HARRINGTON AND OTHERS, 1959, p. 0306

Taenicephalus gouldi (Frederickson). BELL and ELLINWOOD, 1962, p. 401, Pl. 57, figs. 1–9

REMARKS: Measured across the palpebral lobes and along the axis, the cranidium of *Taenicephalus gouldi* is broader than long, distinguishing *T. gouldi* from other species of *Taenicephalus*. Most specimens also exhibit a subequal brim and border, a glabella wider than long, a glabella higher above frontal area than in other species of *Taenicephalus* that have the subequal brim and border.

OCCURRENCE: *Taenicephalus gouldi* is common in the *Parabolinoides* Subzone of the *Taenicephalus* Zone. It has been found at HB 73.8, 77.8; HD 85–88, 84.6, 85.1; HE 90.8; HF 15.6; HG 51; HH 74.3; HI 69.5; GC 94.2; FC 108.6; JC 69.6; SP 111.9, 117.4; BM 92.7; YO 79.7, 81.1.

Taenicephalus shumardi (Hall)
(Pl. 12, figs. 21–22, 25–26)

Conocephalites shumardi HALL, 1863, p. 154, Pl. 7, figs. 1–2, Pl. 8, fig. 32

Taenicephalus shumardi (Hall). WALCOTT, 1924b, p. 59, Pl. 13, fig. 1; WALCOTT, 1925, p. 117, Pl. 17, figs. 15–17; RESSER, 1942b, Pl. 20, fig. 21; SHIMER and SHROCK, 1944, p. 633, Pl. 266, fig. 17; BERG, 1953, p. 565–566, Pl. 59, figs. 11–14; WILSON, 1951, p. 652–653, Pl. 95, figs. 21–23, 25; LOCHMAN, *in* HARRINGTON AND OTHERS, 1959, p. 0274, Fig. 202, no. 10; LOCHMAN and HU, 1960, p. 811–812, Pl. 95, figs. 12–23, 31; BELL and ELLINWOOD, 1962, p. 402, Pl. 57, figs. 10–21

Taenicephalus peali RESSER, 1942b (part), p. 99, Pl. 19, figs. 17–23 (not figs. 15–16: *T. gallupensis* n.sp.)

Taenicephalus holmesi RESSER, 1942b, p. 100, Pl. 19, figs. 24–27

Taenicephalus speciosus RESSER, 1942b, p. 100, Pl. 20, fig. 19

Taenicephalus castlensis RESSER, 1942b, p. 106, Pl. 21, figs. 24–25

Taenicephalus wyomingensis RESSER, 1942b, p. 106–107, Pl. 21, fig. 32

Taenicephalus cordillerensis Miller. DELAND and SHAW, 1956, p. 559, Pl. 67, fig. 3 (not *T. cordillerensis* MILLER, 1936, p. 33–34, Pl. 8, figs. 40–41)

From recent discussions and accompanying illustrations of *Taenicephalus shumardi*, plus measurement of nearly 200 specimens from Montana and Wyoming, three simple ratios have been derived that distinguish *T. shumardi* from other known species of the genus. These measurements (including those of Hall's illustration and Berg's photograph of the holotype) indicate that the axial length of the cranidium is greater than the width across the palpebral lobes. The width of the base of the glabella just anterior to the occipital furrow is at least as great as the axial length of the glabella exclusive of the occipital ring and furrow. This feature was pointed out by Hall (1863, p. 164) in his original description of the species. The brim is at least as wide as the border and may be wider.

In *T. altus* Nelson and *T. gallupensis* n.sp. the glabellar length is greater than its width. In *T. gouldi* (Frederickson) the cranidial width is greater than its length. In *T. cordillerensis* Miller (1936, Pl. 8, figs. 40–41; Resser, 1942b, Pl. 19, fig. 33) the brim is narrower than the border, and the cranidial width is equal to or greater than its axial length. *T. wichitaensis* Resser (1942b, p. 105, Pl. 21, figs. 13–17; Frederickson, 1949, p. 362, Pl. 72, figs. 1–2) conforms very well to the dimensions of *T. shumardi* and probably is conspecific.

Resser (1942b, p. 99–107) established many species of *Taenicephalus*, each from its own locality. Large collections of topotype material from all of his localities in the "Dry Creek

Shale" (Snowy Range Formation) except those in the Wind River and Big Horn mountains (which contain *T. cordillerensis* Miller and *T. wyomingensis* Resser respectively) contain none of Resser's "locality-species" but only a variable population of *T. shumardi* along with *T. gallupensis* and *T. gouldi*.

The cranidium of *Taenicephalus* from western Wyoming that DeLand and Shaw (1956, p. 559, Pl. 67, fig. 3) illustrated under the heading of *T. cordillerensis* does not conform to Miller's original diagnosis of that species. Miller says (1936, p. 34),

"The cranidium of this species is similar to that of *T. shumardi* (Hall) but differs in being proportionately broader. The glabella of *T. cordillerensis* is more rounded and less conical, not squarely truncate in front as in *T. shumardi*."

DeLand and Shaw's illustrated cranidium is longer than broad, and the glabella is strongly conical and squarely truncate. In addition, the brim of their specimen is considerably wider than the border, which does not agree with either Miller's or Resser's (1942b, Pl. 19, fig. 33) illustrations of the species, but conforms very well to *T. shumardi*.

DeLand and Shaw (1956, p. 559) are correct in stating that *T. holmesi* Resser and *T. speciosus* Resser are conspecific with their illustrated specimens of *T. cordillerensis* (actually *T. shumardi*). Topotype specimens of these two species, and also *T. peali* Resser, fall well within the morphologic limits of *T. shumardi*. DeLand and Shaw examined *T. wyomingensis* Resser and believe that it belongs with their *T. cordillerensis*. Following their diagnosis, *T. wyomingensis* is included in the synonymy of *T. shumardi*.

OCCURRENCE: *Taenicephalus shumardi* is abundant in the *Taenicephalus* Zone. It has been found at HB 73.8; HC 14.6; HD 84.6, 86.6, 85–88; HE 89.3, 90.8; HF 15.5, 15.6, 19; HG 47.7, 51, 56; HH 72.3, 74.3; HI 69.5; HK 78.7; GC 93.5, 94.2; FC 108.6, 131.2; FP 123; JC 69.6; BC 69.3, 73.3; SP 111.9, 117.4, 118.4; BP 98.7, 102.4; BM 92.7; SC 40.1, 42.7, 43.8, 47.5, 50.7, 52.3, 54.9, 56.7; CF 62.3, 64.2, 65.6, 67.1, 69.6; MC 117.1; FOX 73.5; GR 74.1; SL 81.1, 81.5.

Family PLETHOPELTIDAE Raymond, 1924
Genus *Stenopilus* Clark, 1924
Stenopilus ? sp.
(Pl. 15, fig. 7)

REMARKS: Three cranidia are referred doubtfully to *Stenopilus* on the basis of their elliptical shape and smooth convexity. They are mentioned to record the presence of this kind of trilobite in the Trempealeauan of the West.

OCCURRENCE: *Stenopilus* ? sp. is very rare in the Trempealeauan at BM 296.8; UYO 267.6, 283.0.

Family PTEROCEPHALIIDAE Kobayashi, 1935
Genus *Aphelaspis* Resser, 1935
Aphelaspis sp. undet.
(Pl. 8, fig. 1)

DESCRIPTION: Cranidium small (average less than 5.0 mm), quadrate, moderately convex longitudinally; glabella slightly elevated above fixed cheeks, slightly tapered, nearly truncate, may be keeled or evenly arched transversely; glabellar furrows absent or faint; dorsal furrow moderately impressed, with incipient anterior pits; occipital node may be present; frontal area long, about one third length of cranidium; brim convex, downsloping; border short, about one third as long as brim, slightly upturned; marginal furrow shallow, gently arcuate; fixed cheeks half as wide as glabella at midline; palpebral lobes near midline of glabella, long, with distinct palpebral furrows. Posterior limbs probably narrow, straplike.

Free cheeks and pygidium unknown.

REMARKS: This species of *Aphelaspis* is characterized by its short border and incipient anterior pits. Comparison of the brim and border shows that the border is shorter than that of the species described by Palmer (1955a, p. 747, fig. 5), including *A. walcotti* which also has been described from Wyoming by Shaw (1956, p. 51). *Aphelaspis* sp., mentioned by

Lochman and Duncan (1944, p. 21, 32, 41), is illustrated by Duncan (1937, M.A. thesis, Montana State Univ., p. 22, Pl. 3, fig. 25) but is not the same as this species.

OCCURRENCE: Seven cranidia of *Aphelaspis* sp. were found in a bed of intraclastic limestone 2.5 feet above the base of the Dry Creek Shale in the section above Bighorn Lake in the Bridger Mountains (BL 2.5). Probably the species represents the upper part of the *Aphelaspis* Zone of the Dresbachian Stage, indicating that the zone is present in the Dry Creek Shale in Montana, as it is in Wyoming (Shaw, 1956, p. 48).

Genus *Camaraspis* Ulrich, 1924

Camaraspis ULRICH, 1924, p. 94
Camaraspoides FREDERICKSON, 1949, p. 349
TYPE SPECIES: *Arionellus* (*Agraulos*) *convexus* WHITFIELD, 1878, p. 57

REMARKS: Frederickson (1949, p. 349) comments that, "*Camaraspoides* does show a family relationship to *Camaraspis* Ulrich and Resser. The former may be readily distinguished, however, by the deeper dorsal furrow, presence of glabellar furrows, the convex border, and especially by the furrowed pygidium as contrasted to the smooth, unfurrowed pygidium of *Camaraspis*." Cranidia from the Snowy Range show various combinations of these characteristics. Some have glabellar furrows but shallow marginal furrows and barely distinguishable borders, whereas others have no glabellar furrows but do have deep dorsal furrows. A few are consistently more deeply furrowed than the others.

No smooth, unfurrowed pygidia were found in Montana or Wyoming. Deeply furrowed pygidia occur with smooth cranidia of *Camaraspis convexa* as in the central Appalachians (Wilson, 1951, p. 630, Pl. 90, figs. 5–7).

Examination of topotype material from Berkey's locality in the Mill Street Conglomerate (*see* Nelson, 1951, p. 775) and of Frederickson's specimens of *Camaraspoides* led to the same conclusion as that reached by Wilson (1951, p. 631): *Camaraspoides* is identical to *Camaraspis* in every proportion, the only difference being the depth of furrows on the cranidium. Wilson continued to recognize *Camaraspoides* because of its wide distribution. A slight difference in cranidial relief seems insufficient ground for its recognition as a separate genus.

Camaraspis berkeyi (Resser)
(Pl. 10, fig. 1)

Agraulos convexus Whitfield. BERKEY, 1898, p. 288, Pl. 20, figs. 9–11, Pl. 21, figs. 3, 7
Agraulos convexus Whitfield var. A. BERKEY, 1898, p. 288, Pl. 20, figs. 1–2, Pl. 21, fig. 5 (the holotype designated by Resser)
Modocia berkeyi Resser, 1935, p. 42
Camaraspoides berkeyi (Resser). FREDERICKSON, 1949, p. 349–350, Pl. 68, figs. 1–9; WILSON, 1951, p. 631, Pl. 90, fig. 9; NELSON, 1951, p. 774–775, Pl. 107, figs. 6, 14

REMARKS: *Camaraspis berkeyi* resembles *C. convexa* in every respect except depth of the dorsal, marginal and glabellar furrows, and elevation of the glabella. Cranidial furrows are deeper in *C. berkeyi,* and the glabella more elevated.

Study of topotype materal from Berkey's locality in Minnesota and of Frederickson's specimens of *Camaraspoides berkeyi* shows that the degree of cranidial relief is a consistent distinguishing feature between *C. convexa* and *C. berkeyi.*

Possibly the deeper furrows and increased convexity of *C. berkeyi* are responses to ecological factors. In Minnesota the species is found only in a conglomerate that overlaps Precambrian basalt, and incorporates boulders of basalt. Frederickson (1956, oral communication) mentioned that the Honey Creek Formation at his "locality 6" (Frederickson, 1949, p. 345) also directly overlies Precambrian igneous rock and is conglomerate. In Texas, Montana-Wyoming, and the central Appalachians (Wilson, 1951) this species is found in carbonate strata, and the cranidia are uniformly smaller than those from the conglomerates. Greater depth of furrows might strengthen a gently arched carapace. Perhaps where water was relatively placid or only intermittently agitated, the extra strength afforded by deep furrowing was needed only in the earlier molts, with smaller thinner shells. After this stage was passed, the organism could survive with a smooth shell. Where the sea lapped against cliffs of igneous rock, where boulder conglomerates were forming in strong currents, older individuals could not survive without the deeper furrows, and therefore only the deeply furrowed large individuals are found in the conglomerates. This implies the possibility that in the areas of carbonate rock specimens referred to *C. berkeyi* may be early growth stages of *C. convexa,* and that in the areas of conglomerates they may be ecological variants of *C. convexa.*

OCCURRENCE: *Camaraspis berkeyi* is rare in the *Camaraspis* Subzone of the *Elvinia* Zone at HG 47.5; GR 15.9.

Camaraspis convexa (Whitfield)
(Pl. 10, figs. 3, 6)

Arionellus (*Agraulos*) *convexus* WHITFIELD, 1878, p. 57
Camaraspis convexa (Whitfield). FREDERICKSON, 1948, p. 798, Pl. 123, figs. 12–13 (synonymy to date); BELL, FENIAK, and KURTZ, 1952, p. 181, Pl. 29, figs. 2a–f (synonymy to date)
Camaraspis plana FREDERICKSON, 1948, p. 799, Pl. 123, figs. 14–15; DELAND and SHAW, 1956, p. 549, Pl. 65, fig. 1, Pl. 66, fig. 13

REMARKS: Cranidia of *Camaraspis* range in convexity from slightly arched (*C. plana* Frederickson) to strongly arched (*C. convexa*). Specimens here support the contention of Bell, Feniak, and Kurtz (1952, p. 181–182) that smaller individuals normally are less convex than larger ones. The smaller, flatter specimens have not been found associated with the larger, more convex ones, but this is as likely the result of selective sorting as of the existence of two separate species. It is impossible to make a clear distinction between *C. plana* and *C. convexa,* except at the extremes of their variation. Moderately convex cranidia, which are more abundant than either very flat or very convex ones, cannot be placed with certainty in either category.

One cranidium has tiny puncta covering the frontal area and fixed cheeks.

OCCURRENCE: *Camaraspis convexa* is common at the top of the *Elvinia* Zone at HC 7.8; HD 84.1; HG 45.8; HH 68.9; SP 106; CF 29.2; MC 104.4; YO 65.9; GR 15.9. Its presence marks the *Camaraspis* Subzone of the *Elvinia* Zone.

Genus *Dytremacephalus* Palmer, 1955
Dytremacephalus ? sp. undet.
(Pl. 8, fig. 2)

REMARKS: This species has deep anterior pits, upturned border, ocular ridges, a dorsal furrow that widens posteriorly, and two pairs of glabellar furrows; it may be a species of *Dytremacephalus.*

OCCURRENCE: Four cranidia were found in a bed of limestone-pebble conglomerate at the base of the Dry Creek Shale in the Bill Smith Creek section (BC 0). Palmer (1955a, p. 750) reports species of *Dytremacephalus* from the *Aphelaspis* and post-*Aphelaspis* (*Dunderbergia*) zones.

Genus *Pterocephalia* Roemer, 1849
Pterocephalia sanctisabae Roemer
(Pl. 8, figs. 25, 28–29)

Pterocephalia sanctisabae ROEMER, 1849, p. 421; 1852, p. 92, Pl. 11, figs. la–d; BRIDGE, 1933, p. 232, Pl. 2, figs. 26–27; KOBAYASHI, 1936b, p. 172, Pl. 21, figs. 10–12; BRIDGE, *in* BRIDGE and GIRTY, 1937, p. 246, Pl. 67, figs. la–d, Pl. 68, figs. 7–43; WILSON, 1949, p. 42, Pl. 10, figs. 1–3; FREDERICKSON, 1949, p. 355, Pl. 69, figs. 1–4; WILSON, 1951, p. 647, Pl. 91, fig. 24; PALMER, 1960, p. 88–89, Pl. 9, figs. 7–8, 13 (extensive synonymy to date)
Pterocephalia bridgei RESSER, 1938, p. 40; LOCHMAN, 1950a, p. 334, Pl. 47, figs. 14–18 (including synonymy); LOCHMAN and HU, 1960, p. 814, Pl. 96, figs. 28–33

DESCRIPTION: Frontal area long, broad, flat, with border 5–9 times longer than brim; glabella elongate, tapered, somewhat truncate, with rather deep glabellar furrows; pygidium large, ovate with strong pleural furrows.

REMARKS: Palmer (1960, p. 86–89) analyzed this species and reviewed its nomenclatural history. He concludes that it is very widespread in the *Elvinia* Zone and includes in its synonymy many species names which are not repeated here because his paper is recent and easily available. The species which Lochman and Hu (1960) called *P. bridgei* is listed, in light of Palmer's conclusion that the species are synonymous.

OCCURRENCE: *Pterocephalia sanctisabae* is rare in the *Elvinia* Zone: cranidia and pygidia were found at HG 45.8, 47.5; NG 48, pygidia at BC 63.8; SC 27.

Family PTYCHASPIDIDAE Raymond, 1924
Genus *Ptychaspis* Hall, 1863
Ptychaspis granulosa (Owen)
(Pl. 14, figs. 1–3)

Dikelocephalus granulosus OWEN, 1852, p. 575, Table 1, figs. 5, 7
Ptychaspis granulosa (Owen). WHITFIELD, 1878, p. 54; 1882, p. 185, Pl. 1, fig. 24; NELSON, 1951, p. 779, Pl. 110, fig. 8; BELL, FENIAK, and KURTZ, 1952, p. 193, Pl. 34, figs. 6a–b, Pl. 35, figs. la–e (complete synonymy); BERG and ROSS, 1959, p. 112, Pl. 22, fig. 12; LOCHMAN and HU, 1959, p. 424, Pl. 60, figs. 37–44

DESCRIPTION: Cranidium about twice as wide as long; glabella nearly parallel-sided, outlined by deep glabellar furrow, somewhat flattened over axis, and sunken nearly to level of broad fixed cheeks; frontal area steeply downsloping, nearly vertical; ornamentation consisting of coarse granules on anterior segment of glabella and on fixed cheeks adjacent and slightly posterior to that segment, and coarse transverse lirae across frontal area and fixed cheeks to edge of granulated area. Pygidium transverse, outline rhomboid with flatly convex, slightly downsloping pleural lobes, nearly flat, border becoming slightly wider distally; ornament fine but distinct lirae on borders, parallel to margins, becoming weaker on pleural lobes and absent on axis.

REMARKS: Specimens from the Snowy Range agree in every essential feature with those described from the Franconia Formation by Bell, Feniak, and Kurtz (1952) except in the liration of the pygidium. The Franconia and Snowy Range pygidia are identical in form and outline, but the former show no ornament. The Franconia sandstone is probably too coarse-grained to show such relatively light ornamentation. Ornamentation of *P. striata* (Bell, Feniak, and Kurtz, 1952, Pl. 35, figs. 2b, d, f) is very coarse and therefore distinct even in sandstone, contrasting to the light lirae on the limestone pygidia from Montana. Lochman and Hu (1959, Pl. 60) illustrate cranidia and pygidia that agree with Snowy Range specimens in all characteristics.

This species differs from *P. bullasa* Lochman and Hu (1959, p. 422) in its flatter and more sunken glabella, fewer granules farther forward on the fixed cheeks, more steeply downsloping frontal area, and especially in its pygidium which is more rhomboid than semielliptical, has a relatively wide, flat border, and is ornamented by light lirae. Bell and Ellinwood (1962) report *P. bullasa* in the lower part of the *Ptychaspis-Prosaukia* Zone in central Texas. It is absent from collections in Montana and Wyoming.

P. granulosa occurs only in the lower part of the *Ptychaspis-Prosaukia* Zone in the upper Mississippi Valley. It is rare in the middle of that zone, where replaced by *P. striata* Whitfield (Bell, Feniak, and Kurtz, 1952, p. 177, Table 1); it extends only rarely into the range of *Idahoia serapio* (Grant, 1962, Figs. 3, 5–6). In Montana and Wyoming its range extends throughout the *Idahoia* Zone. Biostratigraphic segregation of granulose forms from striated forms, which occurs in the sandstone regions, is not present in the carbonates of Montana and Wyoming. Instead there is one longer-ranging species with granules on the cephalon and striations on the pygidium.

OCCURRENCE: *Ptychaspis granulosa* is rare to moderately common in the *Idahoia wyomingensis* Subzone at HD 125.1; HI 115.8; GC 126.2; FC 151; JC 109.4; RP 132.2; BM 144.4; in the *Idahoia wisconsensis* Subzone at HD 140.4; HH 124.4; GC 137.3; FP 179.5; BC 109.9, 116.7; RP 146.1; MC 170.6; YO 135.7; and in the *Idahoia serapio* Subzone at HD 146.2; HH 128.8, 132.8; HI 121.2, 124.3; SP 161; BM 156.9, 163.8; MC 185.3

Ptychaspis cf. *P. miniscaensis* (Owen)
(Pl. 14, fig. 33)

Dikelocephalus miniscaensis Owen, 1852, p. 574, Table 1, figs. 3a–b, 12, Table 1A, figs. 4–5
Ptychaspis miniscaensis (Owen). Hall, 1863, p. 171, Pl. 6, figs. 41–46, Pl. 10, figs. 21–22; Bell, Feniak, and Kurtz, 1952, p. 193, Pl. 35, figs. 3a–b, Pl. 36, figs. 1a–f (synonymy to date)

Remarks: Several small cranidia are comparable to *P. miniscaensis* in their tapered glabellas, gently downsloping frontal areas, and obsolescent anterior glabellar furrows. They differ from specimens of that species from the upper Mississippi Valley in their wider fixed cheeks and posterior limbs, and slightly wider frontal areas. On most specimens only the posterior glabellar furrow is visible, and it extends across the glabella. One peculiar specimen with the typical tapered glabella and sloping frontal area has two deep glabellar furrows crossing the glabella, each glabellar segment and the occipital ring has a small median node.

This species occurs in the same biostratigraphic position as *P. granulosa*. In Minnesota and Wisconsin *P. miniscaensis* occurs with *Prosaukia,* above *P. granulosa* and *P. striata.*

P. cf. *P. miniscaensis* most closely resembles figure 48 of Hall (1863, Pl. 6) and figure 3a of Bell, Feniak, and Kurtz (1952, Pl. 35). It is close to *P. minuta* Whitfield (1878, p. 55; 1882, p. 186, Pl. 1, figs. 25–26) in its small size and shallow glabellar furrows but is distinguished by its tapered glabella and gently sloping frontal area.

Occurrence: *Ptychaspis* cf. *P. miniscaensis* is very rare in the *I. serapio* Subzone of the *Idahoia* Zone at HH 128.8; HI 121.2; BM 202.2.

Family Saukiidae Ulrich and Resser, 1930
Genus *Prosaukia* Ulrich and Resser, 1933
Prosaukia sp. undet.
(Pl. 14, fig. 32)

Remarks: One well-preserved pygidium from BM 225.3 belongs to a species of *Prosaukia.* It resembles the pygidium of *P. misa* (Hall) illustrated by Ulrich and Resser (1933, p. 141–144, Pl. 24, figs. 6, 8) and by Shimer and Shrock (1944, Pl. 261, fig. 10).

Occurrence: *Prosaukia* sp. is very rare in the *Prosaukia* Zone at BM 225.3.

Saukid gen. et sp. undet.
(Pl. 14, fig. 36–37)

Description: Cranidium rectangular with parallel-sided, anteriorly truncate glabella having two pairs of glabellar furrows; fixed cheeks narrow; eyes long and narrow; frontal area moderately downsloping, with weak hint of marginal furrow at sides; anterior facial sutures slightly divergent; posterior half of glabella and frontal area ornamented by striations, anterior half of glabella marked by small pustules. Pygidium small, with thick axial lobe and four pairs of irregular pleura bending backward distally; margin smooth.

Remarks: The pustulose ornamentation of the glabella indicates relationship with *Saukia,* but the slight indentations at the position of a marginal furrow show a possible link with *Saukiella* or perhaps even with *Prosaukia.* Not enough material of this species is preserved to make possible a positive generic identification. It is mentioned and figured to show that "saukid" trilobites are present, although very rare, in the Trempealeauan of Montana.

Occurrence: "Saukid" sp. was found in the Trempealeauan at HJ 255.2; ME 36.1.

Family Shumardiidae Lake, 1907
Genus *Idiomesus* Raymond, 1924
Idiomesus sp. undet.
(Pl. 14, fig. 38)

Description: Cranidium small, semicircular, convex, with moderate relief; glabella long, occupying most of cranidial length, tapering at both ends and marked by two incomplete pairs of glabellar furrows and one connected pair; anterior of glabella notched on axial line; fixed cheeks convex, wider than glabella, and where exfoliated have few small pustules scattered at random and one row of pustules paralleling side of glabella; frontal area simple, short, less convex than fixed cheeks, slightly flattened anterior to notch in glabella; anterior facial sutures parallel just anterior to eyes, anterior margin evenly curved.

REMARKS: This species most closely resembles *I. levisensis* (Rasetti), differing by its anterior glabellar notch, slightly flatter, less anteriorly tapered glabella, proportionately longer frontal area and deeper glabellar furrows. The anterior glabellar notch is similar to that in species of *Missisquoia* Shaw. This species differs from species of *Missisquoia* in its undivided frontal area, wider and more semicircular fixed cheeks, and connected pair of posterior glabellar furrows. It differs from species of *Holcacephalus* Resser in possessing deep glabellar furrows.

OCCURRENCE: *Idiomesus* sp. is rare in the Trempealeauan at BM 249.2, associated with *Dikelocephalus* sp. and *Pseudagnostus* cf. *P. laevis.*

Family INCERTAE SEDIS

Genus *Ellipsocephaloides* Kobayashi, 1935

Ellipsocephaloides silvestris Resser

(Pl. 14, fig. 31)

Ellipsocephaloides silvestris RESSER, 1942b, p. 64, Pl. 11, figs. 1–3; BELL and ELLINWOOD, 1962, p. 406, Pl. 59, figs. 10–12

DESCRIPTION: Brim narrow, ropelike, border narrow, palpebral lobes prominent, with distinct palpebral furrows. The faint axial boss on the frontal area that is mentioned by Resser (1942b, p. 64) and illustrated by Bell and Ellinwood (1962) is present on the Montana specimens, but barely visible.

REMARKS: *E. silvestris* differs from *E. argutus* Resser and *E. curtus* (Whitfield) by its much narrower fixed cheeks and by possession of a marginal furrow separating a distinct brim and border. It differs from *E. gracilis* Feniak, which also has narrow fixed cheeks, by its marginal furrow, brim, and border. It resembles some species of *Monocheilus* in its quadrate glabella but differs in its posteriorly truncate eyes and much shorter frontal area that is just as long at the anterolateral corners as on the axial line, *i.e.,* not nasute.

OCCURRENCE: *Ellipsocephaloides silvestris* is rare in the *Idahoia wisconsensis* Subzone at BC 114.2; in the *I. serapio* Subzone at BM 156.9; and in the *Prosaukia* Zone at BM 202.2.

Class ARACHNIDA

Subclass MEROSTOMATA

Order AGLASPIDA Raasch, 1939

(Pl. 15, fig. 30)

REMARKS: Many acetic acid residues contain small fragmentary plates of corneous material that are covered with a variety of pustules. These fragments are thin, translucent, flat or slightly curved, and their pustules are irregularly distributed and more than one size. Some are elongate and curved transversely, as though fragments of a spine or telson. These phosphatic pustulose fragments correspond closely to Raasch's descriptions and illustrations (1939, p. 51–58, Pl. 3, figs. 1–2, Pl. 6, fig. 10, Pl. 7, figs. 4, 6) of the carapaces of Aglaspids.

OCCURRENCE: Aglaspid fragments are sporadic in acetic acid residues from samples throughout the Snowy Range Formation. No detailed listing of their occurrence is given, but their presence is recorded in lists of fossils in measured sections.

Phylum ECHINODERMATA

Subphylum PELMATOZOA

REMARKS: Pelmatozoan fragments are abundant throughout the Franconian and Trempealeauan rocks of southwestern Montana and northwestern Wyoming. Columnals occur in most of the fossiliferous beds. Those of the Franconian are small discs with holes; many of the Trempealeauan columnals are pentagonal or five-rayed. According to Caster (1942, p. 110) the five-rayed columnals were identified by Dr. Edwin Kirk as crinoid columnals.

Many samples contain small unornamented calyces. These may be cystoid or perhaps crinoid calyces. Most of them are undistorted and composed of a single large crystal of calcite.

One irregularly hexagonal pelmatozoan plate also is indeterminate as to class. It is cystoid or crinoid, and either a large crystal of calcite or a fibrous bundle of crystals in such continuity with one another that it has a striated appearance.

OCCURRENCE: Pelmatozoan fragments, especially columnals, are abundant throughout the Franconian and Trempealeauan rocks of the Snowy Range Formation. No detailed listing of their occurrence is given, but their presence is recorded in the list of fossils for each fossiliferous bed.

Phylum CHORDATA (?)
Subphylum STOMOCHORDA
Class GRAPTOLITHINA Bronn, 1846
Order DENDROIDEA Nicholson, 1872
Family DENDROGRAPHTIDAE Roemer *in* Frech, 1897
Genus *Callograptus* Hall, 1865
Callograptus staufferi Ruedemann
(Pl. 15, figs. 27–28)

Callograptus staufferi RUEDEMANN, 1933, p. 319, Pl. 50, figs. 1–7, Pl. 55, figs. 1–2, 5; DECKER, 1936, p. 304; 1956, p. 1699–1704, Pl. 1, figs. 6–7; SHIMER and SHROCK, 1944, p. 65, Pl. 20, figs. 4–5; RUEDEMANN, 1947, p. 204, Pl. 15, fig. 16, Pl. 16, figs. 7–15

REMARKS: *Callograptus staufferi* is characterized by its small size, dichotomous branching, and indistinct thecae that cling close to the stipe. The few specimens of this study fit Ruedemann's descriptions and illustrations closely. The species is much finer and more delicately constructed than *C. antiquus* Ruedemann.

C. staufferi is Trempealeauan. Specimens from the upper part of the Grove Creek Member suggest that none of the part of Snowy Range Formation preserved in the Yellowstone Park area is Ordovician.

OCCURRENCE: *Callograptus staufferi* is rare in the Trempealeauan at SL 274.5, 278.3, 283.4, 283.4 (float).

Miscellaneous graptolite fragments

REMARKS: Individual thecate and nonthecate stipes have been found at several localities in the upper part of the Grove Creek Member. Thecate stipes probably are individual branches of Dendrograptidae. Nonthecate fragments, much thicker than the thecate portions, probably represent parts of the nema. These fragments cannot be identified; they are mentioned to record the occurrence of graptolites in the Trempealeauan portion of the Snowy Range Formation.

OCCURRENCE: Graptolite fragments are rare in the Trempealeauan at UYO 283.0; KZ 13.1, 26.7; FOX 249.8; SL 274.5, 278.3, 279.9, 283.4

CONODONTS
Order CONODONTOPHORIDA Eichenberg, 1930
Genus *Westergaardodina* Müller, 1959

REMARKS: Acetic acid residues from many localities contained small (ca. 1 mm), chitinophosphatic, bilaterally symmetrical objects which are rounded on one end and have two or three sharp-pointed prongs on the other. One side of each prong normally is flat, the other side gently convex; the plane of symmetry therefore passes between the prongs of the two-pronged type and along the middle of the mid-prong of the three-pronged type. Similar objects were described from Cambrian localities in Europe by Westergård (1953), who called them simply "*Problematicum* no. 1." Müller (1959) examined many such objects from the Cambrian of Europe and North America and, by detailed mineralogical and morphological comparisons, concluded that they are basically the same as objects from higher in the section which have been called "conodonts."

Müller devised a taxonomy for these objects, separating them into several genera and many species. Those here belong to two of his species: the more numerous form is *Westergaardodina bicuspidata* Müller. These are relatively large and robust, characterized by two prongs or cusps. The less numerous form is *W. tricuspidata* Müller, characterized by smaller size and three, relatively slender prongs.

The two- and three-pronged forms originally were grouped together as *problematica,* the system used by Westergård. Therefore the following list of occurrences does not distinguish the two forms, but is only the record of occurrences of the genus.

OCCURRENCE: *Westergaardodina* is rare, but it has been found in all zones of the Franconian; in the *Elvinia* Zone at GC 63; in the *Taenicephalus* Zone at JC 81; BC 87.1, 98.6; FOX 88.8, 94.2; GR 27.1; in the *Idahoia wyomingensis* Subzone at FC 143.2; BC 106.4; SP 150.6; YO 128.4; SL 108.2; in the *I. wisconsensis* Subzone at BM 150.6; in the *I. serapio* Subzone at HI 121.2; FOX 124.2, 135.9, 148.6; and in the *Prosaukia* Zone at RP 189.1.

Westergaardodina bicuspidata Müller
(Pl. 15, figs. 33–34)

Problematicum 1 WESTERGAARD, 1953, p. 465–468, Pl. 5, figs. 1–5, 13–14 (only)
Westergaardodina bicuspidata MÜLLER, 1959, p. 468, Pl. 15, figs. 1, 4, 7, 9–10, 14

REMARKS: This species is U-shaped, with two sharp prongs. According to Müller it may have a rudimentary middle prong, but this has not been observed here.

Westergaardodina tricuspidata Müller
(Pl. 15, fig. 31)

Westergaardodina tricuspidata MÜLLER, 1959, p. 470, Pl. 15, figs. 3, 5–6

REMARKS: This species is shaped like a trident, with the prongs rather slender. The middle prong is longest.

PROBLEMATICUM
(Pl. 15, fig. 26)

REMARKS: A shallow, veined, leaf-shaped impression was found at the top of the Grove Creek Member at KZ 26.7. It is 25 mm long and 16 mm wide, with a central impressed axial line and at least five pairs of impressed "veins" that branch obliquely from the axis. It occurs in association with fragments of graptolites and a fragment of *Apheoorthis* sp.

A similar but more circular impression is described from the Grove Creek Member in the Wind River Canyon of Wyoming by Caster (1942, p. 104–112, Pl. 1). He assigned it to the medusa *Laotira cambria* Walcott (1896, p. 613, Pl. 32, figs. 1–8; 1898a, p. 32–41, Pls. 5–19, 21–23).

The specimen does not appear to have radial symmetry, but the "veins" might be a partial or somewhat distorted impression of the canal system of a medusa. Presence of the *problematicum* among fragments of graptolites suggests that it may be a detached pneumatophore from a planktonic graptolite. Dr. M. L. Glaessner (1962, oral communication) does not think that it resembles specimens of Precambrian "pennatulids" that he has observed in Australia.

CALCAREOUS ALGAE
Form-genus *Collenia* Walcott, 1914
Collenia magna Fenton and Fenton
(Pl. 5, figs. 5, 7–8)

Collenia magna FENTON and FENTON, 1939, p. 103, Pl. 5, figs. 1–2; DORF and LOCHMAN, 1940, p. 545, Pl. 1, fig. 2, Pl. 3, figs. 1–2; LOCHMAN, 1949, p. 37; MCMANNIS, 1955, p. 1395

REMARKS: This species forms columns of limestone, very fine-grained, 1–5 feet high, 6–18 inches in diameter, normally closely spaced, with 3–6 inches of shale or pebbly limestone between them. It occurs in layered colonies, making bioherms up to 25 feet high. The limestone normally is greenish; much of it is subtly laminated and stylolitic. Laminae are convex upward, fossil fragments are rare, and dolomite, if present, is secondary (*see* thin-section description from HG 45.8). Where the edges of the bioherm are exposed, shale beds and pebbly limestone arch upward against it.

OCCURRENCE: The base of the *Collenia magna* bioherm at most localities indicates the base of the Sage Member of the Snowy Range Formation. The bioherm is present in most sections that were measured; in some places it is only 1 foot thick. It is present in the *Elvinia* Zone at HC 0–6.5; HD 62–70; HE 77–80.5; HF 0–5; HG 32–43.5; HH 48–62; HI 56–57; FP 106.5–107.5; JC 59–61; BL 53; BC 46.3–66; SP 86–108; BP 75.5–90.5; BM 82.5–88.1; MC 106–109; YO 50.5–63; FOX 39–53; BB 49.5–56; GR 0–6.5; SL 51.5–71. For the most part, the bioherm is confined to the lower part of the *Elvinia* Zone, extending up into the *Camaraspis* Subzone only at Flathead Pass and Sacajawea Peak sections.

Form-genus *Tetonophycus* Fenton and Fenton, 1939
Tetonophycus blackwelderi Fenton and Fenton
(Pl. 5, figs. 3–4, 6)

Tetonophycus blackwelderii FENTON and FENTON, 1939, p. 99–101, fig. 2, Pl. 4, figs. 1–2

REMARKS: This species grows in beds, rather than columns, forming low, upwardly convex mounds that range in diameter about 6–18 inches and in height from 1 to about 12 inches. The most characteristic feature of the structure is the division between the basal portion, bedded and pebbly, and the upper portion, which forms low mounds on the upper surface. The upper half normally is slightly dolomitic and exhibits growth laminae in cross section. Where tops of the mounds are truncated by erosion, concentric circles with cores are visible. The total thickness of a bed of this species is about 1–2 feet.

OCCURRENCE: Beds of *Tetonophycus blackwelderi* are present in the *Taenicephalus* Zone at YO 78.1, 83.1; in the *Idahoia wyomingensis* Subzone at YO 116.9; SL 100, 101; and in the *I. serapio* Subzone at YO 157.1, 162.3, 166.6. They are much more common in the Trempealeauan at MC 268.7, 269.7, 283.5, 209.5; YO 172,8, 208.3, 235.7, 240.7, 252, 265.5, 268.3, 274.3, 277.3, 285.5; UYO 267.6, 272.6; FOX 202.8, 204.7, 216.9, 218.9, 224.1, 229.4, 234.6, 242.7, 245.8, 248, 250.3, 256–267; UFOX 36.5, 50.4, 53.1, 54.5, 57.6, 59.8, 61.6, 66–69; KZ 7.1, 10, 12–1, 13.1; SL 231.7, 233.8, 236.3, 239.3, 240.1, 242.1, 249.1, 255–273.

REFERENCES

Barnes, V. E., and Bell, W. C., 1954, Cambrian rocks of Central Texas, p. 35–69 *in* San Angelo Geological Society [Guidebook], Cambrian field trip—Llano area, [Texas]: San Angelo Geol. Soc., 139 p.

Barnes, V. E., and others, 1959, Stratigraphy of the pre-Simpson Paleozoic subsurface rocks of Texas and southeast New Mexico: Univ. Texas Pub. 5924, v. 1, 2, 836 p., 65 Pls.

Beecher, C. E., 1891, Development of the Brachiopoda: Am. Jour. Sci., ser. 3, v. 41, p. 343–357, Pl. 17

Bell, W. C., 1941, Cambrian Brachiopoda from Montana: Jour. Paleontology, v. 15, p. 193–255, Pls. 28–37

—— 1944, Early Upper Cambrian brachiopods, p. 144–153, Pls. 18, 19 *in* Lochman, C., and Duncan, D., Early Upper Cambrian faunas of central Montana: Geol. Soc. America Special Paper 54, 181 p.

—— 1948, Acetic acid-etching techniques applied to Cambrian brachiopods: Jour. Paleontology, v. 22, p. 101–102

Bell, W. C., and Ellinwood, H. L., 1962, Upper Franconian and Lower Trempealeauan Cambrian trilobites and brachiopods, Wilberns formations, Central Texas: Jour. Paleontology, v. 36, p. 385–423, 1 Fig., Pls. 51–64

Bell, W. C., Berg, R. R., and Nelson, C. A., 1956, Croixan type area–upper Mississippi Valley, p. 415–446, Figs. 1–4 *in* Rodgers, J., *Editor,* El sistema Cambrico, su paleogeografia y el problema de su base (Symposium): Mexico, 20th Internat. Geol. Cong., pt. 2, 762 p.

Bell, W. C., Feniak, O. W., and Kurtz, V. E., 1952, Trilobites of the Franconia formation, southeast Minnesota: Jour. Paleontology, v. 26, p. 175–198, Pls. 29–38

Berg, R. R., 1953, Franconian trilobites from Minnesota and Wisconsin: Jour. Paleontology, v. 27, p. 553–568, Pls. 59–61

—— 1954, Franconia formation of Minnesota and Wisconsin: Geol. Soc. America Bull., v. 65, p. 857–882, 9 Figs., 1 Pl.

Berg, R. R., and Ross, R. J., 1959, Trilobites from the Peerless and Manitou formations, Colorado: Jour. Paleontology, v. 33, p. 106–119, Figs. 1, 2, Pls. 21, 22

Berg, R. R., Nelson, C. A., and Bell, W. C., 1956, Upper Cambrian rocks in southeastern Minnesota, p. 1–23, 5 Figs. *in* Schwartz, G. M., *Editor,* Lower Paleozoic of the upper Mississippi Valley: Geol. Soc. America Guidebook for Field Trips, Minneapolis Mtg., 110 p.

Berkey, C. P., 1898, Geology of the St. Croix Dalles, Part 3, Paleontology: Am. Geologist, p. 270–294, Pls. 17–21

Bridge, J., 1933, p. 231–234 *in* Sellards, E. H., Adkins, W. S., and Plummer, F. B., *Editors,* The geology of Texas. V. 1, Stratigraphy: Univ. Texas Bull. 3232, 1007 p.

Bridge, J., and Girty, G. H., 1937, A redescription of Ferdinand Roemer's Paleozoic types from Texas: U.S. Geol. Survey Prof. Paper 186–M, p. 239–271, Pls. 66–70

Bridge, J., Barnes, V. E., and Cloud, P. E., Jr., 1947, Stratigraphy of the Upper Cambrian, Llano uplift, Texas; Geol. Soc. America Bull., v. 58, p. 109–124, 8 Pls.

Bulman, O. M. B., 1955, Graptolithina, Part V *of* Moore, R. C., *Editor,* Treatise on invertebrate paleontology: Geol. Soc. America and Univ. Kansas Press, 101 p., 72 Figs.

Caster, K. E., 1942, A laotirid from the Upper Cambrian of Wyoming: Am. Jour. Sci., v. 240, p. 104–112, 1 Pl.

Clark, T. H., 1924, The paleontology of the Beekmantown series at Levis, Quebec: Bull. Am. Paleontology, v. 10, no. 41, 134 p.

Cloud, P. E., Jr., 1942, Notes on stromatolites: Am. Jour. Sci., v. 240, p. 363–379, Fig. 1, Pls. 1, 2

Cloud, P. E., Jr., and Barnes, V. E., 1948, The Ellenburger Group of Central Texas: Univ. Texas Pub. 4621, 473 p., 44 Pls.

—— 1957, Early Ordovician sea in Central Texas, p. 163–214, 3 Figs., *in* Ladd, H., *Editor,* Treatise on marine ecology and paleoecology, Volume 2, Paleoecology: Geol. Soc. America Memoir 67, 1077 p.

Cohee, G. V., and others, 1956, Nature, usage and nomenclature of rock-stratigraphic units (American Commission on Stratigraphic Nomenclature Report): Am. Assoc. Petroleum Geologists Bull., v. 40, p. 2003–2014

Darton, N. H., 1904, Comparison of the stratigraphy of the Black Hills, Bighorn Mountains, and Rocky Mountain Front Range: Geol. Soc. America Bull., v. 15, p. 379–448, Pls. 23–36

Decker, C. E., 1936, Some tentative correlations on the basis of graptolites of Oklahoma and Arkansas: Am. Assoc. Petroleum Geologists Bull., v. 20, p. 301–311

—— 1956, Place of graptolites in Animal Kingdom: Am. Assoc. Petroleum Geologists Bull., v. 40, p. 1699–1704, 1 Pl.

Deiss, C., 1936, Revision of type Cambrian formations and sections of Montana and Yellowstone National Park: Geol. Soc. America Bull., v. 47, p. 1257–1342, 10 Figs., 2 Pls.

Deland, C. R., and Shaw, A. B., 1956, Upper Cambrian trilobites from western Wyoming: Jour. Paleontology, v. 30, p. 542–562, Pls. 63–67

Dorf, E., and Lochman, C., 1940, Upper Cambrian formations in southern Montana: Geol. Soc. America Bull., v. 51, p. 541–556, 2 Figs., 5 Pls.

Emmons, W. H., and Calkins, F. C., 1913, Geology and ore deposits of the Phillipsburg quadrangle, Montana: U.S. Geol. Survey Prof. Paper 78, 271 p.

Evitt, W. R., 2d, 1949, Stereophotography as a tool of the paleontologist: Jour. Paleontology, v. 23, p. 566–570, Pl. 88

Fenton, C. L., and Fenton, M. A., 1939, Precambrian and Paleozoic algae: Geol. Soc. America Bull., v. 50, p. 89–126, 9 Figs., 11 Pls.

Folk, R. L., 1954, The distinction between grain size and mineral composition in sedimentary-rock nomenclature: Jour. Geology, v. 62, p. 344–359, 1 Pl.

—— 1957, Petrology of sedimentary rocks: Univ. Texas course syllabus, Austin, Texas, Hemphill's, p. Q1–P27

—— 1959, Practical petrographic classification of limestones: Am. Assoc. Petroleum Geologists Bull., v. 43, p. 1–38, 41 Figs.

Frederickson, E. A., 1948, Upper Cambrian trilobites from Oklahoma: Jour. Paleontology, v. 22, p. 798–803, Pl. 123

—— 1949, Trilobite fauna of the Upper Cambrian Honey Creek formation: Jour. Paleontology, v. 23, p. 341–363, Pls. 68–72

—— 1956, Cambrian of Oklahoma, p. 483–508, Figs. 1–7, *in* Rodgers, J., *Editor,* El sistema Cambrico, su paleogeografia y el problema de su base (Symposium): Mexico, 20th Internat. Geol. Cong., pt. 2, 762 p.

Gaines, R. B., 1951, The statistical study of *Irvingella,* Upper Cambrian trilobite: Texas Jour. Sci., v. 3, p. 606–616

Gott, P. F., 1945, Procedure of simplified stereophotography of fossils: Jour. Paleontology, v. 19, p. 390–395, 9 Figs.

Grant, R. E., 1956, Trilobite distribution, upper Franconia formation, Wabasha County, Minnesota (Abstract): Geol. Soc. America Bull., v. 67, pt. 2, p. 1700–1701

—— 1962, Trilobite distribution, upper Franconia formation (Upper-Cambrian) southeastern Minnesota: Jour. Paleontology, v. 36, p. 965–998, Pl. 139, 10 Figs.

Hague, A., and others, 1899, Geology of the Yellowstone National Park: U.S. Geol. Survey Mon. 32, pt. 2, 893 p., 121 Pls.

Hall, J., 1861, Report of the superintendent of the Geological Survey, exhibiting the progress of the work: Madison, Wisc. Geol. Survey, 52 p.

—— 1862, Physical geography and general geology, p. 1–72 *in* Hall, J., and Whitney, J. D., Report of the geological survey of the state of Wisconsin. Volume 1: Wisc., Geol. Survey Rept., 455 p., 10 Pls., 2 maps

—— 1863, Preliminary notice of the fauna of the Potsdam sandstone: N.Y. State Cabinet Nat. History 16th Ann. Rept., p. 119–209, 11 Pls.

—— 1873, Notes on some new or imperfectly known forms among the Brachiopoda, *etc.:* N.Y. State Cabinet Nat. History, 23d Ann. Rept., p. 244–247

Hall, J., and Whitfield, R. P., 1877, Paleontology, p. 199–231 *in* U.S. Geological Exploration 40th Parallel Rept. (King), v. 4, 669 p., 7 Pls.

Hanson, A. M., 1952, Cambrian stratigraphy in southwestern Montana: Mont. Bur. Mines and Geology Memoir 33, 46 p., 9 Pls.

Harrington, H. J., and others, 1959, Arthropoda 1, Part O *of* Moore, R. C., *Editor,* Treatise on invertebrate paleontology: Geol. Soc. America and Univ. Kans. Press, 560 p., 415 Figs.

Howell, B. F., and Lochman, C., 1939, Succession of Late Cambrian faunas in the Northern Hemisphere: Jour. Paleontology, v. 13, p. 115–122, 1 Fig.

Howell, B. F., and Van Houten, F. B., 1940, A new sponge from the Cambrian of Wyoming: Wagner Free Inst. Sci. Bull., v. 15, p. 1–8

Howell, B. F., and others, 1944, Correlation of the Cambrian formations of North America: Geol. Soc. America Bull., v. 55, p. 993–1003, 1 Pl.

Knight, J. B., 1947, Some new Cambrian bellerophont gastropods: Smithsonian Misc. Coll., v. 106, no. 17, p. 1–11, Pls. 1–2

Kobayashi, T., 1933a, Faunal study of the Wanwanian (basal Ordovician) Series, with special notes on the Ribeiridae and the Ellesmereoceroids: Tokyo Imp. Univ. Faculty Sci., sec. 2, v. 3, pt. 7, p. 249–328, Pls. 1–10

—— 1933b, Upper Cambrian of the Wuhutsui Basin, Liotung, with special reference to the limit of the Chaumitian (or Upper Cambrian) of eastern Asia, and its subdivision: Japanese Jour. Geology and Geography, v. 11, p. 55–155, Pls. 9–15

—— 1935a, The *Briscoia* fauna of the late Upper Cambrian in Alaska with descriptions of a few Upper Cambrian trilobites from Montana and Nevada: Japanese Jour. Geology and Geography, v. 12, p. 39–57, Pls. 8–10

—— 1935b, The Cambro-Ordovician formations and faunas of South Chosen. Part 3, Cambrian faunas of South Chosen with a special study on the Cambrian trilobite genera and families: Tokyo Imp. Univ. Faculty Sci., sec. 2, v. 4, pt. 2, p. 49–344, Pls. 1–24

—— 1936a, Cambrian and Lower Ordovician trilobites from northwestern Canada: Jour. Paleontology, v. 10, p. 157–167, Pl. 21

—— 1936b, The Dikelokephalininae (nov.), its distribution, migration and evolution: Japanese Jour. Geology and Geography, v. 13, p. 163–178

—— 1937, The Cambro-Ordovician shelly faunas of South America: Tokyo Imp. Univ. Faculty Sci., sec. 2, v. 4, pt. 4, p. 369–522, Pls. 1–8

—— 1938, Upper Cambrian fossils from British Columbia with a discussion on the isolated occurrence of the so-called "*Olenus*" beds of Mt. Jubilee: Japanese Jour. Geology and Geography, v. 15, p. 149–192, Pls. 15–16

—— 1939, On the Agnostids (Part 1): Tokyo Imp. Univ. Faculty Sci., sec. 2, v. 5, pt. 5, p. 69–198, 1 Table

Lake, P., 1907, A monograph of the British Cambrian trilobites: London Paleontograph. Soc., pt. 2, p. 29–48, Pls. 3–4

de Laubenfels, M. W., 1955, Porifera, Part E *of* Moore, R. C., *Editor,* Treatise on invertebrate paleontology: Geol. Soc. America and Univ. Kans. Press, 122 p., 89 Figs.

Lochman, C., 1938, Upper Cambrian faunas of the Cap Mountain formation of Central Texas: Jour. Paleontology, v. 12, p. 72–85, 1 Fig., Pls. 17–18

—— 1940, Faunas of the basal Bonneterre dolomite (Upper Cambrian) of southeastern Missouri: Jour. Paleontology, v. 14, p. 1–53, Pls. 1–5

—— 1949, Paleoecology of the Cambrian in Montana and Wyoming, p. 31–71, 8 Pls. *in* Report of the Committee on a Treatise on Marine Ecology and Paleoecology: Washington, D.C., Natl. Research Council, 1948–1949, no. 9, 121 p.

—— 1950a, Upper Cambrian faunas of the Little Rocky Mountains, Montana: Jour. Paleontology, v. 24, p. 322–349, Pls. 46–51

—— 1950b, Status of the Dry Creek shale of central Montana: Am. Assoc. Petroleum Geologists Bull., v. 34, p. 2200–2222, 10 Figs.

—— 1953a, Notes on Cambrian trilobites—homonyms and synonyms: Jour. Paleontology, v. 27, p. 886–889

—— 1953b, Analysis of nine Cambrian trilobite families: Jour. Paleontology, v. 27, p. 889–896, Fig. 1

—— 1956, The Cambrian of the middle central interior states of the United States, p. 447–481, 3 Figs. *in* Rodgers, J., *Editor,* El sistema Cambrico, su paleogeografia y el problema de su base (Symposium): Mexico, 20th Internat. Geol. Cong., pt. 2, 762 p.

—— 1957, Paleoecology of the Cambrian in Montana and Wyoming, p. 117–162, 7 Figs. *in* Ladd, H., *Editor,* Treatise on marine ecology and paleoecology. V. 2, Paleoecology: Geol. Soc. America, Memoir 67, 1077 p.

—— 1958, *Sulcocephalus* Wilson 1948 to replace *Berkeia* Resser 1937, and *Burnetiella* to replace *Burnetia* Walcott 1924: Jour. Paleontology, v. 32, no. 1, p. 247

Lochman, C., and Duncan, D., 1944, Early Upper Cambrian faunas of central Montana: Geol. Soc. America Special Paper 54, 180 p., 19 Pls.

Lochman C., and Hu, C-H, 1959, A *Ptychaspis* faunule from the Bear River Range, southeastern Idaho: Jour. Paleontology, v. 33, p. 404–427, 1 Fig., Pls. 57–60

—— 1960, Upper Cambrian faunas from the northwest Wind River Mountains, Wyoming. Part 1: Jour. Paleontology, v. 34, p. 793–834, Figs. 1–4, Pls. 95–100

Lochman-Balk, C., 1956a, The evolution of some Upper Cambrian and Lower Ordovician trilobite families: Jour. Paleontology, v. 30, p. 445–462, Figs. 1–7, Pl. 47

—— 1956b, The Cambrian of the Rocky Mountains and southwest deserts of the United States and adjoining Sonora Province, Mexico, p. 529–662, Pls. 1–8 *in* Rodgers, J., *Editor,* El sistema Cambrico, su Paleogeografia y el problema de su base (Symposium): Mexico, 20th Internat. Geol. Cong., pt. 2, 762 p.

—— 1957, Paleoecology of the Cambrian in Montana and Wyoming: Geol. Soc. America Memoir 67, p. 117–162, 7 Figs., 1 Pl.

Lochman-Balk, C., and Wilson, J. L., 1958, Cambrian biostratigraphy in North America: Jour. Paleontology, v. 32, p. 312–350, 18 Figs.

Lorenz, H. W., and McMurtrey, R. G., 1956, Geology and occurrence of ground water in the Townsend Valley, Montana: U.S. Geol. Survey Water Supply Paper 1360–C, 290 p., Figs. 29–40, Pls. 19–20, Tables 1–5

McMannis, W. J., 1955, Geology of the Bridger Range, Montana: Geol. Soc. America Bull., v. 66, p. 1385–1430, 5 Figs., 8 Pls.

Miller, B. M., 1936, Cambrian trilobites from northwestern Wyoming: Jour. Paleontology, v. 10, p. 23–34, Pl. 8

Miller, S. A., 1889, North American geology and paleontology: Cincinnati, 664 p., 1194 Figs.

Moore, R. C., 1955, Invertebrates and geologic time scale, p. 547–574, 13 Figs. *in* Poldervaart, Arie, *Editor,* Crust of the earth: Geol. Soc. America Special Paper 62, 762 p.

Müller, K. J., 1959, Kambrische Conodonten: Zeitsch. Deut. Geol. Gesellschaft, p. 434–485, 11 Figs., Pls. 11–15, 3 Tables

Nelson, C. A., 1951, Cambrian trilobites from the St. Croix Valley: Jour. Paleontology, v. 25, p. 765–784, Pls. 106–110

—— 1956, Upper Croixan stratigraphy, upper Mississippi Valley: Geol. Soc. America Bull., v. 67, p. 165–184, 10 Figs.

Owen, D. D., 1852, Report of a geological survey of Wisconsin, Iowa and Minnesota: Philadelphia, Lippencott, Granbo and Co., 638 p.

Palmer, A. R., 1955a, Faunas of the Riley formation in central Texas: Jour. Paleontology, v. 28, p. 709–786, Pls. 76–92

—— 1955b, Upper Cambrian Agnostidae of the Eureka district, Nevada: Jour. Paleontology, v. 29, p. 86–101, Pls. 19–20

—— 1960, Trilobites of the Upper Cambrian Dunderberg Shale, Eureka district: U.S. Geol. Survey Prof. Paper 334–C, p. 53–109, Figs. 5–22, Pls. 4–11

Peale, A. C., 1893, The Paleozoic section in the vicinity of Three Forks, Montana: U.S. Geol. Survey Bull. 110, 56 p., 2 Figs., 6 Pls.

Pierce, W. G., 1957, Heart Mountain and South Fork detachment thrusts of Wyoming: Am. Assoc. Petroleum Geologists Bull., v. 41, p. 591–626, 20 Figs.

Raasch, G. O., 1939, Cambrian Merostomata: Geol. Soc. America Special Paper 19, 146 p., 21 Pls.

—— 1951, Revision of Croixan Dikelocephalidae: Ill. Acad. Sci. Trans., v. 44, p. 137–151 (Reprinted 1952, Ill. Geol. Survey Circ. 179, p. 137–151)

Rasetti, F., 1944, Upper Cambrian trilobites from the Levis conglomerate: Jour. Paleontology, v. 18, p. 229–259, Pls. 36–39

—— 1945, New Upper Cambrian trilobites from the Levis conglomerate: Jour. Paleontology, v. 19, p. 462–478, Pls. 60–62

—— 1947, Notes on techniques in invertebrate paleontology: Jour. Paleontology, v. 21, p. 397–399

Raymond, P. E., 1924, New Upper Cambrian and Lower Ordovician trilobites from Vermont: Boston Soc. Nat. History Proc., v. 37, p. 389–466, Pls. 12–14

—— 1937, Upper Cambrian and Lower Ordovician trilobites and Ostracoda from Vermont: Geol. Soc. America Bull., v. 48, p. 1079–1146, 4 Pls.

Resser, C. E., 1935, Nomenclature of some Cambrian trilobites: Smithsonian Misc. Coll., v. 93, no. 4, p. 1–46

—— 1936, Second contribution to nomenclature of Cambrian trilobites: Smithsonian Misc. Coll., v. 95, no. 4, p. 1–29

—— 1937, Third contribution to nomenclature of Cambrian trilobites: Smithsonian Misc. Coll., v. 95, no. 22, p. 1–29

—— 1938, Fourth contribution to nomenclature of Cambrian fossils: Smithsonian Misc. Coll., v. 97, no. 10, p. 1–43

—— 1942a, Fifth contribution to nomenclature of Cambrian fossils: Smithsonian Misc. Coll., v. 101, no. 15, p. 1–58

—— 1942b, New Upper Cambrian trilobites: Smithsonian Misc. Coll., v. 103, no. 5, p. 1–136, Pls. 1–21

Rodgers, J., 1956, The known Cambrian deposits of the southern and central Appalachian Mountains, p. 355–384, Figs. 1–2 *in* Rodgers, J., *Editor,* El sistema Cambrico, su paleogeografia y el problema de su base (Symposium): Mexico, 20th Internat. Geol. Cong., pt. 2, 762 p.

Roemer, F., 1849, Texas, mit besonderer Rucksicht auf deutsche Auswanderung und die physischen Verhaltnisse des Landes, 14: Bonn, Germany, 464 p.

—— 1852, Die Kreidebildungen von Texas und ihre organischen Einschlusse: Bonn, Germany, 100 p.

Ruedemann, R., 1933, The Cambrian of the upper Mississippi Valley. Part 3, Graptolithoidea: Milwaukee Public Mus. Bull., v. 12, p. 309–348, Pls. 46–55

—— 1934, Paleozoic plankton of North America: Geol. Soc. America Memoir 2, 141 p., 26 Pls.

—— 1947, Graptolites of North America: Geol. Soc. America Memoir 19, 652 p., 92 Pls.

Schuchert, C., and Cooper, G. A., 1931, Synopsis of the brachiopod genera of the suborders Orthoidea and Pentameroidea, with notes on the Telotremata: Am. Jour. Sci., ser. 5, v. 22, p. 241–251

—— 1932, Brachiopod genera of the suborders Orthoidea and Pentameroidea: New Haven, Peabody Mus. Nat. History Memoir, v. 4, pt. 1, p. i–xii, 1–270, 36 Figs., 29 Pls.

Shaw, A. B., 1951, New Late Cambrian trilobites, [Pt. 1] *of* The paleontology of northwestern Vermont: Jour. Paleontology, v. 25, p. 97–114, Pls. 21–24

—— 1952, Fauna of the Upper Cambrian Rockledge conglomerate near St. Albans, [Pt. 2] *of* The paleontology of northwestern Vermont: Jour. Paleontology, v. 26, p. 458–483, 5 Figs., Pl. 57

—— 1953, Miscellaneous Cambrian fossils, [Pt. 3] *of* The paleontology of northwestern Vermont: Jour. Paleontology, v. 27, p. 137–146, 2 Figs., Pl. 18

—— 1954, Correlation of the Paleozoic formations of Wyoming: Wyo. Geol. Assoc. 9th Ann. Field Conf. Guidebook, Chart 2

—— 1956, A Cambrian *Aphelaspis* fauna from Steele Butte, near Boulder, Wyoming: Jour. Paleontology, v. 30, p. 48–52, Pls. 9–13

Shaw, A. B., and DeLand, C. R., 1955, Cambrian of southwestern Wyoming: Wyo. Geol. Assoc. 10th Ann. Field Conf. Guidebook, p. 38–42, Figs. 1–2

Shimer, H. W., and Shrock, R. R., 1944, Index fossils of North America: Cambridge, The Technology Press, Mass. Inst. Technology; New York, John Wiley and Sons, 837 p., 303 Pls.

Shrock, R. R., and Twenhofel, W. H., 1953, Principles of invertebrate paleontology (2d ed.): New York, McGraw-Hill Book Co., 816 p.

Shumard, B. F., 1861, The Primordial Zone of Texas, with descriptions of new fossils: Am. Jour. Sci., 2d ser., v. 32, p. 213–221

—— 1862, Notice of some new and imperfectly known fossils from the Primordial Zone (Potsdam Sandstone and Calciferous Sand Group) of Wisconsin and Minnesota: St. Louis Acad. Sci. Trans., v. 2, p. 101–107

Sloss, L. L., 1950, Paleozoic sedimentation in Montana area: Am. Assoc. Petroleum Geologists Bull., v. 34, p. 423–451, 11 Figs.

Sloss, L. L., and Laird, W. M., 1947, Devonian System in central and northwestern Montana: Am. Assoc. Petroleum Geologists Bull., v. 31, p. 1404–1430, 8 Figs.

Sloss, L. L., and Moritz, C. A., 1951, Paleozoic stratigraphy of southwestern Montana: Am. Assoc. Petroleum Geologists Bull., v. 35, p. 2135–2169, 11 Figs.

Stauffer, C. R., Schwartz, G. M., and Thiel, G. A., 1939, St. Croixan classification of Minnesota: Geol. Soc. America Bull., v. 50, p. 1227–1244

Størmer, L., 1949, Classe des trilobites, p. 44–246 *in* Piveteau, J., *Editor,* Traite de paleontology: Paris, Masson & Cie., v. 3, 1063 p.

Twenhofel, W. H., Raasch, G. O., and Thwaites, F. T., 1935, Cambrian strata of Wisconsin: Geol. Soc. America Bull., v. 46, p. 1687–1744, 1 Fig., Pl. 151

Ulrich, E. O., 1924, Notes on new names in table of formations and on physical evidence of breaks between Paleozoic systems in Wisconsin: Wis. Acad. Sci. Arts and Letters Trans., v. 21, p. 71–107

Ulrich, E. O., and Cooper, G. A., 1936, New genera and species of Ozarkian and Canadian brachiopods: Jour. Paleontology, v. 10, p. 616–631

—— 1938, Ozarkian and Canadian Brachiopoda: Geol. Soc. America Special Paper 13, 323 p., 57 Pls.

Ulrich, E. O., and Resser, C. E., 1930, The Cambrian of the upper Mississippi Valley. Part 1, Trilobita; Dikelocephalinae and Osceolinae: Milwaukee Public Mus. Bull., v. 12, no. 1, p. 1–122, Pls. 1–23

U.S. Department of Agriculture, Forest Service, 1941, Shoshone National Forest (with map): Washington, D.C., U.S. Govt. Printing Office, 24 p.

—— 1947a, Gallatin National Forest (east half), Montana: Principal Meridian, Montana: Washington, D.C., U.S. Govt. Printing Office, map

—— 1947b, Gallatin National Forest (west half), Montana: Principal Meridian, Montana: Washington, D.C., U.S. Govt. Printing Office, map

Walcott, C. D., 1879, Descriptions of new species of fossils from the Calciferous formation: New York State Mus. 32d Ann. Rept., p. 129–131 (also preprint, January 3, 1879, p. 1–4)

—— 1884, Paleontology of the Eureka district: U.S. Geol. Survey Mon. 8, 298 p., 24 Pls.

—— 1886, Second contribution to the studies on the Cambrian faunas of North America: U.S. Geol. Survey Bull. 30, 225 p., 33 Pls.

—— 1891, Description of new forms of Upper Cambrian fossils: U.S. Natl. Mus. Proc., *for* 1890, no. 820, v. 13, p. 266–279, Pls. 20–21

—— 1896, Fossil jelly fishes from the Middle Cambrian Terrane: U.S. Natl Mus. Proc., v. 18, p. 611–614, Pls. 31–32

—— 1898a, Fossil Medusae: U.S. Geol. Survey Mon. 30, 201 p., 47 Pls.

—— 1898b, Cambrian Brachiopoda: *Obolus* and *Lingulella,* with description of new species: U.S. Natl. Mus. Proc., v. 21, p. 385–420, Pls. 26–28

—— 1899, Cambrian fossils, p. 440–478, Pls. 60–65 *in* Hague, Arnold, and others, Geology of the Yellowstone National Park: U.S. Geol. Survey Mon. 32, pt. 2, 893 p.

—— 1902, Cambrian Brachiopoda: *Acrotreta, Linnarssonella, Obolus,* with descriptions of new species: U.S. Natl. Mus. Proc., v. 25, p. 577–612

—— 1905, Cambrian Brachiopoda, with descriptions of new genera and species: U.S. Natl. Mus. Proc., v. 28, p. 227–337

—— 1912a, Cambrian Brachiopoda: U.S. Geol. Survey Mon. 51, pt. 1, 872 p.; pt. 2, 361 p., 104 Pls.

—— 1912b, New York Potsdam-Hoyt fauna: Smithsonian Misc. Coll., v. 57, no. 9, p. 251–304, Pls. 37–49

—— 1914a, *Dikelocephalus* and other genera of the Dikelocephalinae: Smithsonian Misc. Coll., v. 57, no. 13, p. 345–412, Pls. 60–70

—— 1914b, Precambrian Algonkian algal flora: Smithsonian Misc. Coll., v. 64, no. 2, p. 77–156, Pls. 4–23

—— 1916a, Cambrian trilobites: Smithsonian Misc. Coll., v. 64, no. 3, p. 157–258, Pls. 24–38

—— 1916b, Cambrian trilobites: Smithsonian Misc. Coll., v. 64, no. 5, p. 303–456, Pls. 45–67

—— 1924a, Cambrian and Ozarkian Brachiopoda, Ozarkian Cephalopoda and Notostraca: Smithsonian Misc. Coll., v. 67, p. 477–554, Pls. 106–126

—— 1924b, Cambrian and Lower Ozarkian trilobites: Smithsonian Misc. Coll., v. 75, no. 2, p. 53–60, Pls. 9–14

—— 1925, Cambrian and Ozarkian trilobites: Smithsonian Misc. Coll., v. 75, no. 3, p. 61–146, Pls. 15–24

Weed, W. H., 1896, Yellowstone National Park folio: U.S. Geol. Survey Geol. Atlas, folio no. 30, 6 p., 11 figs., maps

—— 1899a, Fort Benton folio, Montana: U.S. Geol. Survey Geol. Atlas, folio no. 55, 7 p., maps

—— 1899b, Little Belt Mountains folio, Montana: U.S. Geol. Survey Geol. Atlas, folio no. 56, 9 p., maps

—— 1900, Geology of the Little Belt Mountains, Montana: U.S. Geol. Survey 20th Ann. Rept., 1898–99, pt. 3, p. 257–461

Weed, W. H., and Pirsson, L. V., 1896, The geology of the Little Rocky Mountains: Jour. Geology, v. 4, p. 399–428

Westergård, A. H., 1953, Two problematic fossils from the Cambrian in Sweden: Stockholm, Geologiska Foreningen, Forhandlingar, bd. 75, hafte 4, p. 465–468, Pl. 5

Wheeler, H. E., and Mallory, V. S., 1953, Designation of stratigraphic units: Am. Assoc. Petroleum Geologists Bull., v. 37, p. 2407–2421, 3 Figs.

—— 1956, Factors in lithostratigraphy: Am. Assoc. Petroleum Geologists Bull., v. 40, p. 2711–2723, 6 Figs.

Whitfield, R. P., 1877, Descriptions of new species of fossils from the Potsdam, Jurassic, and Cretaceous formations of the Black Hills of South Dakota: U.S. Geog. and Geol. Survey, Rocky Mtn. Region, Rept. Black Hills, Dakota; Prelim. Rept., 49 p.

—— 1878, Preliminary descriptions of new species of fossils from the lower geological formations of Wisconsin: Wis. Geol. Survey Ann. Rept., 1877, p. 50–67

—— 1880, Paleontology of the Black Hills of Dakota, p. 325–468, Pls. 1–16 *in* Newton, H., and Jenney, W. P., U.S. Geog. and Geol. Survey, Rocky Mtn. Region, Rept. Black Hills, Dakota, 566 p.

—— 1882, Species from the Potsdam sandstone: Wis. Geol. Survey Ann. Rept., 1873–79, v. 4, pt. 3, p. 163–363, Pls. 1–2

—— 1883, List of Wisconsin fossils: Wis. Geol. Survey Ann. Rept., 1873, v. 1, pt. 2, p. 362–375

Wilson, J. L., 1948, Two Upper Cambrian *Elvinia* zone trilobite genera: Jour. Paleontology, v. 22, p. 30–34, Pl. 8

—— 1949, The trilobite fauna of the *Elvinia* zone in the basal Wilberns limestone of Texas: Jour. Paleontology, v. 23, p. 25–44, Pls. 9–11

—— 1951, Franconian trilobites of the central Appalachians: Jour. Paleontology, v. 25, p. 617–654, Pls. 89–95

—— 1952, Upper Cambrian stratigraphy in the central Appalachians: Geol. Soc. America Bull., v. 63, p. 275–322, 4 Figs., 4 Pls.

—— 1954, Late Cambrian and Early Ordovician trilobites from the Marathon uplift, Texas: Jour. Paleontology, v. 28, p. 249–285, Pls. 24–27

Wilson, J. L., and Frederickson, E. A., 1950, The *Irvingella major* ("*Ptychopleurites*") faunizone of the Upper Cambrian: Am. Jour. Sci., v. 248, p. 891–902, Pl. 1

Winchell, A., 1864, Notice of a small collection of fossils from the Potsdam sandstone of Wisconsin and the Lake Superior sandstone of Michigan: Am. Jour. Sci., 2d ser., v. 37, p. 226–232

Winchell, N. H., 1886, New species of fossils: Minn. Geol. Survey 14th Ann. Rept., p. 313–318

Young, R. S., 1956, Lower Canadian brachiopods from Virginia: Jour. Paleontology, v. 30, p. 1165–1169, Pl. 124

EXPLANATION OF PLATES 5–15

REPOSITORIES: Most of the collection is at the U.S. National Museum, Washington, D.C.; illustrated specimens deposited there are designated by USNM numbers. Most of the small brachiopods are at the University of Texas; illustrated representatives have UT catalogue numbers.

PHOTOGRAPHY: At least one of the best preserved specimens of each species was photographed. Stereoscopic effect was obtained by using a bellows camera mounted on a swivel, according to the technique described by Gott (1945) and Evitt (1949). Each fossil was given a white coating to bring out details of morphology and to give the photographs a uniform tone. Trilobites and large brachiopods were coated with magnesium oxide by holding the specimen over a burning magnesium ribbon (Rasetti, 1947, p. 397). Small and fragile brachiopods were coated with ammonium chloride (Gott, 1945, p. 394) because it is soluble in water and can be removed from delicate shells with a wet brush.

Each fossil was magnified enough to make a picture slightly less than 1 inch wide. This partly destroys immediate appreciation of relative sizes among the fossils, but is necessary in order to construct plates with three rows of stereophotographs.

PLATE 5. PHOTOGRAPHS OF OUTCROPS AND CALCAREOUS ALGAE

Figures | Page

1, 2. Typical rock exposures 70, 74

(1) Sage Member at Fox Creek, characteristic alternation of green shale with beds of limestone or limestone-pebble conglomerate. Nearly all fossils were found in the limestone or conglomerate beds. (2) Ledge formed by Grove Creek Member at locality above Swamp Lake; lower slope, mostly covered, is Sage Member, upper slope is weathered Bighorn Formation, possibly brecciated by Heart Mountain thrust fault. Ledge is 26 feet high; basal 17 feet is Grove Creek, upper 9 feet is Bighorn.

3, 4, 6. *Tetonophycus blackwelderi* Fenton and Fenton 27, 146

(3) Naturally exposed cross-section at UFOX 65.9 showing mound-shaped growth lines and abrupt contact between upper and lower parts of bed. (4) Small mound at Fox Creek formed by calcareous algae, with beds of shale draped over top; small limestone pods irregularly distributed along beds of shale below. (6) Upper surface of algal mound at UFOX 65.9.

5, 7, 8. *Collenia magna* Fenton and Fenton 24, 145

(5) Isolated small column in shale below main mass of bioherm at Fox Creek; also appearing below and to left of hammer in fig. 7. Surrounding shale is calcareous, drapes over column. (7) Three-stage bioherm at Fox Creek with thick columns. Shale and limestone beds to left of bioherm thicken toward it, butt against or drape over it, contain calcareous debris probably eroded from it. (8) Three-layered bioherm with thinner columns at Swamp Lake, each layer about 5 feet high with pebbly, shaly limestone beds between layers, total thickness about 19 feet. Here bioherm also is discontinuous, with shale and limestone beds butting against it, fossiliferous calcareous cement between columns.

PHOTOGRAPHS OF OUTCROPS AND CALCAREOUS ALGAE

GRANT, PLATE 5
Geological Society of America Memoir 96

LIMESTONE-PEBBLE CONGLOMERATE

PLATE 6. LIMESTONE-PEBBLE CONGLOMERATE

Figures Page

1. Polished surface of poorly sorted conglomerate from YO 196.9 (× 0.75) 14, 24
   Pebbles and fossil fragments in matrix of sparry calcite, many pebbles with limonite rims indicating oxidation prior to consolidation; those near top sharply truncated, overlain by microcrystalline limestone (*see* Pl. 7, fig. 3).
2. Naturally exposed conglomerate from North Grove Creek (× 0.75) 16
   Shows random orientation and pebble with hole in it, characteristic of Grove Creek Member.
3. Limestone pods occupying ripple depressions in calcareous shale at GR 235.6 (× 0.50) 14
   Evidence for hypothesis that pebbles in limestone-pebble conglomerate originated in this manner.
4. Green shale at FOX 77.5 (Sage Member) 15
   Has many pods of limestone, probably formed as above (fig. 3). Hammer rests on lens of fossil fragments cemented by sparry calcite. Overlying bed of limestone-pebble conglomerate probably formed by cementation of a gravel of these pods.
5. Dolomitized edgewise conglomerate at KZ 19–20, in Grove Creek Member 16
   Has tightly cemented pods in dolomitized shale below bed of conglomerate. Random orientation of pebbles in conglomerate is evidence for hypothesis that gravels were concentrated suddenly, possibly by storm waves.

PLATE 7. PHOTOMICROGRAPHS OF ROCKS, SNOWY RANGE FORMATION
(Grid squares 0.2 mm per side)

Figures Page

1. HA 45.8. Sage Member. 12, 24
Dolomitized glauconitic intraclastic biosparite; constituent particles partly replaced and pitted by dolomite, probably during Devonian weathering.
2. HA 65.7. Maywood unit. 18, 26
Finely crystalline dolomite, about 70 per cent, replacing all but 25 per cent of microcrystalline calcite and sparry calcite cement, and 5 per cent angular quartz silt, some grains with overgrowths. Fabric indicates a few intraclasts, nearly obliterated by dolomitization.
3. YO 196.9. Sage Member. 15, 24
Fossiliferous intrasparite; intraclasts of slightly dolomitic pelmicrite, along with fossil fragments and allochemical calcite distributed randomly, cemented by sparry calcite. Some intraclasts with limonitic rims (*see* Pl. 6, fig. 1).
4. FD 98. Maywood unit. 18, 26
Homogenous medium-crystalline dolomite; probably was calcareous algal limestone before dolomitization: externally resembles algal limestone of Sage Member.
5. BP 245.5. Grove Creek Member. 15, 26
Fossiliferous finely and coarsely crystalline dolomite, with traces of quartz silt and glauconite; fossils in all stages of alteration by dolomite, from unaltered to completely replaced; dolomite rhombs with inclusions of hematite or pyrite, some oxidized to form ankerite banding within rhombs.
6. YO 238.2. Sage Member. 12, 24
Dolomitic illitic shale with limonite stain; illite flakes oriented parallel to bedding, limonite derived from recent weathering of scattered pyrite.

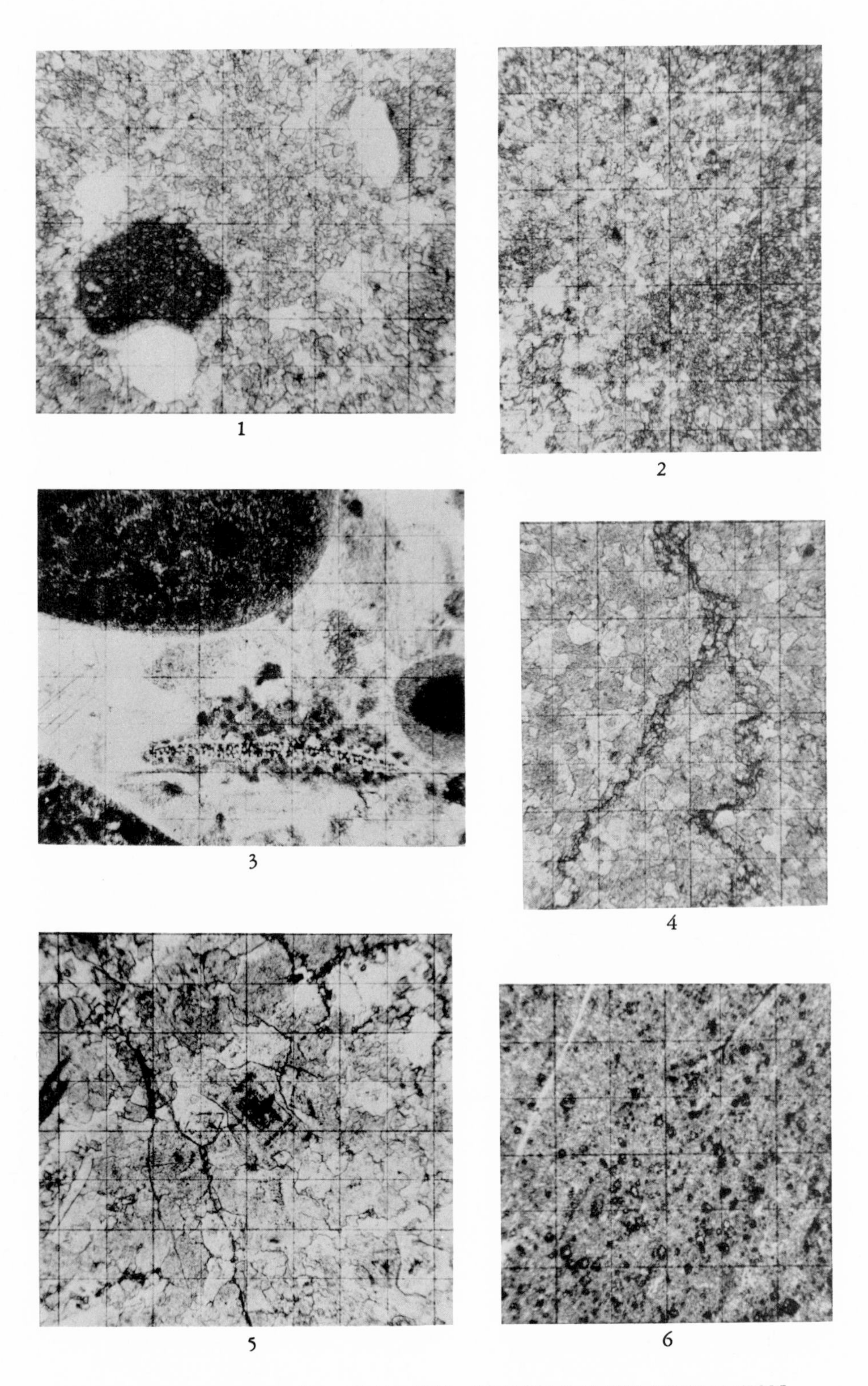

PHOTOMICROGRAPHS OF ROCKS, SNOWY RANGE FORMATION

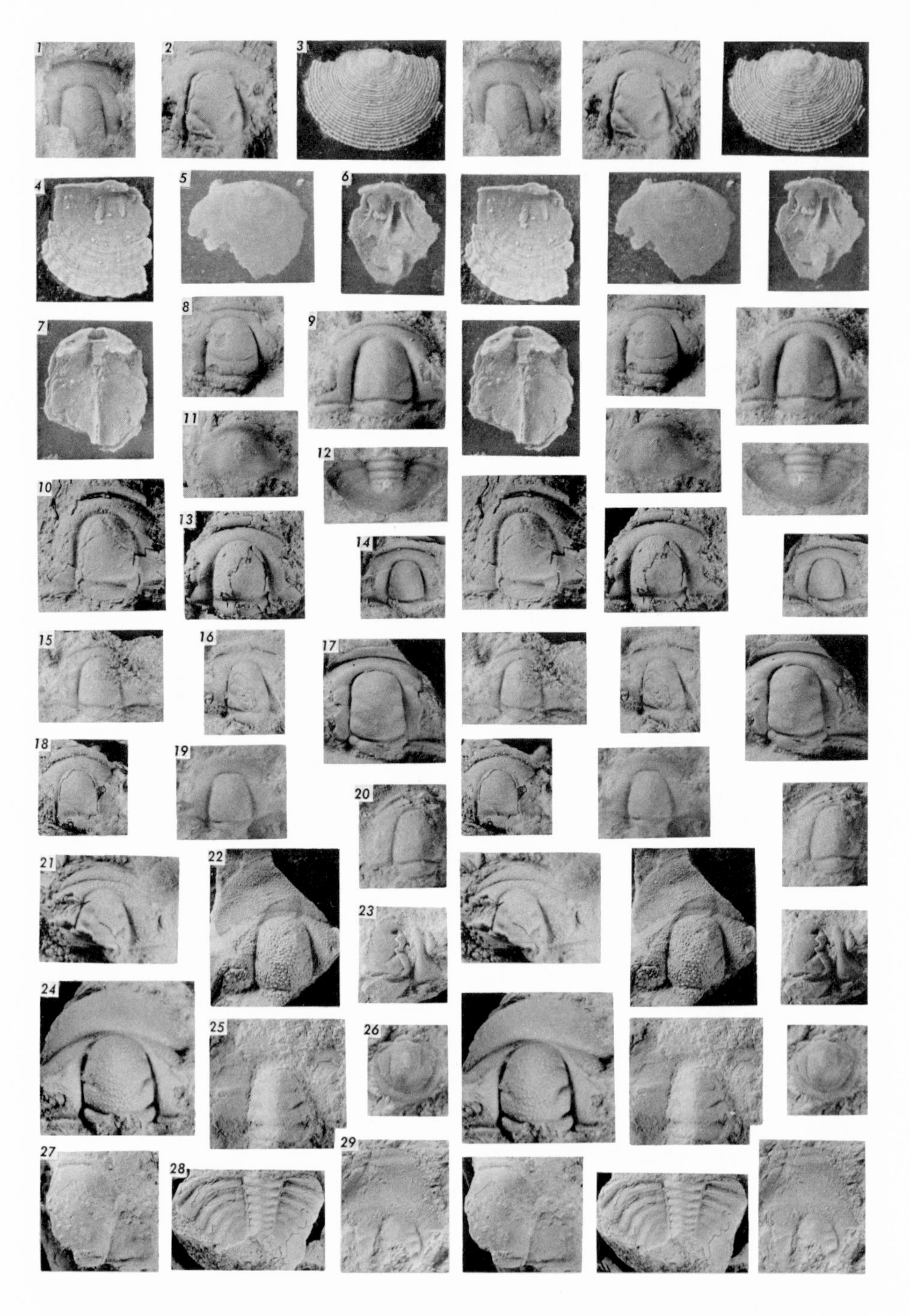

DRESBACHIAN AND *ELVINIA* ZONE FOSSILS

PLATE 8. DRESBACHIAN AND *ELVINIA* ZONE FOSSILS

Figures | Page

1. *Aphelaspis* sp. undet. 138
   Cranidium, ×2.5, BL 2.5, USNM 142253
2. *Dytremacephalus* ? sp. undet. 140
   Cranidium, ×3.5, BC O, USNM 142254

3–4. *Micromitra modesta* (Lochman). 96
   (3) Exterior of pedicle valve, ×11, BL 2.5, UT-12097. (4) Interior of fragmentary brachial valve, ×12, HG 47.7, UT-12098

5–7. *Apsotreta expansa* Palmer. 99
   (5) Exterior of pedicle valve, ×12, FOX 3.5, UT-12099a. (6) Interior of pedicle valve, showing internal pedicle opening and trough, ×12, FOX 3.5, UT-12099b. (7) Interior of brachial valve, showing propareas, median groove and median septum ×12, FOX 3.5, UT-12099c

8. *Irvingella* (*Parairvingella*) *eurekensis* Resser. 127
   Cranidium, ×3.5, HG 36, USNM 142260
9. *Dellea saratogensis* (Resser). 130
   Cranidium, ×3.5, NG "top of reef," USNM 142261

10, 14. *Dellea suada* (Walcott). 130
   (10) Cranidium with features similar to those of *Deadwoodia duris*, ×2, HG 36, USNM 142262. (14) Cranidium typical of *D. suada*, ×2, FC 93.7, USNM 142263

11. *Bynumina terrenda* Wilson. 126
   Cranidium, ×4, FP 88, USNM 142264
12. *Dellea* sp. 128
   Pygidium belonging to a species of Dellea, ×3.5, HG 36, USNM 142265
13. *Dellea juvenalis* Frederickson. 129
   Cranidium, ×2, YG 3.4a, USNM 142266

15–16. *Dellea snoburgensis* (Wilson). 129
   (15) Cranidium with recurved posterior limb, ×2.5, HG 36, USNM 142267. (16) Cranidium showing elongate glabella, ×2, HH 65.9, USNM 142268

17. *Deadwoodia duris* (Walcott). 128
   Cranidium, ×2, NG "top of reef," USNM 142269
18. *Dellea butlerensis* Frederickson 129
   Cranidium, ×2, NG "top of reef," USNM 144270
19. *Pinctus* ? *artus* Grant n. sp. 112
   Holotype cranidium, ×5, HG 36, USNM 142271
20. *Sulcocephalus* sp. 2. 113
   Poorly preserved cranidium, ×3.5, GR 10.7, USNM 142272
21. *Sulcocephalus granulosus* Wilson. 113
   Cranidium, ×3.5, YG 3.4a, USNM 142273

22, 24. *Burnetiella ectypa* (Resser) 110
   (22) Cranidium with low glabella and long frontal area, ×2, GR 10.7, USNM 142274. (24) Cranidium with high glabella and shorter frontal area, ×1.5, BC 63.8, USNM 142275

23. *Kindbladia* cf. *K. wichitaensis* (Resser). 111
   Fragment of cranidium, ×2.5, FP 88, USNM 142276

25, 28, 29. *Pterocephalia sanctisabae* Roemer. 140
   (25) Fragmentary cranidium, ×1.5, HG 47.5, USNM 142277. (28) Pygidium, ×1, BC 63.8, USNM 142278. (29) Cranidium with frontal area, ×2.5, NG "top of reef," USNM 142279

26. *Homagnostus* cf. *H. tumidosus* (Hall and Whitfield). 107
   Pygidium, ×8.5, HG 47.5, USNM 142280
27. *Cheilocephalus* sp. undet. 109
   Right half of cranidium, ×1.5, BB 49.5, USNM 142281

PLATE 9. *ELVINIA* ZONE FOSSILS

Figures | Page

1. *Homagnostus* cf. *H. tumidosus* (Hall and Whitfield). … 107
Cranidium with weak anterior median furrow, ×3.5, YO 65.9, USNM 142282

2–3, 5. *Pseudagnostus sentosus* Grant n. sp. … 108
(2) Cranidium, ×4, HG 47.5, USNM 142434. (3) Immature pygidium ×6, HH 132.8, USNM 142283. (5) Holotype pygidium, ×4, HG 63.5, USNM 142284

4, 6, 8–10, 12–14, 16, 19. *Linnarssonella girtyi* Walcott. … 100
(4) Exterior of pedicle valve with holes drilled by predaceous gastropod or other organism, ×12, SL 64.7, UT-12124a. (6) Interior of small pedicle valve, ×12, SL 64.7, UT-12124b. (8) Exterior of typical brachial valve, ×12, FOX 33.8, UT-12125a. (9) Interior of thick elongate brachial valve (*L. elongata* of Bell, 1941), ×12, CF 31.6, UT-12126. (10) Exterior of resupinate brachial valve. This type is common, but less abundant than the convex type. ×7, HG 36, UT-12127. (12) Interior of typical brachial valve, ×12, SL 64.7, UT-12124c. (13) Interior of small thin brachial valve, ×12, SL 64.7, UT-12124d. (14) Profile of exterior of typical pedicle valve, ×12, HH 70.1, UT-12128. (16) Interior of typical pedicle valve, ×12, FOX 33.8, UT-12125b. (19) Interior of thick pedicle valve. ×8.5, FOX 33.8, UT-12125c

7, 11, 15. *Lingulella desiderata* (Walcott). … 95
(7) Two small valves together, exterior view of brachial valve, ×12, BP 97.3, UT-12129. (11) Two valves together, exterior view of pedicle valve, ×2.5, HG 36, UT-12130. (15) Two valves together, exterior view of pedicle valve and view of part of interior of brachial valve to right, ×2, HD 112.1, USNM 142297

17–18, 20, 23. *Pseudodicellomus mosaicus* (Bell). … 95
(17) Partly exfoliated exterior of brachial valve, ×2.5, GC 93.5, UT-12132. (18) Partly exfoliated exterior of pedicle valve, ×3.5, HD 117.9, USNM 142289. (20) Interior of fragment of pedicle valve, ×3.5, CF 56.2, UT-12134. (23) Interior of fragment of brachial valve, ×6, MC 164.4, UT-12135

21, 24–25, 27. *Angulotreta glabra* Grant, n. sp. … 98
(21) Apical view of exterior of pedicle valve, ×12, MC 105.4, UT-12136. (24) Interior of holotype pedicle valve, ×12, SL 43.9, UT-12137a. (25) View of pseudointerarea of pedicle valve, ×12, YO 52.3, UT-12138. (27) Interior of brachial valve, ×12, SL 43.9, UT-12137b

22. *Elvinia roemeri* (Shumard). … 115
Fragment of cranidium, ×1.5, GR 15.9, USNM 142306

26. *Hyolithes primordialis* (Hall). … 106
Shell filled with limestone, ×1.5, HG 36, USNM 142307

28. *Kyphocephalus* ? sp. … 111
Cranidium, ×7.5, BC 63.8, USNM 142308

29, 32. *Dokimocephalus intermedius* (Resser). … 111
(29) Cranidium, ×2, GR 10.7, USNM 142309. (32) Pygidium, ×2, GR 10.7, USNM 142310

30, 33. *Lingulella perattenuata* (Whitfield). … 96
(30) Exterior of pedicle valve, ×2, GR 44–1–W2 (collected by James L. Wilson at North Grove Creek. Valve associated with *Comanchia lippa*, probably near GR 56.3), USNM 142311. (33) Interior of pedicle valve, ×8.5, HG 56, UT-12144

31. *Kyphocephalus bridgerensis* Miller. … 111
Cranidium, ×1.5, NG "top of reef," USNM 142313

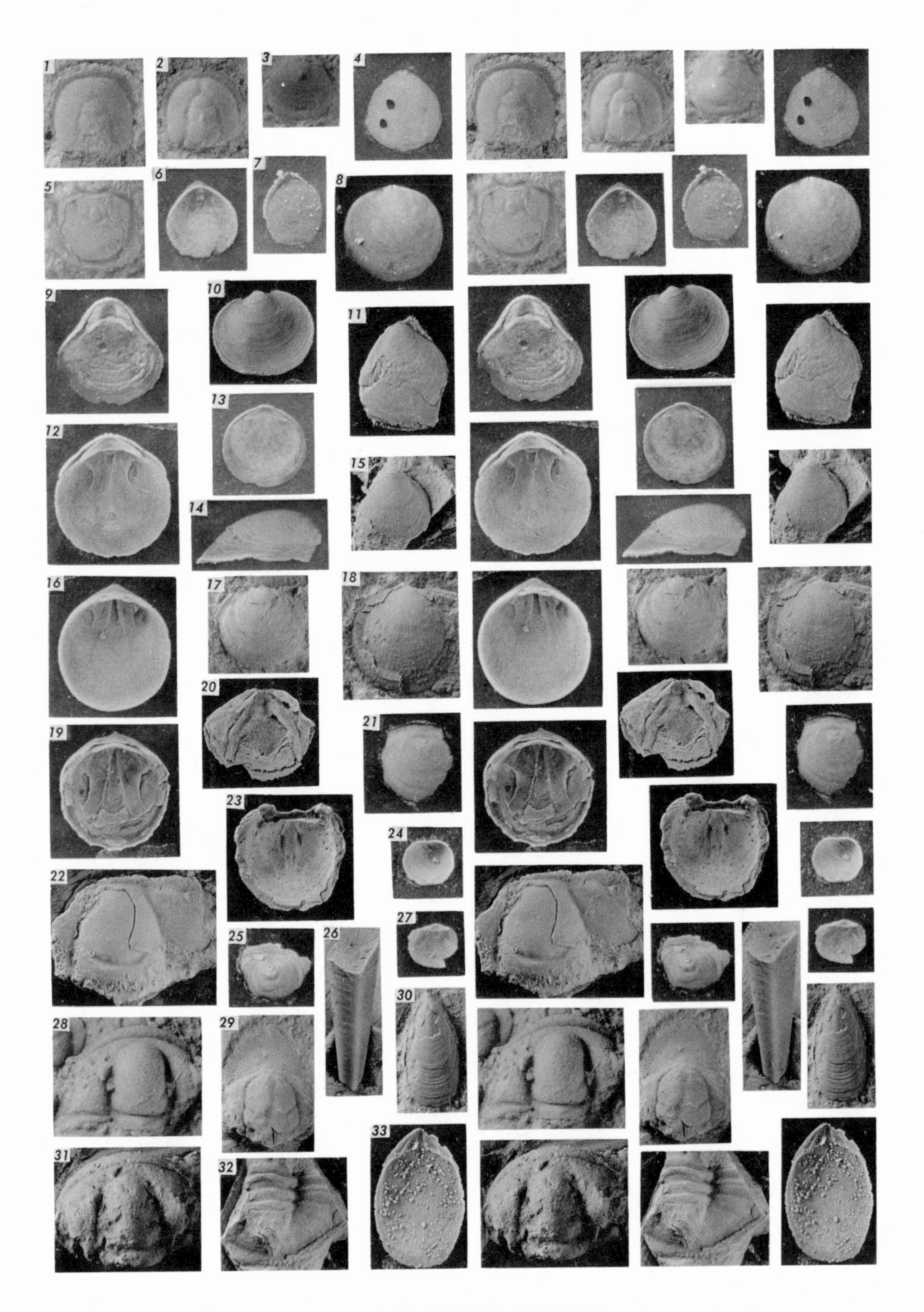

ELVINIA ZONE FOSSILS

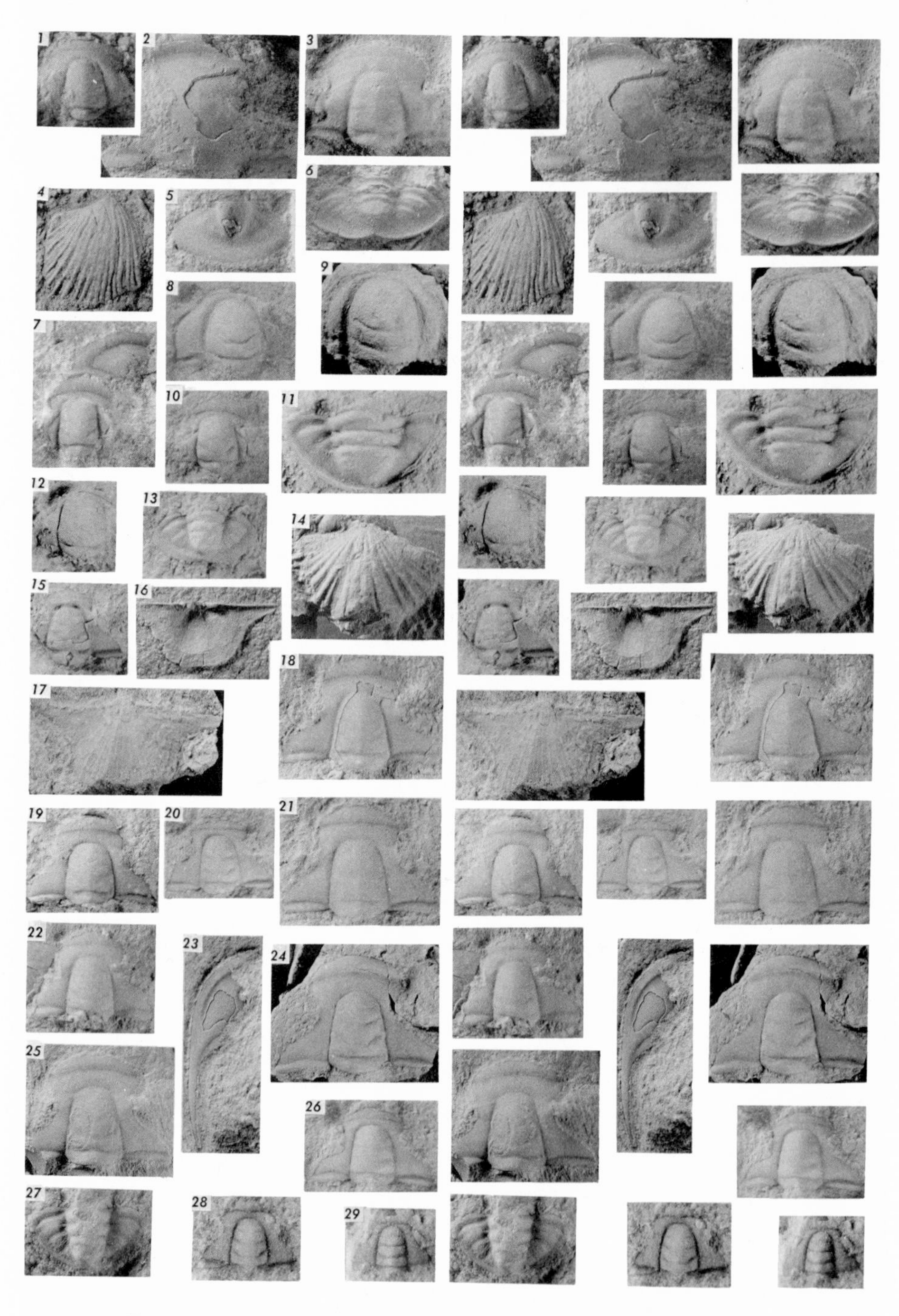

ELVINIA ZONE AND *TAENICEPHALUS* ZONE FOSSILS

GRANT, PLATE 10
Geological Society of America Memoir 96

Plate 10. *ELVINIA* ZONE AND *TAENICEPHALUS* ZONE FOSSILS

Figures | Page

1. *Camaraspis berkeyi* (Resser). 139
Cranidium, ×5, HG 47.5, USNM 142314

2, 5. *Housia vacuna* (Walcott). 117
(2) Cranidium, ×1.5, MC 105.4, USNM 142315. (5) Pygidium, ×2, MC 105.4, USNM 142316

3, 6. *Camaraspis convexa* (Whitfield). 140
(3) Cranidium with furrows nearly as deep as in *C. berkeyi,* ×2.5, HH 68.9, USNM 142317. (6) Pygidium with obvious furrows, ×2.5, HH 68.9, USNM 142318

4. *Ocnerorthis monticola* Bell. 103
Exterior of fragmentary topotype pedicle valve, ×3.5, CF 29.2, USNM 142319

7, 10, 13. *Comanchia lippa* Grant n. sp. 117
(7) Cranidium with associated free cheek, ×4, MC 111.7, USNM 142320. (10) Holotype cranidium ×5, MC 111.7, USNM 142321. (13) Pygidium, ×4, GC 85.8, USNM 142322

8–9, 11. *Irvingella major* Ulrich and Resser. 126
(8) Immature cranidium with large frontal area, ×4, MC 111.7, USNM 142323. (9) Mature cranidium with normal frontal area, ×1.5, YO 69.4, USNM 142324. (11) Pygidium, ×2.5, HD 80.4, USNM 142325

12. *Kiowaia* cf. *K. timberensis* Frederickson. 130
Poorly preserved cranidium, ×2, YO 69.4, USNM 142326

14. *Huenella texana* var. *fortis* Grant n. var. 104
Exterior of strongly ribbed holotype pedicle valve, ×2, YO 69.4, USNM 142327

15. *Kendallina biforota* (Berg). 131
Cranidium, ×2, DC 6.9W (collected by Lochman-Balk near type locality of Dry Creek Shale, Accola, Montana), USNM 142328

16–17. *Otusia sandbergi* (Winchell). 103
(16) Interior of brachial valve, ×2, SL 76.8 (float), USNM 142329. (17) Exterior of brachial valve, ×2.5, HG 47.7, USNM 142330

18, 21–22. *Parabolinoides expansus* Nelson. 135
(18) Cranidium, ×2.5, YG 39/1, USNM 142331. (21) Cranidium, ×3, YG 3.2, USNM 142332. (22) Cranidium, ×3.5, YG 39/1, USNM 142333

19. *Parabolinoides hebe* Frederickson. 135
Cranidium with slightly divergent anterior facial sutures, ×2, FOX 65.4, USNM 142334

20, 23–27. *Parabolinoides contractus* Frederickson. 134
(20) Immature cranidium with features intermediate between those of *P. contractus* and *P. hebe,* ×4, YG 39/1, USNM 142335. (23) Free cheek, × 1.5, YG 3.2, USNM 142336. (24) Cranidium, ×1.5, YO 75.7, USNM 142337. (25) Cranidium, ×1.5, YG 3.2, USNM 142338. (26) Immature cranidium with features intermediate between those of *P. contractus* and *P. expansa,* ×4, YG 39/1, USNM 142339. (27) Pygidium with one pair of marginal spines, ×2.5, YG 39/1, USNM 142340

28–29. *Parabolinoides* sp. 133
(28) Meraspid cranidium of an undetermined species of *Parabolinoides,* ×7.5, YG 39/1, USNM 142341. (29) Earlier meraspid molt of cranidium of undetermined species of *Parabolinoides,* ×8.5, YG 39/1, USNM 142342

PLATE 11. *TAENICEPHALUS* ZONE FOSSILS

Figures	Page
1–5. *Parabolinoides cordillerensis* (Lochman).	134
(1) Cranidium with raised border and recurved marginal furrow, ×2, FOX 65.4, USNM 142343. (2) Cranidium with straight marginal furrow containing shallow median pit, ×2.5, YG 3.2, USNM 142344. (3) Free cheek, ×1, YG 3.2, USNM 142345. (4) Cranidium with flat frontal area and median pit in marginal furrow, ×2, YO 75.7, USNM 142346. (5) Pygidium with one pair of well-developed marginal spines and marginal undulations perhaps marking rudimentary spines, ×3.5, YG 3.2, USNM 142347
6, 8. *Huenella texana* (Walcott).	104
(6) Exteriors of pedicle and brachial valves, ×2, HB 73.8, USNM 142348. (8) Exterior of strongly ribbed brachial valve, ×3.5, GR 74.1, USNM 142349
7, 9. *Huenella abnormis* (Walcott).	104
(7) Exterior of pedicle valve, ×2, BP 98.7, USNM 142350. (9) Exterior of very smooth brachial valve, ×2, BC 69.3, USNM 142351
10, 13. *Eoorthis remnicha* (Winchell).	102
(10) Exterior of brachial valve, ×1.5, YO 73.9, USNM 142352. (13) Internal mold of brachial valve, ×2, SP 109.9, USNM 142353
11–12, 14, 15, 17–18. *Ceratreta hebes* Bell.	100
(11) Interior of pedicle valve, showing posterior internal pedicle tube, ×7.5, SP 116.4, UT-12176a. (12) Interior of similar pedicle valve, ×8, HB 77.3, UT-12177a. (14) Interior of brachial valve, ×7.5, SP 116.4, UT-12176b. (15) Interior of thick brachial valve with callosities at posterolateral corners, ×12, HB 77.8, UT-12177b. (17) Apical view of exterior of pedicle valve, showing slit-shaped external pedicle opening, ×7.5, HK 77.2, UT-12178. (18) Exterior of brachial valve, ×7.5, SL 77.8, UT-12179
16, 19. *Eoorthis remnicha* var. *A*. Grant n. var.	103
(16) Internal mold of brachial valve, ×3, HF 15.6, USNM 142360. (19) Interior of brachial valve, ×2, SL 76.8 (float), USNM 142361
20–21, 23?24. *Angulotreta tetonensis* (Walcott).	98
(20) Interior of pedicle valve, ×8, CF 40, UT-12182. (21) Interior of brachial valve, ×7.5, CF 56.2, UT-12183a. (23) Pseudo-interarea of pedicle valve, ×7.5, YO 75.7, UT-12184. (24) Exterior of typical brachial valve, ×7.5, CF 56.2, UT-12183b
22, 25–26. *Billingsella plicatella* Walcott.	102
(22) Exterior of pedicle valve, ×2, HI 67.7, USNM 142366. (25) Internal mold of brachial valve, ×2.5, MC 117.1, USNM 142367. (26) Internal mold of pedicle valve, ×2.5, MC 117.1, USNM 142368
27. *Pelagiella primordialis* (Hall).	105
Steinkern, ×2.5, SP 117.4, USNM 142369

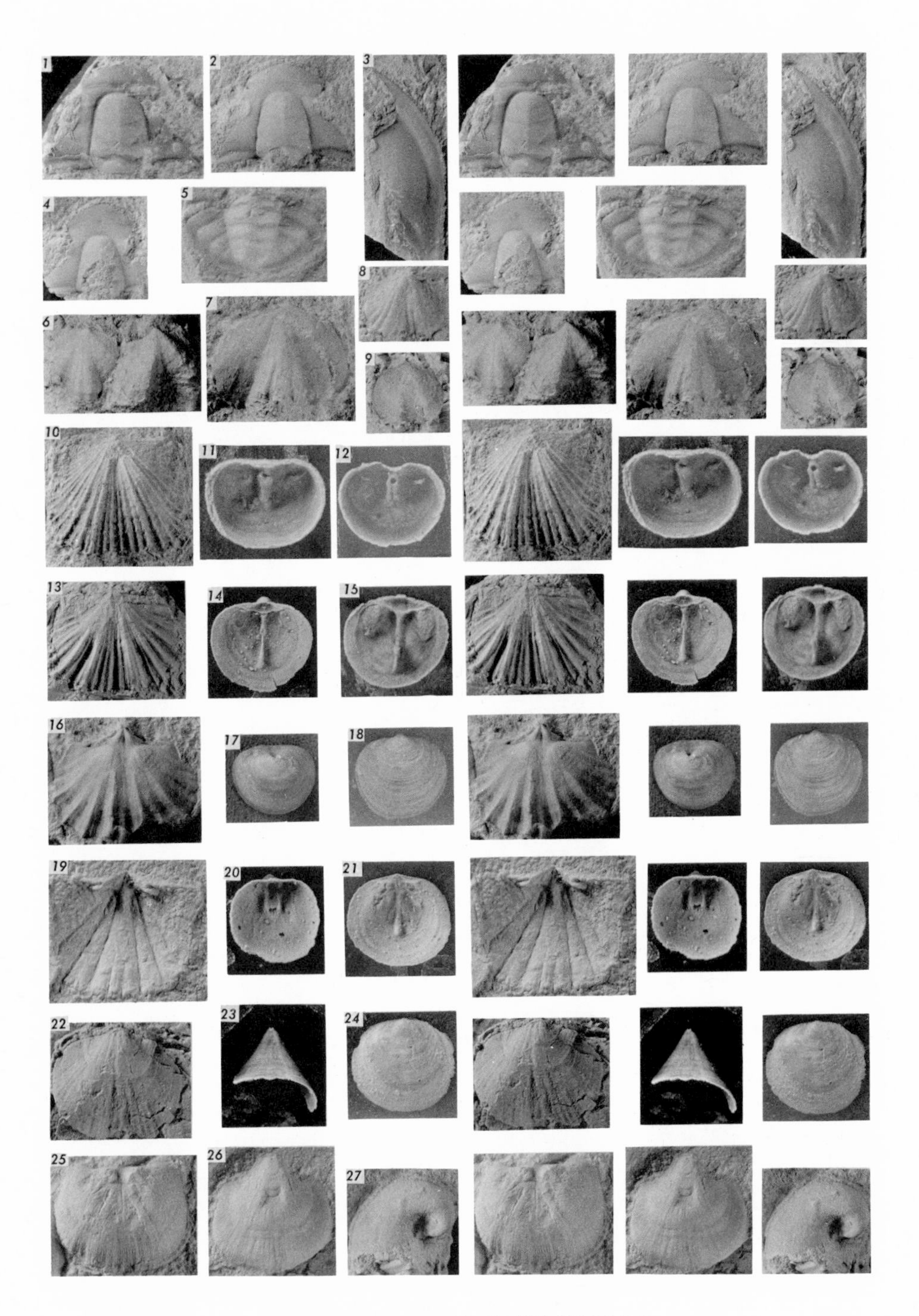

TAENICEPHALUS ZONE FOSSILS

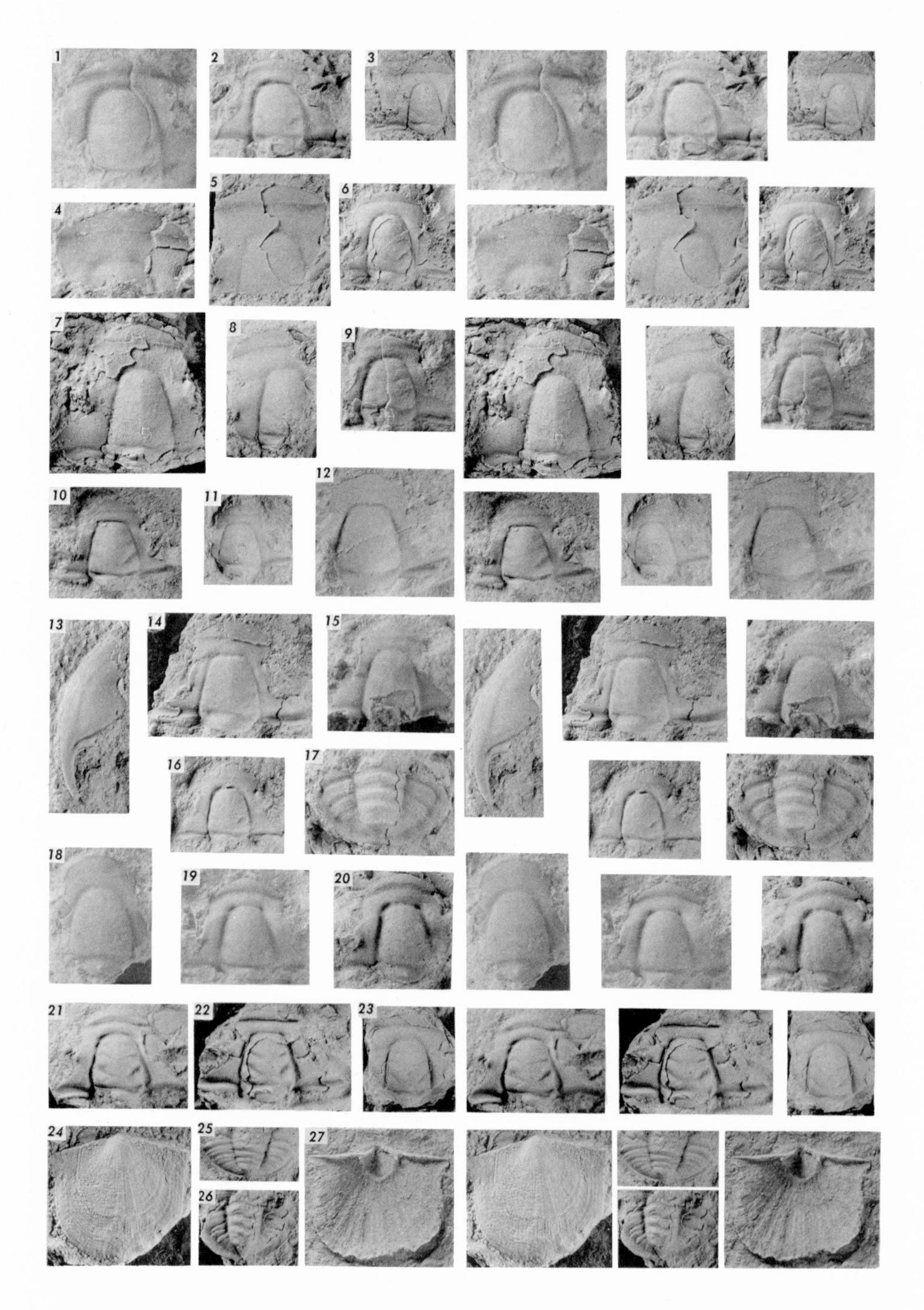

TAENICEPHALUS ZONE FOSSILS

PLATE 12. *TAENICEPHALUS* ZONE FOSSILS

Figures Page

1–2. *Taenicephalus gouldi* (Frederickson). 137
(1) Fragmentary cranidium with narrow brim, ×5, YO 81.1, USNM 142370. (2) More complete cranidium with blunt glabella, ×3, JC 69.6, USNM 142371

3, 5–6. *Orygmaspis firma* Frederickson. 132
(3) Cranidium, ×1.5, NG 3D, USNM 142372. (5) Anterior of cranidium with raised border, ×2, GC 93.5, USNM 142373. (6) Cranidium with downsloping brim and flat border, ×2, GC 93.5, USNM 142374

4, 7. *Orygmaspis llanoensis* (Walcott). 133
(4) Anterior part of cranidium with flat frontal area and very shallow marginal furrow, ×2, HE 90.8, USNM 142375. (7) Cranidium with pustules in marginal furrow exposed by exfoliation, ×2, BC 69.3, USNM 142376

8. *Wilbernia halli* var. *A* Ellinwood. 124
Cranidium with widely divergent anterior facial sutures, but other features of frontal area similar to those of *O. firma,* ×1.5, DC 6.9W (collected by Lochman-Balk near type locality of Dry Creek Shale, Accola, Montana), USNM 142377

9–14. *Maustonia nasuta* (Hall). 132
(9) Partly exfoliated cranidium illustrating similarity of this species to *Taenicephalus shumardi,* ×2.5, SP 117.4, USNM 142378. (10) Cranidium with high glabella, ×2.5, CF 62.3, USNM 142379. (11) Cranidium with typical frontal area. ×1.5, CF 62.3, USNM 142380. (12) Cranidium closely resembling Hall's type specimen, ×3, CF 62.3, USNM 142381. (13) Free cheek, ×1.5, CF 65.6, USNM 142382. (14) Cranidium, ×1.5, CF 65.6, USNM 142383

15–18. *Kendallina eryon* (Hall). 131
(15) Cranidium with limbs and glabella showing relationship to species of *Parabolinoides,* ×3.5, SL 81.1, USNM 142384. (16) Cranidium ×2.5, SC 42.7, USNM 142385. (17) Pygidium, ×2.5, HI 67.7, USNM 142386. (18) Cranidium with smooth frontal area, ×3.5, YO 70.7, USNM 142387

19–20. *Taenicephalus gallupensis* Grant n. sp. 136
(19) Holotype cranidium, ×4, BC 67.3, USNM 142388. (20) Larger cranidium, ×2.5, HF 15.6, USNM 142389

21–22, 25–26. *Taenicephalus shumardi* (Hall). 137
(21) Cranidium with slightly arcuate marginal furrow, ×1.5, SP 111.9, USNM 142391. (22) Cranidium with straight marginal furrow, ×1.5, SC 52.3, USNM 142390. (25) Pygidium, ×2, SC 52.3, USNM 142392. (26) Pygidium, ×2, HH 72.3, USNM 142393

23. *Wilbernia halli* Resser. 124
Cranidium, ×2, DC 6.9W (collected by Lochman-Balk near type locality of Dry Creek Shale, Accola, Montana), USNM 142394

24. *Billingsella perfecta* Ulrich and Cooper. 101
Exterior of slightly alate pedicle valve, ×1.5, FOX 98.4, USNM 142395

27. *Eoorthis remnicha* (Winchell). 102
Interior of slightly alate pedicle valve, ×2, SL 76.8 (float), USNM 142396

PLATE 13. *TAENICEPHALUS* ZONE AND *IDAHOIA* ZONE FOSSILS

Figures		Page
1–2, 4–5.	*Billingsella perfecta* Ulrich and Cooper. (1) Exterior of silicified pedicle valve, ×2, CF 40, USNM 142397. (2) Exterior of silicified brachial valve, ×2, CF 40, USNM 142397. (4) Interior of silicified pedicle valve, ×2, CF 40, USNM 142399. (5) Interior of silicified brachial valve, ×2, CF 40, USNM 142398	101
3, 6–12.	*Angulotreta vescula* Grant n. sp. (3) Interior of pedicle valve, ×8, CF 56.2, UT-12210a. (6) Interior of holotype pedicle valve showing broad base of pseudo-interarea, ×8, CF 56.2, UT-12210b. (7) Interior of small pedicle valve, ×12, HK 86.5, UT-12211. (8) Interior of brachial valve, ×12, SP 119.8, UT-12212a. (9) Exterior of brachial valve, ×8, SP 119.8, UT-12212b. (10) Interior of small brachial valve, ×12, HD 102.1, UT-12213. (11) Profile of exterior of pedicle valve, ×8, CF 56.2, UT-12210c. (12) Apical view of exterior of pedicle valve, ×8, CF 56.2, UT-12210d	99
13–14.	*Pseudagnostus josephus* (Hall). (13) Cranidium, ×4, HD 146.2, USNM 142409. (14) Pygidium, ×3.5, HG 77.3, USNM 142410	108
15.	*Croixana bipunctata* (Shumard). Cranidium, ×2.5, HG 77.3, USNM 142411	131
16–17.	*Saratogia carita* Grant n. sp. (16) Cranidium, ×2, BC 103.6, USNM 142412. (17) Holotype cranidium, ×3.5, HG 77.3, USNM 142413	121
18–20.	*Saratogia fracida* Grant n. sp. (18) Typical cranidium, ×2, SP 150.6, USNM 142414. (19) Holotype cranidium, ×1.5, SP 150.6, USNM 142415. (20) Elongate cranidium with divergent anterior facial sutures, intermediate between this species and *S. amplifrons,* ×2.5, SP 150.6, USNM 142416	122
21.	*Saratogia fria* Lochman and Hu. Typical cranidium, ×1.5, SP 161, USNM 142417	122
22–25.	*Idahoia wyomingensis* Resser. (22) Cranidium with downsloping border, ×2, HG 81.3, USNM 142418. (23) Cranidium, ×3.5, SP 156, USNM 142419. (24) Typical cranidium with occipital spine, ×1.5, HG 81.3, USNM 142420. (25) Pydigium, ×2, HG 81.3, USNM 142421	119
26.	*Lytospira* ? sp. Phosphatic shell from acetic acid residue, ×12, BC 130.5, UT-12223	106
27.	*Wilbernia diademata* (Hall). Cranidium, ×1, HG 81.3, USNM 142423	123
28–32.	*Sinuella vaticina* (Hall). (28) Limestone steinkern, ×3.5, RP 84.9, USNM 142424. (29) Dolomite steinkern, from acetic acid residue, ×12, FC 143.2, UT-12226a. (30) Phosphatic shell of immature individual, from acetic acid residue, ×12, HH 124.4, UT-12227. (31) Egg case of *S. vaticina* from acetic acid residue, ×12, FC 143.2, UT-12226b. (32) Egg case of *S. vaticina,* from acid residue, ×12, FC 143.2, UT-12226c	105

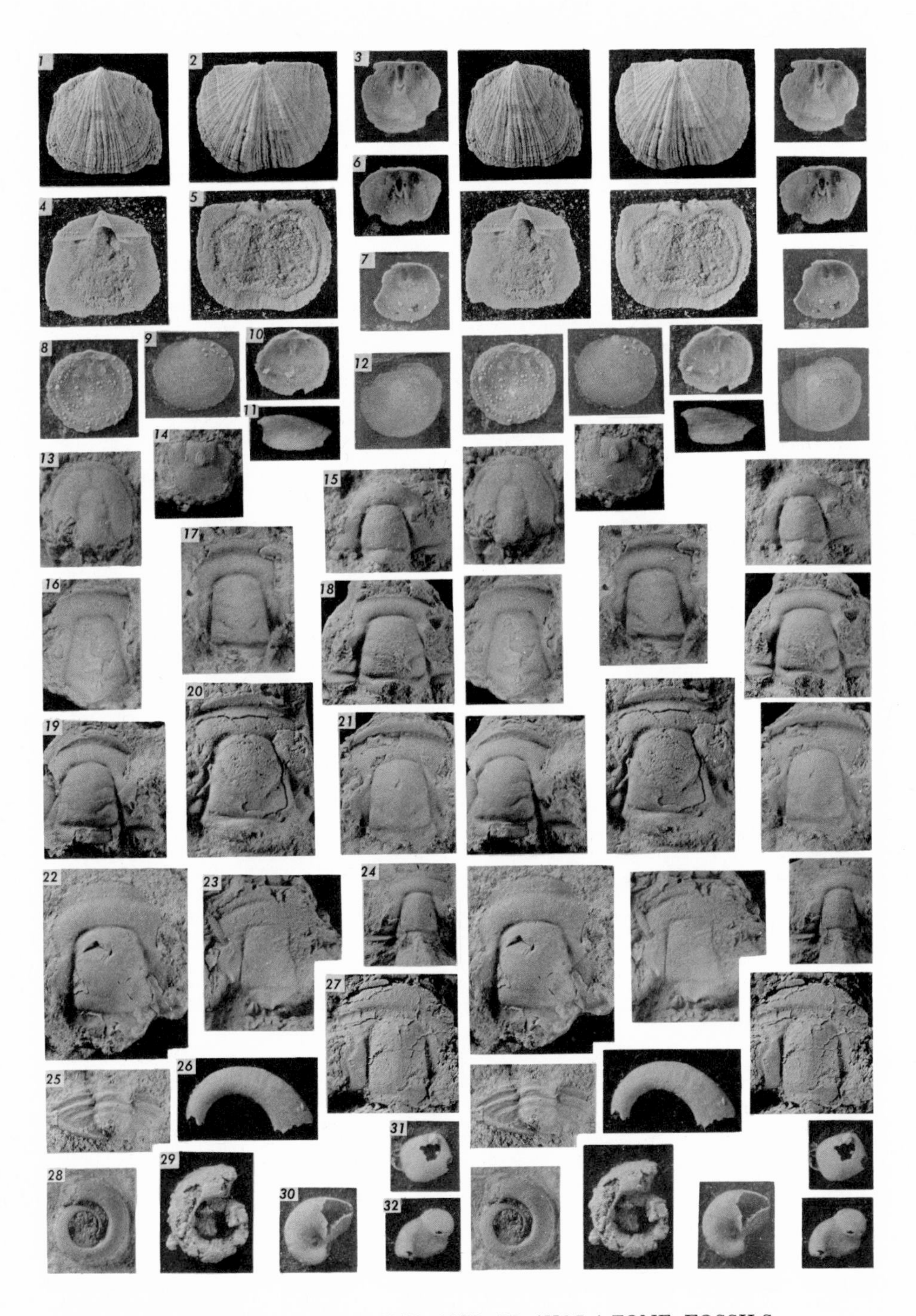

TAENICEPHALUS ZONE AND *IDAHOIA* ZONE FOSSILS

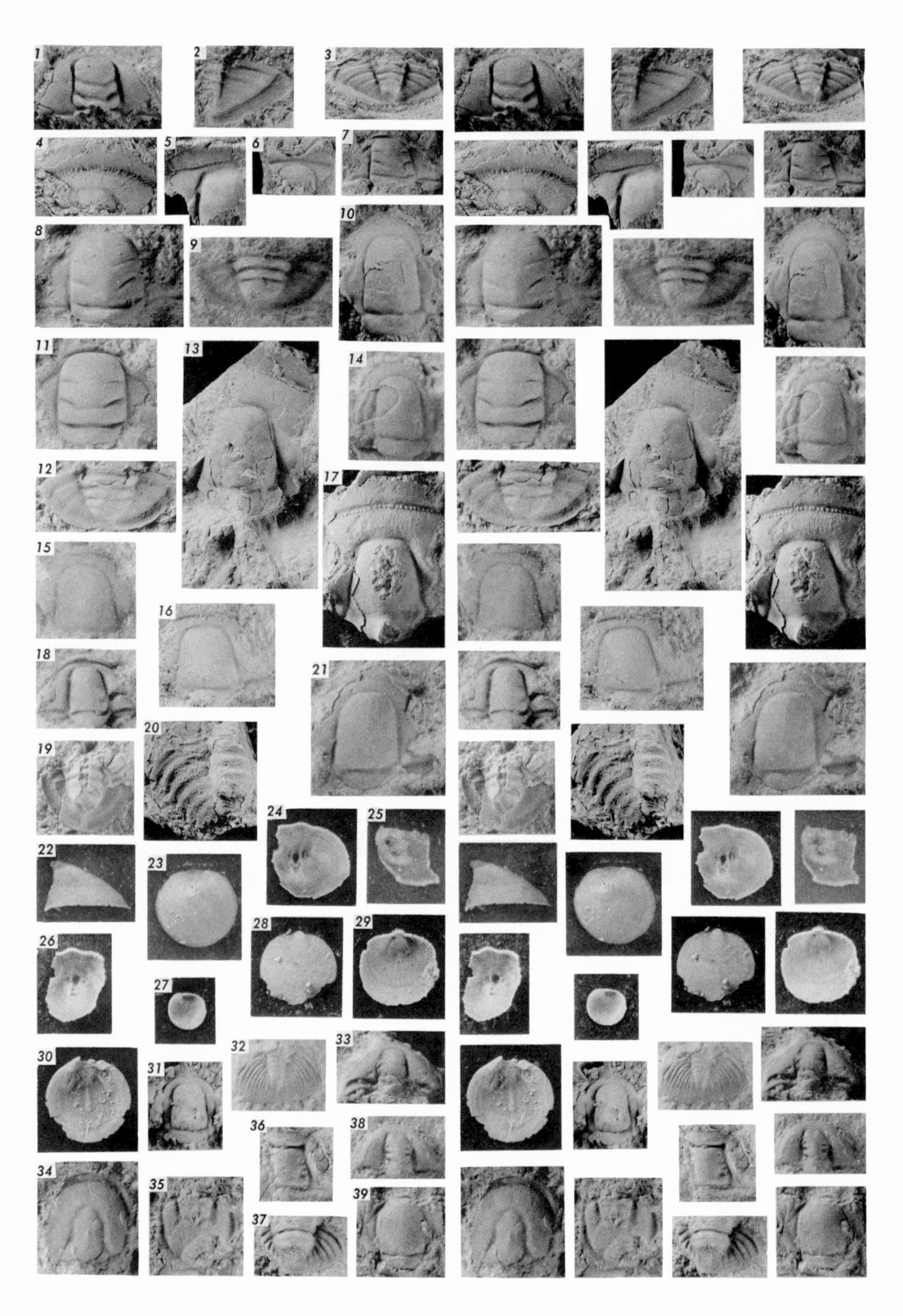

IDAHOIA ZONE AND *PROSAUKIA* ZONE FOSSILS

Plate 14. *IDAHOIA* ZONE AND *PROSAUKIA* ZONE FOSSILS

Figures — Page

1–3. *Ptychaspis granulosa* (Owen). 141
(1) Cranidium with left palpebral lobe, ×1.5, MC 170.6, USNM 142255. (2) Right half of pygidium, with obvious striations, ×2, HH 128.8, USNM 142256. (3) Complete pygidium with weak striations, ×2, YO 135.7, USNM 142257

4. *Wilbernia explanata* (Whitfield). 123
Impression in modeling clay of anterior of cranidium, ×1, FC 143.2, USNM 142258

5. *Wilbernia expansa* Frederickson. 123
Part of cranidium, ×1, SP 150.6, USNM 142259

6. *Wilbernia pero* (Walcott). 124
Anterior of cranidium, ×1.5, MC 164.4, USNM 142285

7–9. *Drumaspis briscoensis* Resser. 115
(7) Small, slightly distorted cranidium, ×1.5, SP 156, USNM 142286. (8) Cranidium, ×3, MC 170.6, USNM 142287. (9) Pygidium, ×4, SP 156, USNM 142288

10, 14. *Monocheilus demissus* Grant n. sp. 109
(10) Holotype cranidium, ×3.5, FC 151, USNM 142289. (14) Cranidium, ×5, SP 156, USNM 142290

11–12. *Drumaspis idahoensis* Resser. 115
(11) Cranidium, ×3.5, HI 124.3, USNM 142291. (12) Pygidium, ×3, HI 124.3, USNM 142292

13. *Idahoia wisconsensis* (Owen). 119
Typical cranidium, ×1, RP 91.1, USNM 142293

15–16, 20. *Maladia americana* Walcott. 116
(15) Cranidium, ×4, HI 124.3, USNM 142294. (16) Cranidium, ×2, YO 159.5, USNM 142295. (20) Pygidium, ×1, HD 142, USNM 142296

17. *Idahoia serapio* Walcott. 118
Cranidium, ×1.5, HD 146.2, USNM 142298

18–19. *Pinctus ? pullus* Grant n. sp. 112
(18) Holotype cranidium, ×6, HD 146.2, USNM 142300. (19) Pygidium with small cranidium near axis, ×3.5, HD 148.2, USNM 142301

21. *Stigmacephaloides curvabilis* Ellinwood. 135
Cranidium, ×3.5, BM 182.1, USNM 142302

22–30. *Angulotreta catheta* Grant n. sp. 97
(22) Profile of exterior of pedicle valve, ×12, UYO 216.9, UT-12246a. (23) Apical view of exterior of pedicle valve, ×12, UYO 216.9, UT-12246b. (24) Interior of holotype pedicle valve, ×12, UYO 216.9, UT-12246c. (25) Interior of broken pedicle valve showing ring in pedicle foramen, ×12, UYO 216.9, UT-12246d. (26) Interior of pedicle valve, ×12, UYO 216.9, UT-12246e. (27) Interior of small, smooth pedicle valve, ×12, FOX 202.4, UT-12247. (28) Exterior of brachial valve, ×12, UYO 216.9, UT-12246f. (29) Interior of brachial valve, ×12, YO 172.8, UT-12248. (30) Interior of brachial valve, ×12, UYO 216.9, UT-12246g

31. *Ellipsocephaloides silvestris* Resser. 143
Cranidium, ×6, BM 202.2, USNM 142303

32. *Prosaukia* sp. 142
Cranidium, ×1.5, HH 128.8, USNM 142305

33. *Ptychaspis* cf. *P. miniscaensis* (Owen). 142
Cranidium, ×4, HH 128.8, USNM 142305

34–35. *Pseudagnostus* cf. *P. laevis* Palmer. 108
(34) Cranidium with weak anterior median furrow, ×4, BM 249.2, USNM 142312. (35) Pygidium with pair of muscle scars at anterior end of pseudo-lobe, ×4, YO 240.7, USNM 142319

36–37. *Saukids*. 142
(36) Part of cranidium, ×1.5, ME 36.1, USNM 142354. (37) Pygidium, ×2.5, HJ 255.2, USNM 142335

38. *Idiomesus* sp. 142
Cranidium, ×3.5, BM 249.2, USNM 142356

39. *Monocheilus* cf. *M. truncatus* Ellinwood. 109
Fragmentary cranidium, ×4, BM 284, USNM 142357

PLATE 15. *ILLAENURUS* ZONE FOSSILS

Figures | Page

1–2. *Dikelocephalus* sp. undet. 110
(1) Cranidium, ×4, BM 249.2, USNM 142358. (2) right half of pygidium, ×1, BM 249.2, USNM 142359

3–5. *Briscoia dalyi* (Walcott). 110
(3) Anterior part of cranidium, ×1.5, UFOX 55, USNM 142362. (4) Cranidium with anterior of frontal area missing, ×0.75, UFOX 55, USNM 142363. (5) Left half of pygidium without margin, ×2.5, UYO 216.9, USNM 142364

6. *Finkelnburgia osceola* (Walcott). 103
Exterior of brachial valve, ×2, MC 293.5, USNM 142365

7. *Stenopilus* ? sp. 138
Small cranidium, ×7, UYO 283.0, USNM 142399

8, 11. *Rasettia snowyensis* Grant n. sp. 127
(8) Exfoliated cranidium, ×2, HJ 246.2, USNM 142400. (11) Holotype pygidium, ×1.5, MC 290.5, USNM 142401

9–10, 12. *Geragnostus* ? *insolitus* Grant n. sp. 107
(9) Cranidium and associated pygidium, ×5, MC 293.5, USNM 142402. (10) Holotype pygidium, ×6, MC 293.5, USNM 142403. (12) Pygidium ×6, MC 293.5, USNM 142404

13–14. *Homagnostus* sp. 107
(13) Broken pygidium, ×6, BC 205.5, USNM 142405. (14) Pygidium, ×6, BC 192.6, USNM 142406

15, 18. *Eurekia binodosa* (Hall). 116
(15) Fragment of cranidium, ×1.5, MC 293.5, UT-12268. (18) Pygidium, ×2, MC 290.5, UT-12269

16, 19. *Bynumiella typicalis* Resser. 125
(16) Cranidium, ×6, BC 205.5, USNM 142407. (19) Pygidium, ×3.5, (tentatively assigned) BC 205.5, USNM 142408

17. *Bynumina* sp. undet. 126
Cranidium, ×4, UFOX 55, USNM 142422

20–21. *Illaenurus sinclairensis* Resser. 125
(20) Free cheek, ×1.5, MC 285.5, USNM 142425. (21) Cranidium, ×1.5, BC 191.1, USNM 142426

22. *Illaenurus truncatus* Feniak. 125
Cranidium, ×1.5, BC 192.6, USNM 142427

23. *Illaenurus quadratus* Hall. 125
Cranidium, ×1.5, BC 192.6, USNM 142428

24. *Illaenurus montanensis* Kobayashi. 125
Cranidium, ×1.5, MC 293.5, USNM 142429

25. *Apheoorthis* sp. 101
Fragment of exterior of pedicle (?) valve, ×2.5, KZ 26.7, USNM 142430

26. *Problematicum*. 145
×0.75, KZ 26.7, USNM 142431

27–28. *Callograptus staufferi* Reudemann. 144
(27) Rhabdosome, ×2, SL 283.4 (float), USNM 142432. (28) Narrower rhabdosome, ×2, SL 283.4, USNM 142433

29, 32. *Multivasculatus ovatus* Howell and Van Houten. 94
(29) Siliceous spicule from acetic acid residue, ×12, BM 307.7, UT-12280a. (32) Small siliceous spicule, ×12, BM 307.7, UT-12280b

30. Aglaspid fragment, ×6, FOX 222.9, UT-12281 143

31. *Westergaardodina tricuspidata* Müller. 145
From acetic acid residue, ×12, GR 27.1, UT-12282

33, 34. *Westergaardodina bicuspidata* Müller. 145
(33), ×12, GC 63, UT-12283. (34) ×12, HI 121.2, UT-12284

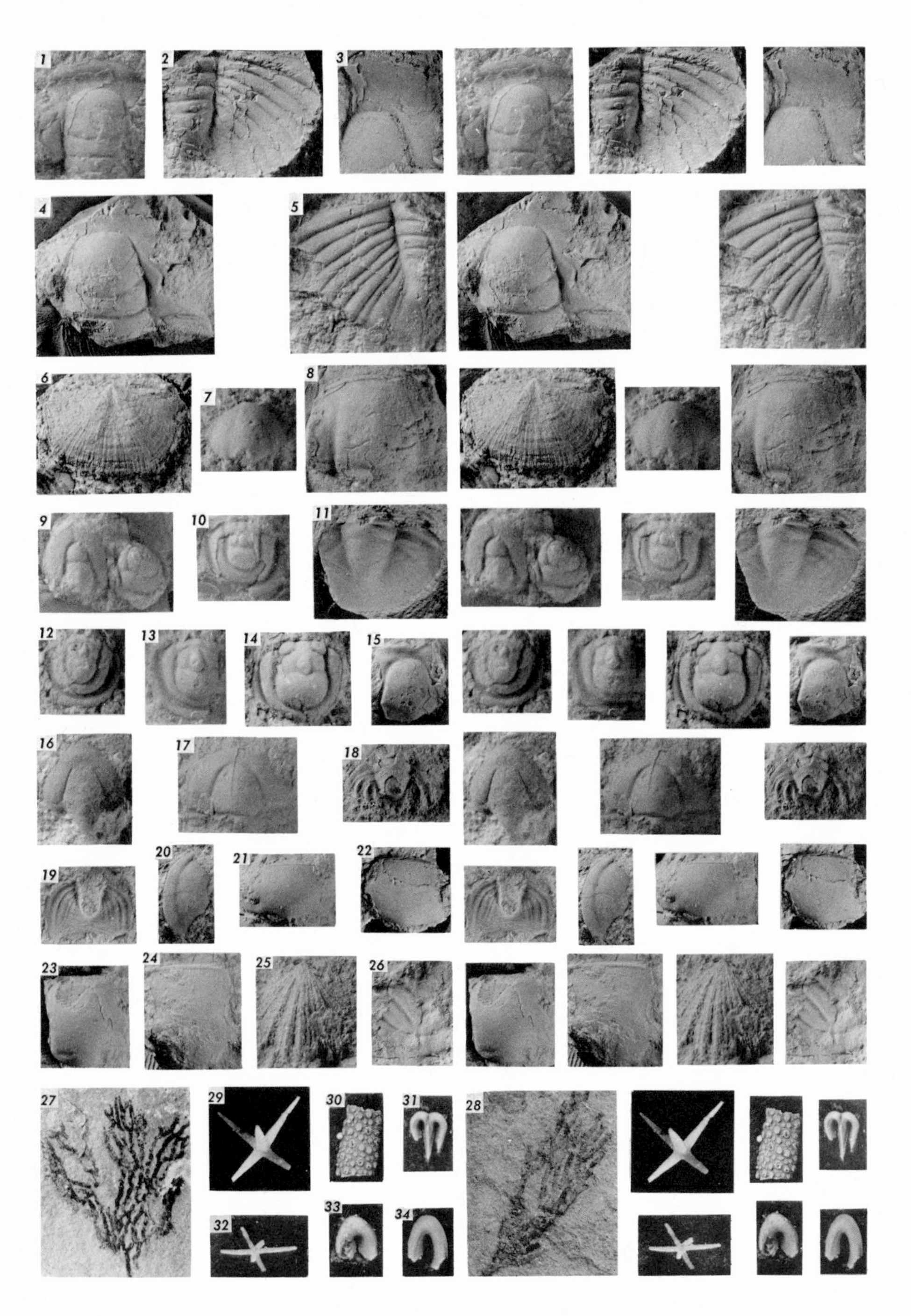

ILLAENURUS ZONE FOSSILS

INDEX

Numbers in **boldface** refer to primary descriptions or discussions. Morphologic terms, zones, and localities used in descriptions of individual taxa are omitted from the index.

Accola, Montana, 11
Acrotreta Kutorga, 97
Aglaspida Raasch, **143**, Pl. 15
Anconochilus idahoensis Lochman and Hu, 105
Angulotreta Palmer, **97**
catheta n. sp., 85, 87, 88, 89, 91, **97**, 98, 99, Pl. 14
glabra n. sp., 82, 97, **98**, 99, Pl. 9
microscopica (Shumard), 97, 98, 99
postapicalis Palmer, 97, 99
tetonensis (Walcott), 84, 90, 91, 97, **98**, Pl. 11
triangularis Palmer, 99
vescula n. sp., 84, 85, 90, 91, 98, **99**, Pl. 13
Angulotreta catheta Zone, **91**, 98
Angulotreta tetonensis Zone, 89, **90**, 91
Angulotreta vescula Zone, 89, **90**, 91
Apachia convexa DeLand, 82
Aphelaspis Resser, **138**
sp., 80, **138**, Pl. 8
walcotti Resser, 81, 138
Aphelaspis Zone, 52, 54, 79, **80**, 81, 82, 89
Apheoorthis Ulrich and Cooper, 89, 101
sp., 88, 92, **101**, Pl. 15
Appalachian Mountains, 3, 83, 139
Apsotreta Palmer, **99**
expansa Palmer, 81, 89, **99**, Pl. 8
Apsotreta expansa Zone, 88, **89**
Arbuckle Mountains, 114

Baldy Mountain (BM), 10, 14, 20, **58**, 87, 142
Beartooth Butte (BB), 7, 9, **73**, 101
Beartooth Mountains, 5, 7, 9
Belgrade, Montana, 44, 45
Belt Series, 19, 23, 28
Bemaspis Frederickson 134, **136**
gouldi Frederickson, 84, 136, **137**
Berkeia Resser, 83, 113
glabellamersa Wilson, 130
typica Resser, 113
wichitaensis Resser, 111
Bernia Frederickson, **133**, 134
obtusa Frederickson, 133, 134, **135**
Bighorn Formation, 10, 16, **17**, 18, 21, 29, 67, 69, 70, 72, 73, 74, 75, 76, 88, Pl. 5
Bighorn Lake (BL), 5, **51**, 89
Big Horn Mountans, 138
Big Snowy Mountains, 10
Billingsella Hall, 90, **101**
alata Bell, 102
coloradoensis (Shumard), 101
exasperata Bell, 102
perfecta Ulrich and Cooper, 84, 85, 90, **101**, 102, Pl. 12, Pl. 13
plicatella Walcott, 84, 85, 90, 101, **102**, Pl. 11
radiata Bell, 101

Bill Smith Creek (BC), 5, 11, **52**, 89
Bozeman, Montana, 5
Bridger Mountains, 4, 5, 7, 9, 10, 11, 12, 13, 14, 16, 17, 19, 20, 21, 30, 46, 48, 49, 50, 51, 52, 54, 55, 57, 58, 94, 136
Bridger Peak (BP), 10, 17, 20, 26, **57**, 87, 88, Pl. 7
Briscoia Walcott, **110**
dalyi (Walcott), 80, 88, **110**, Pl. 15
Briscoia Zone, 80
Burnetiella Lochman, **110**
alta (Resser), 82
ectypa (Resser), 82, **110**, Pl. 8
urania (Walcott), 110, 111
Bynumiella Resser, **125**
typicalis Resser, **125**, Pl. 15
Bynumina Resser, **126**
caelata Resser, 126
globosa Walcott, 126
missouriensis Resser, 126
sp., 88, **126**, Pl. 15
terrenda Wilson, 82, **126**, Pl. 8

Callograptus Hall, 144
antiquus Ruedemann, 144
staufferi Ruedemann, 88, **144**, Pl. 15
Camaraspis Ulrich, 82, 83, 113, 134, **139**
berkeyi (Resser), 82, **139**, Pl. 10
convexa (Whitfield), 139, **140**, Pl. 10
plana Frederickson, 82, **140**
Camaraspis Subzone, 34, 36, 39, 40, 43, 55, 64, 66, 68, **82**, 90
Camaraspoides Frederickson, 134, **139**
berkeyi (Resser), **139**
Cambrian, 3, 4, 9, 10, 15, 19, 29, 31, 32, 33, 34, 36, 37, 38, 40, 42, 43, 44, 45, 46, 47, 48, 49, 50, 51, 52, 54, 56, 57, 58, 59, 60, 61, 62, 63, 64, 65, 66, 67, 68, 69, 70, 72, 73, 74, 75, 76, 78, 79, 89, 92, 103, 106, 144
Cedaria Zone, 106
Ceratreta Bell, 90, **100**
hebes Bell, 84, 85, 90, 97, **100**, Pl. 11
Certreta-Eoorthis Subzone, 12, **90**, 91
Cheilocephalus Berkey, **109**
buttsi Resser, 109
delandi Shaw, 81
sp., 82, **109**, Pl. 8
Clark Fork (of Yellowstone River), 5, 7, 9, 13, 14, 17, 30, 74
Cliffia latagenae (Wilson), 82
Collenia Walcott, **145**
magna Fenton and Fenton, 12, 13, **24**, **29**, 82, 83, 84, 90, **145**, Pl. 5
Comanchia Frederickson, 83, **117**
amplooculata Frederickson, 83, 117
lippa n.sp., 82, 83, **117**, Pl. 10

Conaspis Zone, 41, 80, 85, 108
Crepicephalus Zone, 106
Crinoid fragments, 143
Croixan Series, 3, 4, 28, 79, 80, 81, 88, 89
Croixana Nelson, **131**
  bipunctata (Shumard), 84, 85, **131**, Pl. 13
Crowfoot Ridge (CF), 7, 9, 11, 20, 21, **63**, 90, 95, 101, 103

Deadwood Formation, 10
Deadwoodia Resser, **128**
  duris (Walcott), 82, **128**, 129, 130, Pl. 8
  panope (Walcott), 128
Dellea Wilson, **128**
  butlerensis Frederickson, 82, **129**, Pl. 8
  cf. butlerensis Frederickson, 82
  juvenalis Frederickson, 82, **129**, Pl. 8
  saginata DeLand, 82, 129
  saratogensis (Resser), 82, 129, **130**, Pl. 8
  snoburgensis (Wilson), 82, **129**, Pl. 8
  suada (Walcott), 82, 128, 129, **130**, Pl. 8
Devonian, 4, 10, 14, 17, **18**, 19, 20, 21, 24, 27, 28, 29, 30, 31, 32, 33, 34, 36, 37, 38, 42, 43, 44, 45, 46, 47, 48, 49, 50, 52, 54, 56, 57, 59, 61, 62, 64, 65, 78
Dicellomus Hall, 95
Dikelocephalus Owen, **110**
  norwalkensis Ulrich and Resser, 110
  sp., 88, **110**, Pl. 15
  thwaitesi Ulrich and Resser, 110
Dikelocephalus postrectus Zone, 16, 80, 88
Dokimocephalus Walcott, **111**
  intermedius (Resser), 82, **111**, Pl. 9
Dresbach Formation, 28
Dresbachian Stage, 3, 4, 28, 52, 54, 72, 79, **80**, 81, 89, 98, 99, 120, Pl. 8
Drumaspis Resser, 86, **114**, 127
  briscoensis Resser, 85, 86, **115**, Pl. 14
  deckeri Resser, 114, 115
  idahoensis Resser, 85, 86, 87, **115**, Pl. 14
  nitida Resser, 114
  texana Resser, 114, 115
  walcotti Resser, 114
Dry Creek (DC), 5, 11, 45
Dry Creek Shale Member, 9, **10**, 11, 12, 18, 19, 23, **27**, 28, 32, 33, 36, 37, 38, 40, 43, 44, 45, 46, 48, 49, 50, 51, 54, 55, 57, 58, 60, 62, 63, 64, 66, 67, 69, 71, 74, 76, 77, 78, 81, 82, 89, 90
Dunderberg Shale, 126
Dunderbergia Zone, 72, 80, **81**, 82, 89
Dytremacephalus Palmer, **140**
  ? sp., 80, **140**, Pl. 8

Ellipsocephaloides Kobayashi, **143**
  argutus Resser, 143
  curtus (Whitfield), 143
  gracilis Feniak, 143
  silvestris Resser, 85, 87, **143**, Pl. 14
Elvinia Walcott, 115, 127
  hamburgensis (Resser), 127
  roemeri (Shumard), 82, **115**, Pl. 9
  sp., 82
Elvinia Zone, 32, 33, 34, 36, 37, 38, 39, 40, 41, 43, 44, 46, 47, 49, 50, 51, 52, 53, 55, 58, 60, 62, 63, 64, 66, 68, 71, 73, 76, 77, 78, 79, 81, **82**, 83, 89, 90, 95, 97, 101, 103, 108, 112, 126, 127, 141, Pls. 8–10
Emerson Formation, 10
Eoorthis Walcott, 90, **102**
  indianola (Walcott), 103
  remnicha (Winchell), 84, 85, 90, 100, **102**, 103, 104, Pl. 11, Pl. 12
  remnicha var. *A*, **103**, Pl. 11
Eoorthis Subzone, 85, 88, 90, 134
Eschelmania Wilson, **128**
  convexa Wilson, 129
Eurekia Walcott, **116**
  binodosa, 88, **116**, Pl. 15
  granulosa Walcott, 116

Fairy Lake, 5, 54
Felix Canyon (FC), 5, **48**
Finkelnburgia Walcott, 89, **103**
  buttsi Ulrich and Cooper, 103
  finkelnburgi (Walcott), 103
  missouriensis Ulrich and Cooper, 103
  osceola (Walcott), 88, 91, **103**, Pl. 15
Finkelnburgia osceola Subzone, 89, 91
Flathead Formation, 106
Flathead Pass (FP), 5, 11, 14, **49**, 50
Flying "D" Ranch (FD), 7, 11, 19, 20, 21, 27, **61**, Pl. 7
Fox Creek (FOX), 12, 14, 15, 23, 25, 26, **70**, 81, 89, Pl. 5, Pl. 6
Fox Creek, Upper (UFOX), 17, 25, 27, **72**, Pl. 5
Franconia Formation, 141
Franconian Stage, 3, 4, 16, 28, 32, 33, 34, 35, 36, 37, 38, 39, 40, 42, 43, 44, 46, 47, 48, 49, 50, 51, 52, 53, 54, 56, 58, 59, 60, 62, 63, 64, 65, 66, 67, 68, 70, 72, 73, 74, 75, 76, 77, 78, 79, **81**, 85, 86, 89, 90, 91, 95, 96, 97, 101, 105, 118, 120, 143

Gallatin Gateway, Montana, 61
Gallatin River, 31, 32, 33, 34, 36, 62, 63
Gallatin Valley, 95, 96
Gallup Creek (GC), 10, **46**, 136
Geragnostus Howell, **107**
  brevis Palmer, 107
  ? *insolitus* n.sp., 88, **107**, Pl. 15
Graptolite fragments, 144
Grove Creek Member, 5, 9, 10, 13, 14, 15, 16, 17, 18, 20, 26, **29**, 30, 31, 45, 51, 52, 56, 57, 59, 61, 65, 67, 69, 70, 72, 73, 74, 75, **76**, 87, 88, 92, 101, 144, 145, Pl. 5, 6, 7

Heart Mountain Thrust Fault, 17, 156
Holcacephalus Resser, 143
Homagnostus Howell, **107**
  cf. tumidosus (Hall and Whitfield), 82, **107**, Pl. 8, Pl. 9
  sp., 88, **107**, Pl. 15
Honey Creek Formation, 110, 131, 139
Horseshoe Hills, 5, 9, 10, 11, 12, 14, 16, 17, 19, 20, 21, 30, 31, 40, 41, 94
Horseshoe Hills Section A (HA), 10, 11, 24, 27, **31**, Pl. 7
—— Section B (HB), 14, **32**
—— Section C (HC), **33**
—— Section D (HD), **34**
—— Section E (HE), **36**

Horseshoe Hills Section F (HF), **37**
—— Section G (HG), 24, **38**, 130, 146
—— Section H (HH), **41**, 90
—— Section I (HI), **43**
—— Section J (HJ), 10, 11, 14, 17, 20, **44**
—— Section K (HK), **45**
Housia Walcott, **117**
canadensis (Walcott), 117
ovata Palmer, 117
vacuna (Walcott), 82, **117**, Pl. 10
varro (Walcott), 117
Hoyt Formation, 120
Huenella Walcott, **104**
abnormis (Walcott), 84, 85, 90, **104**, Pl. 11
texana (Walcott), 84, 85, 90, **104**, Pl. 11
texana var. *fortis* n.var., **104**, Pl. 10
Hyolithes Eichwald, 106
attenuatus Walcott, 106
primordialis (Hall), 82, 85, **106**, Pl. 9
princeps Billings, 106
Hypseloconus simplex erectus Shaw, 80
simplex simplex Lochman, 80

Idaho, 10, 105, 114, 118
Idahoia Walcott, 86, **117**, 120, **121**, 123
latifrons (Shumard), 119
serapio Walcott, 85, 86, 87, **118**, 119, 141, Pl. 14
wisconsensis (Owen), 85, 86, 87, 118, **119**, Pl. 14
wyomingensis Resser, 85, 86, 87, 118, **119**, 120, Pl. 13
Idahoia Zone, 32, 35, 39, 40, 42, 43, 46, 47, 48, 49, 50, 53, 54, 56, 57, 59, 65, 68, 71, 73, 77, 80, 81, 84, **85**, 86, 87, 91, 97, 105, 106, 114, 115, 116, 141, Pl. 14
Idahoia serapio Subzone, 35, 42, 43, 50, 53, 54, 56, 57, 59, 65, 68, 71, **87**, 89, 91, 114
Idahoia wisconsensis Subzone, 35, 42, 43, 47, 49, 51, 53, 54, 56, 58, 60, 65, 68, 71, 86, **87**, 114
Idahoia wyomingensis Subzone, 13, 15, 32, 35, 36, 39, 40, 42, 44, 46, 47, 48, 51, 53, 55, 56, 58, 60, 66, 68, 71, **86**, 114
Iddingsia occidentalis DeLand and Shaw, 82
Idiomesus Raymond, **142**
levisensis (Rasetti), 143
sp., 88, **142**, Pl. 14
Illaenurus Hall, **124**
albertensis Resser, 125
montanensis Kobayashi, 88, **125**, Pl. 15
quadratus Hall, 88, **125**, Pl. 15
sinclairensis Resser, 88, **125**, Pl. 15
truncatus Feniak, 88, **125**, Pl. 15
Illaenurus Zone, 45, 52, 57, 59, 61, 65, 67, 69, 70, 72, 75, 77, 80, **88**, 91, Pl. 15
Irvingella Ulrich and Resser, **126**, 127, 130
aff. *flohri* Resser, 82
major Ulrich and Resser, 82, 83, 84, **126**, 127, 130, Pl. 10
Irvingella (*Parairvingella*) Kobayashi, **127**
eurekensis Resser, 82, **127**, Pl. 8
Irvingella major Zonule, 47, 66, 68, **83**, 105

Jefferson Formation, 5, 17, 18, 19, 20, **21**, 31, 32, 33, 34, 36, 38, 43, 44, 45, 47, 48, 50, 52, 54, 56, 59, 61, 62, 63, 64, 65
Johnson Canyon (JC), **50**, 90
Jordan Formation, 3

Kendallina Berg, **131**, 132
biforota (Berg), 84, **131**, Pl. 10
eryon (Hall), 84, **131**, Pl. 12
Kindbladia Frederickson, **111**, 113
affinis (Walcott), 111
cf. wichitaensis (Resser), 82, **111**, Pl. 8
Kiowaia Frederickson, **130**
timberensis Frederickson, 83, **130**, Pl. 10
Kyphocephalus Miller, **111**
bridgerensis Miller, 82, **111**, 112, Pl. 9
ponderosus Wilson, 111, 112
? sp., 82, **111**, Pl. 9
K-Z Ranch (KZ), **74**, 92, 145, Pl. 6

Limestone pebbles (origin of), **14**, 25, 28, 29, Pl. 5, Pl. 6
Lingulella Salter, **95**
desiderata (Walcott), 82, 84, 85, 88, **95**, Pl. 9
perattenuata (Whitfield), 82, 84, **96**, Pl. 9
sp., 80
Linnarssonella Walcott, **100**
elongata Bell, 100
girtyi Walcott, 82, 89, 90, 97, **100**, 103, Pl. 9
Linnarssonella Zone, **89**, 90
Little Belt Mountains, 9, 11, 30, 77
Little Rocky Mountains, 10, 18, 19, 94
Logan, Montana, 31, 32, 33
Lytospira Koken, **106**
? sp., 85, 87, **106**, Pl. 13

Maladia Walcott, **116**
americana Walcott, 85, 87, **116**, Pl. 14
Manhattan, Montana, 34, 36, 38
Maurice Formation, 9
Maustonia Raasch, **132**, 134, 135
cordillerensis Lochman, 134
hedra Kurtz, 135, 136
nasuta (Hall), 84, **132**, Pl. 12
Maywood unit, 4, 9, 10, 13, 16, 17, **18**, 19, 20, 21, 23, 27, 28, 29, **30**, 31, 32, 33, 34, 36, 37, 38, 42, 43, 45, 47, 48, 49, 50, 52, 54, 56, 57, 59, 61, 62, 64, 78, 85, 88, Pl. 7
Meeria Frederickson, 118, 121, 122
lirae Frederickson, 121
modesta Lochman and Hu, 121, 122
Micromitra Meek, **96**
modesta (Lochman), 80, **96**, Pl. 8
Mill Creek (MC), 7, 9, 10, 11, 12, 13, 14, 16, 17, 18, 20, **65**, 83
Minnesota, 83, 108, 114, 119, 124, 131, 139, 142
Missisquoia Shaw, 143
Mississippi Valley, 3, 80, 83, 85, 86, 87, 88, 90, 113, 114, 118, 120, 134, 135, 141, 142
Monocheilus Resser, **109**, 143
anatinus (Hall), 109
cf. truncatus Ellinwood, 88, **109**, Pl. 14
demissus n.sp., 85, **109**, Pl. 14
Montana, 3, 4, 5, 9, 10, 11, 18, 19, 21, 30, 67, 79, 80, 83, 85, 86, 87, 88, 89, 101, 102, 103, 104, 108, 109, 114, 115, 116, 117, 118, 120, 124, 125, 126, 131, 132, 133, 134, 135, 136,

Montana 139, 141, 142, 143
Mount Ellis (ME), 11, 20, **60**
Multivasculatus Howell and Van Houten, **94**
ovatus Howell and Van Houten, 84, 85, 88, **94**, Pl. 15

Nevada, 106, 126
New York, 20
Nixon Gulch (NG), 30, 37, 38, **40**, 111, 127
North Grove Creek (GR), 7, 9, 10, 14, 16, 17, 18, **76**, Pl. 6

Ocnerorthis Bell, **103**
monticola Bell, 82, 90, 102, **103**, Pl. 10
Oklahoma, 3, 83, 85, 90, 110, 114, 117, 131
Open Door Formation, 10
Opisthotreta Palmer, 97
Ordovician, 10, 16, 17, 18, 26, 27, 29, 67, 69, 70, 73, 74, 75, 76, 80, 89, 91, 92, 103, 144
Orygmaspis Resser, 124, 131, **132**
firma Frederickson, 84, **132**, Pl. 12
llanoensis (Walcott), 84, 131, 132, **133**, Pl. 12
Otusia Walcott, **103**
sandbergi (Winchell), 84, 85, 90, **103**, Pl. 10

Parabolinoides Frederickson, 131, 132, **133**, 134
contractus Frederickson, 84, 133, **134**, 135, Pl. 10
cordillerensis (Lochman), 84, **134**, Pl. 11
expansus Nelson, 84, 134, **135**, Pl. 10
hebe Frederickson, 83, 84, 133, 134, **135**, Pl. 10
palatus Berg, 135
Parabolinoides Subzone, 33, 34, 35, 37, 38, 39, 41, 42, 44, 46, 47, 49, 50, 51, 53, 55, 57, 58, 62, 63, 64, 66, 68, 71, 76, 77, **84**, 85, 90, 100
Parabolinoides-Orygmaspis Subzone, 90
Parairvingella Kobayashi, **127**
angustilimbatus Kobayashi, 127
eurekensis Resser, **127**, Pl. 8
intermedia Resser, 127
Park Shale Formation, 19
Pelagiella Matthew, **105**
primordialis (Hall), 84, **105**, Pl. 11
Pelmatozoa, 143
Phoreotropis ? marginata Rasetti, 113
Phosphatic balls, **106**
Pilgrim Formation, 5, **9**, 11, 28, 31, 32, 33, 36, 37, 38, 40, 43, 44, 45, 46, 48, 49, 50, 51, 52, 54, 55, 57, 58, 60, 61, 62, 63, 64, 66, 67, 69, 72, 74, 76, 77, 81
Pinctus Wilson, **112**
? *artus* n.sp., 82, **112**, Pl. 8
latus Wilson, 113
? *pullus* n.sp., 85, 87, **112**, Pl. 14
Platyceras Conrad, 105
Platycolpus Subzone (*see Rasettia* Subzone)
Princeton, Montana, 18
Problematicum, 101, **145**, Pl. 15
Prosaukia Ulrich and Resser, 86, **142**
misa (Hall), 142
sp., 87, **142**, Pl. 14
Prosaukia Zone, Subzone, 53, 59, 65, 67, 70, 75, 77, 79, 80, 81, 86, **87**, 89, 91, Pl. 14
Protospongia Salter, 94
Prototreta Bell, 97
Psalaspis patersoni (Hall), 119, 120
Pseudagnostus Jaekel, **108**
cf. laevis Palmer, 88, **108**, Pl. 14
communis (Hall and Whitfield), 108
josephus (Hall), 84, 85, **108**, Pl. 13
prolongus (Hall and Whitfield), 108
sentosus n.sp., 82, 84, 85, **108**, Pl. 9
Pseudodicellomus Bell, **95**
mosaicus (Bell), 82, 84, 85, 87, 88, **95**, Pl. 9
Pterocephalia Roemer, **140**
bridgei Resser, 140, 141
sanctisabae Roemer, 82, **140**, Pl. 8
Ptychaspis Hall, **141**
bullasa Lochman and Hu, 141
cf. miniscaensis (Owen), 87, **142**, Pl. 14
granulosa (Owen), 85, **141**, 142, Pl. 14
miniscaensis (Owen), 86, 142
minuta Whitfield, 142
striata Whitfield, 141, 142
Ptychaspis Zone, Subzone, 40, 80, 86, 105, 108, 114, 118
Ptychaspis granulosa Subzone, Zonule, 86, 119
Ptychaspis striata Subzone, Zonule, 86
Ptychaspis-Prosaukia Zone, 16, 85, 86, 114, 118, 141
Ptychopleurites Kobayashi, 83
Ptychopleurites Zone, 83

Raaschella occidentalis Lochman, 81
Rasettia Lochman, **127**
capax (Billings), 128
depressa (Rasetti), 128
dubia (Billings), 128
highlandensis (Resser), 128
marcoui (Clark), 128
oklahomensis (Resser), 128
quinnensis (Resser), 128
sinclairensis (Resser), 128
snowyensis n.sp., 88, **127**, Pl. 15
wichitaensis (Resser), 128
Rasettia Subzone (*olim Platycolpus* Subzone), 80, 88
Red Lion Formation, 10
Red Lodge, Montana, 16, 30
Ross Peak (RP), 5, 10, 20, **55**

Sacajawea Peak (SP), 5, 17, **54**
Sage Member, 9, **12**, 13, 14, 16, 19, 20, 24, **28**, 29, 30, 31, 32, 33, 34, 36, 37, 38, 40, 42, 43, 45, 46, 47, 48, 49, 50, 52, 54, 56, 57, 59, 61, 62, 63, 64, 65, 67, 69, 70, 72, 73, 74, 75, 77, 78, 82, 83, 84, 85, 86, 87, 88, 90, Pls. 5–7
Saratogia Walcott, 86, 118, **120**
calcifera Walcott, 120, 121, 122
carita n.sp., 85, 86, **121**, 122, Pl. 13
fracida n.sp., 85, 86, 121, **122**, 123, Pl. 13
fria Lochman and Hu, 85, 86, 121, **122**, Pl. 13
hera Walcott, 120
Saratogia (*Meeria*) Frederickson, 118, 120, 121, 122

lirae Frederickson, 121
modesta Lochman and Hu, 121, 122
Saukia Zone, 80, 88
Saukid undet., **142**, Pl. 14
Saukiella Ulrich and Cooper, 142
Silver Gate, Montana, 67
Sinuella Knight, **105**
minuta Knight, 105, 106
vaticina (Hall), 85, 86, 91, **105**, Pl. 13
Snowy Range, 7
Snowy Range Formation, 4, 5, 7, **9**, 10, 11, 12, 13, 14, 16, 17, 19, 20, 21, 23, 24, 25, 26, 27, 28, 29, 31, 32, 33, 34, 36, 37, 38, 40, 42, 43, 45, 46, 47, 48, 49, 50, 51, 52, 54, 56, 57, 59, 61, 62, 63, 64, **65**, 67, 69, 70, 72, 74, 75, 78, 79, 80, 81, 82, 83, 84, 85, 88, 89, 91, 93, 97, 105, 114, 118, 126, 128, 129, 131, 139, 141, 144
Soda Butte Creek, 5, 9, 13, 14, 17, 30, 67
Squaw Creek (SC), 7, 11, 19, 20, 21, **62**
Steele Butte, Wyoming, 80
Stenopilus Clark, **138**
? sp., **138**, Pl. 15
Stigmacephaloides Ellinwood, **135**
curvabilis Ellinwood, 85, **135**, Pl. 14
Stigmacephalus flexifrons Feniak, 116
St. Lawrence Formation, 3
Sulcocephalus Wilson, 83, 112, **113**, 129, 130
candidus (Resser), 83, 113
granulosus (Wilson), 82, 112, **113**, Pl. 8
latus Wilson, 112
spp. 82, **113**, Pl. 8
typicus (Resser), 129
Swamp Lake (SL), 10, 12, 14, **74**, Pl. 5

Taenicephalus Ulrich and Resser, 131, 132, 134, **136**
altus Nelson, 136, 137
castlensis Resser, 137
cordillerensis Miller, 84, 137
gallupensis n.sp., 84, **136**, 137, Pl. 12
gouldi (Frederickson), **137**, Pl. 12
holmesi Resser, 137
peali Resser, 136, 137
shumardi (Hall), 84, 136, **137**, Pl. 12
speciosus Resser, 137
wichitaensis Resser, 137
wyomingensis Resser, 137
Taenicephalus Zone, 32, 33, 34, 35, 37, 38, 39, 40, 41, 42, 44, 46, 47, 48, 49, 50, 51, 53, 55, 57, 58, 60, 62, 63, 64, 66, 68, 71, 73, 75, 77, 78, 80, 81, 83, **84**, 85, 89, 90, 91, 97, 100, Pl. 10–13
Tetonophycus Fenton and Fenton, **146**
blackwelderi Fenton and Fenton, 13, 15, 24, 25, 26, **27**, **29**, **146**, Pl. 5
Texas, 3, 80, 81, 83, 85, 86, 88, 89, 90, 95, 103, 104, 106, 113, 114, 116, 117, 134, 136, 139, 141
Three Forks, Montana, 10
Trempealeauan Stage, 3, 4, 16, 45, 52, 56, 57, 59, 61, 65, 67, 69, 70, 72, 74, 75, 77, 79, 80, 87, **88**, 89, 91, 94, 96, 97, 103, 108, 120, 126, 138, 142, 143, 144

Upper *Dikelocephalus* Subzone, 80, 88

Westergaardodina Müller, **144**
bicuspidata Müller, **145**, Pl. 15
tricuspidata Müller, **145**, Pl. 15
Wilbernia Walcott, **123**
diademata (Hall), 85, 86, **123**, 124, Pl. 13
expansa Frederickson, 85, **123**, 124, Pl. 14
explanata (Whitfield), 85, 86, **123**, Pl. 14
halli Resser, 84, 123, **124**, Pl. 12
halli Resser var. *A*. Ellinwood, **124**, Pl. 12
pero (Walcott), 85, 123, **124**, Pl. 14
Windfall Formation, 108
Wind River Mountains, 138
Wisconsin, 83, 106, 108, 131, 142
Wyoming, 3, 4, 5, 10, 18, 67, 79, 80, 82, 83, 85, 86, 87, 88, 89, 101, 102, 103, 108, 114, 115, 116, 117, 118, 120, 124, 125, 126, 131, 132, 133, 134, 135, 138, 139, 141, 143, 145
Wyoming Creek (YO), 12, 24, **67**, 107, Pl. 6, 7
Wyoming Creek, Upper (UYO), **69**, 110

Xenocheilos cf. X. spineum Wilson, 82

Yellowstone National Park, 5, 9, 10, 11, 12, 13, 14, 30, 63, 95, 106, 144
Yogo Gulch (YG), 30, **77**, 102

Zortman Member, 10

Manuscript Received By The Society December 12, 1960